THE GREAT CANADIAN OIL PATCH

THE GREAT CANADIAN OIL PATCH

by Earle Gray

Maclean-Hunter Limited

Copyright

Published by

Maclean-Hunter Limited

481 University Avenue
Toronto   Canada

Printed in Canada

Library of Congress catalog card number 70-121120

Table of Contents

Illustrations

Prologue

The future and the past

Canada is an embryonic giant in the world of oil. Confirmation of this will be provided during the 1970's as exploration reveals the wealth of the nation's frontier oil areas, in the remotest corners of the Arctic and in the ocean beds under hundreds of feet of water.

It is ironic that this should be happening so late in Canada, after the petroleum industry has fueled for more than 70 years history's greatest era of industrial and economic growth and spawned some of the world's largest corporations. It is ironic because for nearly a century Canada had been almost entirely dependent on oil imported from other countries, becoming self-sufficient in petroleum hydrocarbons only in 1966. It is ironic because Canada has the largest supply of oil reserves in the world, at the Athabasca tar sands in northern Alberta. It is ironic because it was a Canadian who played an instrumental role in developing the initial refining technology which made possible the birth of the North American oil producing industry. And it is ironic because this oil producing industry was born in Canada with the first well in North America completed expressly for crude oil production.

Industry born in Canada

It was in Ontario in 1858 that North America's oil producing industry was born, and for a brief period, Canada was the world's leading oil producing nation, with its oil products used domestically, in the United States and in Europe. The small oil pools of south-

1

western Ontario — still producing a trickle of oil today — were soon swamped by far more prolific oil fields in the United States.

The petroleum industry grew with phenomenal speed, fueled the internal combustion engines that sped the 20th century into a new age of mobility, fueled and lubricated a technological-industrial revolution, created a new chemical industry, and spawned commercial empires with wealth and power such as the world had never seen. What coal was to the 19th century, petroleum was to the 20th century — only perhaps even more so. No other single event so affected development on the first half of the 20th century as the advent of the petroleum producing industry. Oil soon became the largest commodity in international trade. In the United States, oil and natural gas supplied less than eight percent of total energy requirements at the turn of the century, 28 percent by 1925, nearly 73 percent by 1960. World-wide, oil demand reached half a million barrels a day by the end of the first world war, five million barrels a day by the start of the second world war, 18 million barrels a day by 1957, and 40 million barrels a day by 1970. As in the United States, oil and natural gas supplied three quarters of Canada's energy consumption by the late 1960's, compared with less than 28 percent as recently as 1946.

Growth in demand

Why U.S. firms are larger

Because they were established early, American companies still dominate the world petroleum business. By 1969, net petroleum investment throughout the free world amounted to $98 billion (U.S. dollars), two-thirds of it owned by American oil companies which controlled 60 percent of the free world oil production. Even outside of the United States, U.S. oil companies accounted for nearly half the petroleum industry investment, excluding Communist nations.

Canada may have spawned the petroleum industry, but it soon got left far behind. Edwin L. Drake completed the first U.S. oil well in Pennsylvania in 1859, and within a year oil had been found in West Virginia, Kentucky, Ohio and Kansas; in Colorado in 1862, Wyoming in 1867, California in 1875. For the U.S. oil industry, the 20th century roared in with the Spindletop discovery in Texas in 1901. Spouting oil at a rate of some 100,000 barrels a day, it was the world's first great oil gusher. Oklahoma and Louisiana followed with giant discoveries, and in 1930 a bankrupt wildcatter, "Dad" Joiner, brought in the five-billion-barrel East Texas field, North America's largest oil field for nearly 40 years. By the time the second world war had started, more than 20 billion barrels of recoverable oil reserves had been discovered in the United States, and U.S. oil companies were firmly entrenched.

The early years

In Canada the story was pathetically different. Following the Oil Springs discovery in 1858, a few modest discoveries (giant by the standards of that day) briefly kept Ontario in the forefront of the new oil producing business. But the contrast with what was happening in the United States was drastic. In nearly 90 years — from 1858 to 1947 — exploration in Canada yielded less than 50 million barrels of oil reserves in Ontario; the Turner Valley field in the Alberta foothills; one other major oil field in the Northwest Territories at Norman Wells, a field too remote to be economically exploited; a few very minor oil pools, and some natural gas fields.

Leduc — the turning point

Not until the Leduc discovery near Edmonton in 1947 did petroleum production and exploration become a viable industry in Canada, and in the following 23 years reserves of more than 14 billion barrels of oil, 60 trillion cubic feet of natural gas and 100 million tons of sulphur were discovered by Canadian wildcatters. By 1970 Canada accounted for four percent of free world oil production — some 1.5 million out of a total of 35 million barrels daily. Imported crude still supplied the petroleum requirements of Quebec and the Atlantic provinces, but these were offset by exports to the United States. In 1947, Canada imported 90 percent of its petroleum requirements. By 1970, production of domestic crude oil, natural gas and gas by-products represented more than $1.5 billion in annual shales, and more than a quarter of a billion dollars in net exports.

Demand in the seventies

As the decade of the 1970's began, the world was consuming petroleum at a rate of 40 million barrels every day. Each barrel of oil was worth, at the point of production, anywhere from $2 to $3. By the end of the decade, world demand for oil is expected to have increased to more than 60 million barrels every day.

Capital and exploration expenditures required by the petroleum industry during the 1970's throughout the non-Communist world — for oil and gas production, pipelines, ships, refineries, petrochemical plants and other facilities — have been estimated by the Chase Manhattan Bank at some $250 billion (U.S.). Comparable expenditures during the 1960's amounted to about $150 billion, and during the 1950's to $70 billion. The largest single area of spending will

3

be on exploration and development to provide the new supplies of oil and gas that the growing world markets will soon require.

400 billion barrels needed

To 1970, some 650 billion barrels of recoverable oil reserves had been found throughout the world, of which some 410 billion barrels still remained to be produced. Production during the 1970's is expected to total about 200 billion barrels, half the known, remaining reserves in 1970. At the same time, net reserves during the decade will have to increase by some 200 billion barrels, if proved reserves are to increase at the same relative rate as production. Thus during the 1970's the world petroleum industry will need to find some 400 billion barrels of recoverable oil reserves — 60 percent as much as had been discovered during the preceding 100 years.

North American problem acute

The problem of finding sufficient new oil reserves will be particularly acute in North America. In 1970, Canada and the United States combined to account for some 37 percent of world oil demand, but only 16 percent of the known world oil reserves. Combined Canadian and U.S. oil demand is expected to increase during the 1970's from a rate of 15 million to 20 million barrels every day. Oil consumed in North America during the decade will total about 65 billion barrels. This is about equal to all the known, remaining recoverable oil reserves in North America in 1970, including the most optimistic assessment of the giant Prudhoe Bay field on the Arctic coast of Alaska. Only the discovery of enormous new supplies can prevent North America from becoming increasingly dependent on imports from other areas for its petroleum requirements.

The Arctic

The discovery in January, 1970, of crude oil near the Canadian Arctic coast, east of the Mackenzie River Delta, appears to mark the beginning of success for Canada's frontier oil areas.

Three hundred miles to the west, another oil discovery had been made two years earlier on Alaska's Arctic coast. This was the Prudhoe Bay field, the largest oil find in North America after more than a century of exploration. With some 15 billion barrels of recoverable oil reserves, Prudhoe Bay represented in just one field nearly one quarter of North America's total remaining recoverable oil reserves in 1970.

Prudhoe Bay provided validation of geologic theories which had long held that portions of the circumpolar regions — in Russia, Alas-

Exploratory
drilling
at Prudhoe Bay

The Great Canadian Oil Patch

ka, Canada and elsewhere – constitute one of the world's principal oil areas. The petroleum resources of the circumpolar regions could well rival those of the Middle East, where more than half the world's oil reserves had been discovered to 1970.

On the North Slope of Alaska, the area prospective for oil embraces some 100,000 square miles, between the Brooks Mountain Range and the Arctic Ocean. The Prudhoe Bay field represents only a small fraction of the total reserves expected to be found on the North Slope. Although definitive figures are not possible, geologists have estimated the potential reserves of the North Slope between 50 billion and 70 billion barrels of recoverable oil reserves.

Canada's Arctic potential

On the Canadian side, the Arctic oil potential is much greater. In the Arctic Islands, along the coastal plain of the mainland, and in the Mackenzie River Delta area, the prospective oil areas of the Canadian Arctic embrace some 400,000 square miles on land, four times the prospective area of Alaska's North Slope. Geologic conditions appear to be at least as favorable for large oil reserves on the Canadian side as on the Alaskan side.

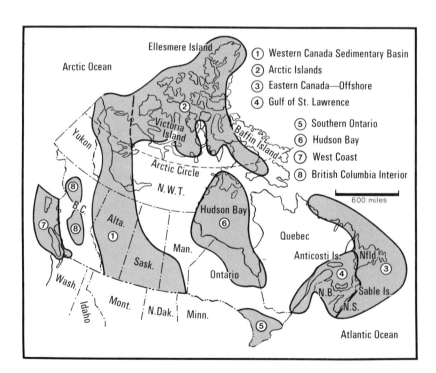

Potential hydrocarbon producing areas

Imperial Oil's Point Atkinson discovery offers confirmation of this. It is Canada's first Arctic oil discovery, 300 miles north of Norman Wells, Imperial's sub-Arctic oil discovery made 50 years earlier.

Atkinson Point

The four provinces of western Canada accounted for something in excess of 95 percent of all the oil and gas discovered in Canada to 1970. Yet these four provinces contain less than a third of Canada's prospective oil bearing areas. The other two thirds, the frontier oil regions, are in the Yukon and Northwest Territories, the Arctic Islands and along the continental shelves beneath the ocean waters bordering the country on three sides.

Not only do the frontier oil regions embrace prospective oil areas more than three times as large as the prospective oil areas of western Canada, but they may be far more prolific. Ninety percent of the world's oil reserves, and all the truly great fields, are contained in sedimentary rocks of the Mesozoic and Cenozoic eras, from 50 million to 225 million years old. Rocks of the Paleozoic era, from 225 million to 600 million years old, account for only 10 percent of the world's oil. Nearly all of the oil found in Western Canada is from rocks of the Paleozoic era. But in Canada's frontier oil eras it is in the younger rocks which have proven so petroliferous elsewhere in the world that the principal oil prospects lie.

Another Middle East?

By 1970, oil companies were spending more than $100 million per year searching for the resources of Canada's frontier oil areas. Point Atkinson was the first reward of that search.

There are in North America, more than 5.5 million cubic miles of rocks of the type in which accumulations of oil and gas are sometimes found. It is these sedimentary rocks, deposited on the shores of ancient oceans, which contain the petroleum resources of the continent.

Sedimentary rock occurrence

The United States has slightly more than half of these rocks — some 2.5 million cubic miles in the "lower 48 states" and about 500,000 cubic miles in Alaska. In Canada, the potential oil bearing rocks have been estimated by the Canadian Petroleum Association to exceed 2.6 million cubic miles.

To 1970, something like 165 billion barrels of recoverable oil reserves (including natural gas liquids as well as crude oil) had been found, and about 100 billion barrels of this had been produced. The lower 48 states had proved up some 135 billion barrels, with about 40 billion barrels left to be produced. Canada had found about 14 billion barrels, with about 10 billion barrels left to be produced. Alaska, with its great Prudhoe Bay field, had accounted for the discovery of up to an estimated 15 billion barrels, of which only a negligible amount had been produced.

No one really knows how much oil is locked in the tiny pores of these 5.5 million cubic miles of sedimentary rocks. Hundreds of "expert" estimates have been made, and nearly all have proven to be far too conservative. In 1919 the director of the U.S. Bureau of Mines warned that "within two to five years the oil fields of this country will reach their maximum production, and from that time on we will face an ever-increasing decline." U.S. oil production in 1919 was little more than one million barrels per day. Fifty years later, the rate was more than eight million barrels per day.

U.S. discovery rate declining

Production and remaining recoverable oil reserves in the U.S. lower 48 states had, however, started declining by 1970. There was still a lot more oil to be found in this the most extensively explored oil area in the world, but it had become increasingly difficult and expensive to find. As a result, oil in the lower 48 states was not being discovered as fast as it was being produced.

The existence of large petroleum supplies in the United States had repeatedly been one of the decisive factors in the course of world history during the first half of the 20th century. The first world war "was won on a wave of petroleum," British Foreign Minister Lord Curzon has observed. Ninety percent of the oil used by the allied forces during that war came from the United States. In the second

Military needs

world war, the United States supplied 70 percent of a vastly greater military demand by the allied forces. It shipped overseas twice as many tons of petroleum products during the war as of all men, weapons, ammunition, food and other supplies combined. During the Korean war the availability of U.S. oil supplies was once again one of the decisive factors in victory. During the Arab-Israeli war of 1957, when the flow of Middle East oil was choked off, it was U.S. oil which prevented a serious world oil shortage. During peace years the availability of large U.S. oil supplies forestalled any possibility of economic or political blackmail by a cartel of a few oil rich nations with a corner on the world's petroleum supplies. In war and peace, the United States has considered few factors to be of such vital importance to its national security as the maintenance of an adequate supply of indigenous petroleum.

U.S. policy during both the 1950's and 1960's fully recognized this contribution of petroleum. Rigid controls on imported oil maintained prices for U.S. crude oil which were the highest of any major world oil producing country, at least $1.25 per barrel above the average crude oil prices elsewhere in the non-Communist world. There is a limit, however, to the amount of premium that even the United States finds desirable to pay for its petroleum supplies in order to stimulate its flagging search for new oil supplies. With the cost of the oil import controls to the U.S. economy estimated as high as $4 billion per year, it appeared that the limit had been reached by 1969.

Cost to U.S. of import controls

It was apparent also by 1969 that the highest crude oil prices in the world were not enough to maintain an adequate level of oil reserves and production in the U.S. lower 48 states. This means that if the United States is to continue to draw the bulk of its petroleum needs from North American sources, so as to ensure security of supply, then it must look increasingly for these supplies to the relatively unexplored oil regions of Alaska and Canada.

A forecast by Oilweek magazine has predicted this growth for the Canadian petroleum industry during the 1970's:

Growth in the seventies

Production of oil and gas liquids, up 230 percent from 1.4 million to 3.3 million barrels per day; natural gas sales, up more than 300 percent from four billion cubic feet per day to 12 billion cubic feet per day; capital expenditures, for production, pipelines, refineries, petrochemical plants and other facilities, plus exploration expenditures, $20 billion, nearly double the $10.5 billion spent during the 1960's.

It is an impressive growth potential, but the full significance lies in the prospects that this holds for the Canadian economy. Consider what effect the establishment of a petroleum producing industry has had on the economy of western Canada, particularly Alberta, during the two decades following the 1947 discovery of oil at Leduc.

In 1945, Alberta had a population of 803,000; personal income per capita was $692, nine percent below the national average; the economy was almost entirely dependent on agriculture, and a declining population seemed inevitable. The discovery of oil at Leduc dramatically changed the outlook for this economically depressed region. Instead of declining, population by 1966 had increased to nearly 1.5 million. Edmonton and Calgary had quadrupled their populations, from 100,000 to 400,000 in Edmonton and from 80,000 to 360,000 in Calgary. Throughout Western Canada the

Influence on Alberta

population was more than one million greater than it would have been without a petroleum producing industry. In Alberta, per capita income rose from nine percent below the national average to four percent above, from $692 to $2,216. A substantial secondary manufacturing industry had been created in the province, the value of manufactured goods increasing from $80 million to $500 million during the 20-year period ended in 1966. By leasing out to industry the oil rights which they own, the governments of the four western provinces collected revenues totalling $3.5 billion during the 23-year period ended in 1969. Three quarters of this was collected by Alberta, which made it, in 1970, the only province without a provincial retail sales tax.

Dramatic spending expected

Most of Canada's petroleum development during the 1970's and 1980's is expected to take place in the frontier oil areas — the Yukon and Northwest Territories, the Arctic Islands, the continental shelf off the Atlantic coast. It is in these regions that the economic effects of petroleum development will be most pronounced. Development of the Canadian north will be stimulated in dramatic fashion. The effects of oil and gas development on the economy of Alberta during the 1950's and 1960's could well be duplicated during the 1970's and 1980's in the Atlantic provinces by the discovery of large oil and gas reserves off the east coast.

Few, if any, industries contributed as much to Canada's economic growth during the 2-1/2 decades following the second world war as the petroleum producing industry. During the next couple of decades, its contribution to the Canadian economy promises to be even more dramatic.

Joint energy policies

It is ironic that there should develop in 1970 a feeling of apprehension in Canada concerning our exports of oil and gas to United States markets.

For years, the Canadian petroleum industry and the government of Canada had been seeking to persuade the United States that it was in the best interests of both nations to allow a greater import of petroleum energy from Canada. For as many years, a large segment of the oil and gas producers in the United States had pressed with all the political force at their command for government curbs on the flow of oil and gas from Canada. But by 1970 there was a growing recognition in the United States that a freer flow of Canadian oil would, indeed, be to their advantage.

Suggestions that the Canadian and U.S. governments might discuss the possibility of joint energy policies aimed at permitting a freer flow of Canadian oil and gas into U.S. markets in the most efficient and economic manner, were greeted with grave concern in the House of Commons. The concern of the opposition members in the House, as New Democratic party leader T. C. Douglas expressed it, was that "we could be getting set up for an extensive sellout of our resources."

"sellout" cries are unfounded

It is difficult to see how increased oil and gas exports to United States markets equates to a "sellout" of our resources to Americans. In order to find, develop and benefit from our potential petroleum resources we will need all the export markets that we can obtain. And if we are lucky enough to sell in the highest priced oil market in the world, then so much the better.

120 billion barrels to be found

By the most ultra-conservative estimate, there are some 120 billion barrels of potential oil reserves in Canada, of which only about 10 percent had been found to 1970. The remaining discovered reserves plus the potential reserves were enough to maintain the 1970 rate of production for 230 years. Should we ever run out of conventional crude oil, we could turn to the enormous bitumen deposit in Alberta's Athabasca tar sands. At only a minor increment over present crude oil costs, the bitumen of the tar sands could yield some 300 billion barrels of synthetic crude oil, enough to maintain Canada's 1970 oil production rate for another 700 years. Finally, there are the nation's vast coal reserves. Capable of being manufactured into substitutes for either crude oil or natural gas, the coal reserves contain many times the amount of energy locked in the Athabasca tar sands. Long before Canada's hydrocarbon energy resources are exhausted, civilization will have likely turned to other sources — nuclear, tidal, solar — to meet all its energy requirements.

Why we need markets

The real challenge is to ensure that the bulk of our potential petroleum resources will not be wasted by being left in the ground, undiscovered, unutilized and benefiting no one. To find, develop and utilize these potential resources we will require all the markets we can obtain. Only if there is an adequate market demand will the indicated $20 billion required for petroleum capital and exploration expenditures in Canada during the 1970's be raised.

In the U.S. lower 48 states it required the drilling of some 300,000 wildcat wells to 1970 to discover 135 billion barrels of oil. With 2.5 million cubic miles of sedimentary rock, that represented approximately one wildcat per eight cubic miles of prospective oil bearing rock. In Canada, some 22,000 wildcats had been drilled to 1970, one

11

per 119 cubic miles of the total 2.6 million cubic miles of sedimentary rocks. In 1970, wildcats were being drilled in Canada at a rate of less than 2,000 per year. At this rate, it would require another 150 years to reach the intensity of exploratory drilling attained in the U.S. lower 48 states by 1970.

Discovery of the early fields

The fact that Canada's oil potential lay dormant for 90 years following the Oil Springs discovery in Ontario reflects no lack of Canadian enterprise. Canadians were among the first oil gamblers. If their efforts bore little fruit, it was because it was difficult to exploit the nation's petroleum potential until the circumstances of geography, geology, technology and economics had all combined to make the time ripe.

The earliest oil fields were found by a combination of two methods: sheer luck, and a rudimentary form of geological science that followed up surface indications. Seepages of oil and gas percolating from the ground pointed the way to the first — and some of the world's largest — oil discoveries. Oil seeps led to Ontario's Oil Springs discovery in 1858; to Drake's discovery at Titusville, Pa., in 1859; to the Turner Valley discovery in Alberta in 1914; to the Norman Wells field in the Northwest Territories in 1920. In Iraq, flames have been burning from a natural gas seep for thousands of years, and are believed to be the Bible's "fiery furnace" where Shadrach, Meshach and Abednego walked. The Turkish Petroleum Company in 1927 drilled a mile and a half from the fiery furnace. It brought in the Kirkuk discovery, a stunning gusher spewing a column of oil 140 feet into the air and flowing oil at a rate of 100,000 barrels a day, one of the world's largest oil fields.

Trendology

Early oil explorers noticed that oil pools often lined up along parallel trends, and "trendology" became a method of oil exploring. They walked along creek beds looking for oil and gas seeps and examining the trends of rock formations, a method dubbed "creekology." Canadian geologists developed the "anticlinal theory," which held that oil was trapped in dome-like structures, or anticlines. In 1848, Sir William Logan, director of the Geological Survey of Canada, noted that the oil seeps on the Gaspe Peninsula were located on anticlines. Thirteen years later T. Sterry Hunt, also with the GSC, concluded that the conditions necessary for an accumulation of oil included a source bed for the oil; a structure, or anticline, and an impervious rock-cap. Trendology, creekology and the anticline theory dominated oil exploration for decades, and produced some of the

Leduc No. 1 blowing in April, 1947. Well is clearing itself of mud contaminated oil which the flames consume.

world's largest oil fields. The same practices were used in Canada, but yielded only sparse and scattered results. The trouble with these methods was the one thing that they all had in common. They relied on surface indications to point the way to oil pools, and this just didn't work in most of western Canada. Few of the oil and gas pools

13

in western Canada are reflected by indications on the surface, in the form of either oil or gas seeps or visible structures. Large reefs, which grew at the edges of ocean beds in the Devonian era (300 million to 400 million years ago), account for more than half of the oil discovered in western Canada to 1970. These reefs are buried from 3,000 to 13,000 feet deep, and there is no known way that you can tell where they might be merely by looking at the surface.

Seismic reflection

The first Devonian oil bearing reef to produce in western Canada was found by Imperial Oil at Leduc, a village near Edmonton, in 1947. It was found with the aid of a seismic survey, a geophysical exploration technique which measures the movement of sound waves through the earth in order to construct relief maps of the subsurface rock layers. This sometimes discloses the presence of subsurface structures which might contain oil or gas.

But reflection seismic was not an established exploration tool until the 1930's and even in the 1960's electronic computer methods for recording and processing the data have greatly improved the effectiveness of seismic exploration in the search for Devonian reefs. Western Canada's oil potential simply had to wait until the exploration scientists had devised methods to see – in however veiled a fashion – the trail markers that in other areas lay on the surface.

Offshore potential

Offshore, too, Canada has had to wait until the time brought the right combination of technical ability and world demand for oil. Along the continental shelves off the world coastlines, to a water depth of 600 feet, lay some nine million square miles of potential oil and gas basins, an area the size of Africa. Offshore areas accounted for 16 percent of world oil production in 1969, and geologists estimate these regions will eventually account for one quarter to a third of the world's petroleum resources. It has only been since the second world war that the industry had the ability to develop oil reserves in any but the shallowest of waters. Giant mobile, floating platforms capable of drilling in water depths of 600 feet or more at locations as far as 200 miles from shore, were not developed until the 1960's. Off Canada's coasts lies nine percent of the world's potential offshore oil and gas basins, a greater potential offshore oil area than that of any other country but Russia.

Arctic Islands

In the Arctic Islands, many geologists believe, oil will be much easier to find in large volume than elsewhere in Canada. Here there are visible the large structures and other surface clues which made petroleum exploration so comparatively simple during the industry's formative years. Despite this, the Arctic Islands have had to await their day too, when new ice breaking techniques, or atomic submarine tankers, or vast submarine pipelines, could lick the problem of economically transporting oil from these ice-locked islands.

Canada missed out on petroleum's first century. It missed out to those areas where, by today's standards, oil was comparatively simple to find. But it won't miss out on the second century. Those first generation oil areas are no longer adequate to meet the world's rapidly growing oil needs. The best of them have already been extensively explored. The oil supplies of tomorrow must come from pools which may be giant-size but which lay better hidden beneath the mask of topographically featureless areas, or beneath hundreds of feet of ocean water, or in remote and inaccessible regions like Canada's far north and the Arctic Islands.

The Second Century

Chapter One

Dr. Gesner and his kerosene

Why drill for oil?

Deliberate efforts to secure crude oil supplies in North America were made only following development of a substantial manufacturing industry capable of converting the crude oil into saleable products.

This was the "coal oil" industry, and no single person can be exclusively credited with its development. But no one made a more vital contribution than a largely unknown Canadian, Dr. Abraham Gesner, physician, surgeon, geologist, chemist, author and inventor. It was Gesner who first produced, and named, kerosene, a product that fueled the lamps of the world for nearly half a century and now fuels jet aircraft. Gesner and others established a flourishing industry in the United States, manufacturing lamp fuel and lubricating oils from coal. Later, the same products were manufactured in the same refineries more cheaply from crude oil. The coal oil industry that Gesner helped establish was almost extinct less than a decade after its founding; but without it, the crude oil discoveries in Ontario in 1858 and Pennsylvania in 1859 would have been of little importance.

The 100-year wonder

Petroleum had been known in various forms and used for diverse purposes for something like 5,000 years before the oil discoveries in Ontario and Pennsylvania almost instantaneously set off one of the world's greatest industrial developments. Now known to scientists as asphaltic pyrobitumens, the heavier forms of petroleum have been referred to by historians as bitumen, tar, pitch, asphalt and, in the Bible, as slime. They were used by Noah to caulk the ark, and they waterproofed the basket that hid Moses in the reeds of the Nile River. In ancient Mesopotamia, the streets of Babylon were paved with pyrobitumen and the walls of Jericho were bonded with it. It was used to waterproof baths, boats and bins, as a cement for pottery and mosaics, in the manufacture of paints, and as an embalming agent for Egyptian mummies.

Petroleum was used in medicine, and in war. The Roman encyclopaedist, Pliny, claimed that bitumen had great powers to check bleeding, assist healing of wounds, straighten out eyelashes, treat leperous spots and gout, and cure chronic coughs and diarrhoea. The Arabs and Persians, turning from the viscous, asphaltic bitumen to more volatile crude oil, developed primitive distillation methods to produce naphtha, used as an illuminating oil and a material of war. In the fire that destroyed Cairo in 1077, some 20,000 jars of naphtha helped feed the conflagration. Even earlier, "Greek Fire" was used with devastating effect in grenades and flame throwers by Arab and Mongol armies. A seventh-century legend has it that the Shah of Persia defeated an elephant-supported Indian army by using hollow iron horses filled with burning oil. The Greeks claimed to have destroyed an enemy fleet by pouring oil on the water and setting it afire. The Chinese drilled oil wells at least 2,000 years ago, used oil and natural gas for both light and heat, and built bamboo pipelines to carry the gas from the wells. In the thirteenth century, Marco Polo found that asphalt deposits and oil wells in the Bakku area of Russia supported a thriving oil business, supplying demand for lamp fuel and medicines.

For
medicinal
purposes

In the Western Hemisphere, natives were using bitumen for much the same purposes. Alexander Mackenzie found the Cree Indians using bitumen from the Athabasca tar sands of northern Alberta to caulk their canoes. In Peru, the natives used it for waterproofing and embalming. In Mexico, it was used as a toothpaste and chewing gum, and almost everywhere in North America it was used as a medicine.

......and
caulking
canoes

First asphaltic deposit discovered by Europeans in the new world was found in Cuba by Spanish explorers in 1526. Soon, such sailors as Drake, Raleigh and De Soto were caulking their ships with material from this and similar deposits along the Gulf of Mexico, in Peru, and from Trinidad's fabled asphalt lake. This lake, located in the crater of an ancient volcano and measuring less than a quarter mile in diameter, has yielded more than 100 million barrels of an asphaltic mixture of bitumen, mud, clay and silt, and in 1970 was still being commercially exploited.

Wonder of the 19th century

Less than a year after Edwin L. Drake completed North America's second commercial oil well near Titusville, Pennsylvania on August 28, 1859, "men began calling the new-born American petroleum industry the wonder of the nineteenth century," according to early oil historians. Within a year of the Drake discovery, hundreds of wells were drilled in search of oil, and production had been found in West Virginia, Kentucky, Ohio and Kansas, as well as in Ontario and Pennsylvania.

Yet Drake's discovery has been described by an authoritative oil historian as "this relatively insignificant event." And so it was, or at least would have been, without the coal oil industry.

Oil springs had been widely known in both eastern Canada and the United States for more than 200 years, and had been exploited for lubricating oils, and for medicine. Wells drilled for salt water brine had already produced appreciable quantities of oil, which was discarded as an unwanted nuisance.

The Lake Erie area

The area centering around Lake Erie is where the oil industry was born in North America, with James Miller Williams' well at Oil Springs, Ontario on the north side of the Lake in 1858, and Drake's discovery on the south side the following year. It was in this region too, that North America's first recorded oil springs were discovered in 1726 by Joseph Delaroch Daillon, a French missionary, who noted "a good kind of oil which the Indians called Antonontons." The site was within 60 miles of Drake's discovery. The oil springs where Drake drilled had been known at least since 1783 when an American General reported that his troops had collected some of the "Barbadoes tar" and "bathed their joints with it," which "freed them immediately from the rheumatic complaints."

Salt drillers really produced the first oil from wells in North America, developed the cable tool method of drilling, and provided the first experienced drillers for the fledgling oil industry. In an era before canned goods and deepfreezes, salt was the major food preservative, and it took 500 pounds to keep a quarter of beef from spoiling. Salt springs and outcrops at first supplied the demand, but drilling for salt brine was well established in West Virginia by 1817, with a score of wells yielding up to 700,000 bushels of salt annually, produced from depths of 100 feet or more. Almost from the start, however, oil, and in some cases gas, was produced with the brine. One well, drilled to 500 feet, was a failure as a brine producer when a pocket of gas blew the tools out of the hole. In 1829 a salt water well near Burksville, Kansas, reportedly flowed oil at a rate of 1,000 barrels a day, ruining a perfectly good salt well and coating the Cumberland River with a sticky film. The inevitable happened: someone set a spark to the oil, and the fire raged along the river for more than 50 miles. All was not lost, however. A group of promoters formed the American Medical Oil Company and sold for medicinal purposes several hundred thousand bottles of oil produced from the well.

Another man bothered with an oil problem was Samuel Kier, who drilled a salt water well to a depth of 469 feet at Tarentum, Pennsylvania, not far from the site of Drake's future discovery. Noting that the unwanted oil produced with the brine from his well smelled suspiciously like the medicine the family doctor had prescribed for his wife, Kier in 1848 started selling his patented "rock oil" as the "most wonderful remedy ever discovered" for rheumatism, gout, neuralgia, chronic coughs and a host of other ailments. Ten years later — and two years before Drake completed his well — Kier had sold an estimated 240,000 bottles of his Rock Oil at $1 each.

240,000 bottles of patent medicine

The discoveries of Williams and Drake were no prolific producers, even by the standards of those days; William's well is reported to have pumped a maximum 37 barrels in 10 hours, while Drake's well was placed on pump production at an estimated rate of eight to ten gallons per day. They established no drilling records; Williams took his well to about 60 feet, and Drake took two years to drill to 69 1/2 feet. By contrast, salt drillers in West Virginia by that time were punching down holes 1,000 feet or more in six to eight months.

What made these wells significant was just this: they were the first to be successfully drilled and completed for the specific purpose of finding and producing crude oil. And the reason they were drilled for this purpose is that the needs of society and the development of technology had been combined to create a real economic value, for the first time, for the hydrocarbon substance known as crude oil. And this is where the great contribution of Dr. Abraham Gesner comes in.

Significance of Drake and Williams

The role played by the creation of coal oil refining technology in the development of the petroleum industry can be summarized simply. The world urgently needed a better source of light — safer, more dependable, cheaper. Coal oil refining provided it, by refining kerosene from a hydrocarbon, coal. Within a few years, a similar illuminating oil was produced more cheaply by the same refineries from another hydrocarbon, crude oil. For half a century — until the electric light bulb eclipsed the kerosene lamp and the petroleum industry stepped into a new era with the development of the internal combustion engine — lamp oil and lubricants were the foundation for one of the most dynamic industries to emerge from the latter half of the 19th century.

The end of the whalers

With the dawn of the 19th century came the industrial revolution, with its wheels, machines, engines, inventions and industry. And with them, too, a problem: how to lubricate the machines of industry. In the factories of Lincoln's day, writes historian Leonard M. Fanning in Men, Money and Oil, "you held your nose against the smell of rancid animal and vegetable oils used to lubricate the spindles and machines. You shouted to be heard over the shrieks and groans of ponderous steam engines. You sat helpless in the railroad coach when the cumbersome locomotive hotboxed to a stop because its bearings had become overheated and acid-eaten."

Illumination was nearly as primitive as in the days of ancient Rome and Greece. Gas light was still a novelty. In homes and offices, factories, ships and stores, men still used flickering candles and a strange assortment of smoking, stinking lamps fueled with whale oil, fish oils, lards of various types and odors, resins from pine pitch, and camphene, a dangerously explosive mixture of redistilled spirits of turpentine and alcohol.

Hunting regions

The premium lamp fuel and lubricant from 1712 until the mid-nineteenth century was the oil from the sperm whale. In pursuit of the depleting supply of the sea monsters, whalers from Nantucket hurled their harpoons in the whale grounds off Newfoundland, the West Indies, Brazil and the Cape Verde Islands, finally rounding Cape Horne to fish the Pacific, "even through Bering's Strait, and into the remotest drawers and lockers of the world," wrote Melville in Moby Dick in 1851. "In the peak year of the trade," writes Samuel W. Twait in Wildcatters, "it meant that over seven hundred ships were in the trade, $70 million of investment, and over 70,000 persons." As the whalers butchered ever farther afield to meet a steadily growing demand, whale oil prices kept pace. By 1850 prices for whale oil had risen to as much as $2.50 per gallon, several days' pay for the average working man of that era.

Rising demand and spiralling prices for any commodity always produces a common result: the search for a better and cheaper alternative. It was gas light and coal oil that finally killed the whaling industry.

Abraham Gesner was born on a homestead at Cornwallis, Nova Scotia, May 2, 1797, one of 12 children of Henry and Sarah Gesner, and was educated, according to a biography written by his son, with "the ordinary instruction of the grammar schools of the day." An avid reader and diligent student, Gesner was also something of an adventurer, and set out on his first career as a horse trader, shipping Nova Scotia and New Brunswick horses to the West Indies. He was shipwrecked twice, and the venture ended in financial failure.

On his trips to the West Indies, Gesner's natural curiosity had led to close inspection of the tar springs on Barbados Island and the famed pitch lake on Trinidad, both of which Gesner correctly deduced were natural asphalts formed by the drying out of petroleum seepages. A quarter of a century later, Gesner's first attempts to produce a new illuminating oil were based on the use of Trinidad asphalt as the raw material.

Gesner's second career stemmed from his marriage to Harriet Webster, daughter of a Kentville, Nova Scotia physician, Dr. Isaac Webster. Within a year, Gesner was following his father-in-law's footsteps, acquiring an education in London, in surgery at Guy's Hospital, and medical instruction at St. Bartholomew's. In 1827, at age 30, Gesner hung up his shingle in the little village of Parrsboro, not far from his family's homestead, and settled down to the quiet life of a country doctor.

But Gesner was far too active, curious, and inquisitive to rusticate in Parrsboro, and soon launched yet another career. While making his medical rounds by horse, Gesner was attracted by the island's finely crystallized rocks, and was soon returning home with his saddlebags crammed with rock specimens. He began reading geological literature, and started what developed into a life-time correspondence with leading scientific men of his day in Europe, Canada, and the United States. He was soon not only reading geologic literature, but also contributing to it. His first book, Remarks on the Geology and Mineralogy of Nova Scotia, a 313-page text published in 1836, was the first attempt to apply modern geological theories to Nova Scotia.

The varied career of Dr. Gesner

Trinidad tar Springs

Geology author

Provincial geologist

It laid great stress on the practical applications, covering newly opened coal mines, undeveloped iron deposits; and it pointed the way to exploitation of other minerals of commercial value. Within two years he had abandoned medicine. He moved to St. John in 1838 to accept an appointment as the first provincial geologist for New Brunswick, and launched a detailed geological examination of the province, again with great emphasis on the economic aspects. His First Report on the Geological Survey of New Brunswick was published in 1839 and followed by similar reports in 1840, 1842 and 1843.

"On foot, on horseback, and by canoe, he pushed through the forests of the province," his biographer, Kendall Beaton, has written in Business History Review magazine. ". . . accompanied by Indian guides, he paddled up its streams, plotting dip and strike, gathering specimens, analyzing finds, theorizing, and – always – keeping a sharp eye out for coal, zinc, lead, iron, manganese, copper, gypsum, salt, and any other mineral deposit which might have, or might be made to have, some commercial value. In charming contrast to geologists of a later day, Dr. Gesner saw no reason why he should not employ in his reports whatever literary skills he possessed to describe in vivid fashion the sights and sounds he encountered in his explorations."

Gesner under seige

His vivid descriptions were, perhaps, too vivid, and his glowing accounts of the economic possibilities, too glowing. In any event, when local interests, prompted by Gesner's reports, opened new coal mines and built iron furnaces they found their enterprises less profitable than hoped, and turned their wrath on Gesner. His employment by the provincial government was abruptly terminated, and Gesner returned to the family homestead at Cornwallis to be with his father, then 87, and resumed his medical practice, while at the same time writing, lecturing, and conducting scientific experiments.

The first illuminating oil

During this period, Gesner produced his first illuminating oil, using asphalt from the pitch lake at Trinidad which he had visited more than two decades earlier. The product was not entirely satisfactory. It smoked, and gave off an offensive odor. The raw material was difficult and expensive to obtain and produced a low yield of about 42 gallons of oil per ton of asphalt.

A peculiar black mineral discovered on the Petitcodiac River in Albert County, New Brunswick, provided a more satisfactory material for the manufacture of illuminating oil. The mineral, later called "Albert mineral" and "Albertite", had the appearance of coal. It was black, and it would burn. Gesner noted that it had "all the essential properties of asphaltum, while it is void of those that constitute true coal." He found that by heating the Albert mineral to high temperatures in a closed retort, he could produce a satisfactory burning oil. In public demonstration in August, 1848, he showed how this burning fluid could be used in lamps. He was thus the first in North America to distill a hydrocarbon into lamp fuel, a fuel that soon glowed in lamps around the world.

Albertite

Success, however, was neither instant nor easy. Gesner himself may not yet have grasped the full significance of his find, for his efforts in the next couple of years seemed directed elsewhere. In 1847 he was appointed commissioner to the Indians by the Nova Scotia government, and in the same year published in London a 388-page guidebook, New Brunswick with notes for Immigrants, followed the next year by The Industrial Resources of Nova Scotia.

Indian com- missioner

Gesner moved his family to Sackville, near Halifax, late in 1850, where his active interest in distillation of burning oils was revived by Thomas Cochrane, 10th Earl of Dundonald, Admiral of the British North American and West India Station, and who was posted at Halifax. Dundonald's interest in the possible applications of hydro-carbon products anteceded Gesner's. Dundonald's father in 1781 had patented a method of distilling coal tar to obtain an illuminating oil, a waterproofing agent and other products, and the family's consider-able fortune had been lost in schemes to implement these and other inventions.

Dundonald

In the Trinidad pitch lake, Dundonald thought he saw an oppor-tunity to put his father's processes to use, and began hatching plans for such applications as paving, waterproofing, coating of water mains and insulation of electric wires. Gesner and Dundonald soon developed concrete proposals to utilize not only the Trinidad pitch but also the Albertite from New Brunswick. Dundonald, then 75, returned to England in 1851, took out a series of patents covering a wide range of applications for natural asphalt, and purchased all the lands surrounding the pitch lake at Trinidad.

Dundonald's patents, however, did not embrace the distillation of burning oil, and it was in this area that Gesner concentrated. His first step was to seek control of a supply of the Albert County mineral, and to this end he brought action in the court at Halifax to show

Gesner goes to New York

23

that this mineral was asphaltum, not coal, and thus not included in the coal rights which had been reserved to the crown in land grants. In the end, the court ruled that coal leases which had been issued in the area embraced also "other mines and minerals".

Gesner was undeterred. He reasoned that similar materials could be had, and in 1853 – at the age of 56 – set off with his family for New York to establish the coal oil business.

The short history of coal oil

"Project for the Formation of a Company to Work the Combined Patent Rights (for the State of New York) of Dr. Abraham Gesner, of Halifax, N.S., and the Right Hon. The Earl of Dundonald, of Middlesex, England ," was the title of an eight-page prospectus issued in March, 1853, by Horatio Eagle, a partner of Eagle & Hazard, ship's agents and brokers, New York. The prospectus offered a public issue of $100,000 in shares of a new company, Asphalt Mining and Kerosene Gas Company (later called North American Kerosene Gas Light Company) which proposed to manufacture a wide range of products: paving materials, waterproofing agents, insulation for underground telegraph wires, railway grease, and, most important, "burning fluids . . . which could be manufactured at a lower cost than the various burning fluids now in use."

Gesner had his financial backing, but the price was high. "Dr. Gesner's services (it may be as well to observe) ," said the prospectus, "have been secured to the company for a term of years, at a moderate salary." Gesner may have also received some allotment of the company's stock, but there is no record of this. When the U.S. patents were issued to Gesner on June 27, 1854, they were assigned to the company.

Gesner's patent

"I, Abraham Gesner, late of the city and county of New York, now of Williamsburg, in the county of Kings and State of New York, have invented and discovered a new and useful manufacture or composition of matter, being a new liquid hydrocarbon, which I denominate Kerosene, and which may be used for illuminating or other purposes," the recital of the patents read. It described how the product was manufactured from almost any hydrocarbon, "petroleum, altha, or soft mineral pitch, asphaltum, or bitumen wherever found". Coal, though not mentioned, was the principal raw material later used. By means of dry distillation followed by further treatment with sulphuric acid and calcinated lime and redistillation, the process yielded three fractions which Gesner called Kerosene A, B and C. The first two were light and highly volatile, similar to what is

24

now called gasoline, and at that time primarily unwanted and dangerous by-products. Kerosene C, heavier and less volatile, was both an
illuminating oil and lubricant.

The term Kerosene is a compound of the Greek word Keros,
meaning wax, from the waxy paraffin obtained in the manufacture;
and camphene, at the time a popular illuminating oil.

By the time the patents were issued, the North American Kerosene
Gas Light Company (as it was later named) had already started
construction of a substantial manufacturing plant along the east bank
of the Newton Creek in Queens County, New York. The plant is
believed to have started operations early in 1854, and although it
probably experienced the start-up troubles common to any new
plant using an untried process, by 1856 the company's advertising
was extolling the virtues of Kerosene as an illuminating oil. It
produced, claimed a consulting chemist hired by the firm, a light 13
times brighter than Sylvic, and four times as bright as even gas light.
It sold for $1 a gallon, and based on the "cost of an equal amount of
light" was one-sixth the cost of sperm oil, a quarter the cost of lard
oil, half the cost of gas light, and two-thirds the cost of camphene.

The first plant

A description of the company's works in the New York Commercial Advertiser on August 24, 1859 (three days before the completion of Drake's well) disclosed a plant that cost $1.25 million,
employed 200 men, used 30,000 tons of coal per year, and had a
manufacturing capacity of 5,000 gallons of kerosene per day. Plant
facilities covered half of a 14-acre site, including "a bulkhead four
hundred and ninety feet long, at which the lighters can discharge
their cargo of coal and receive the oil for shipment." One of the
plant buildings contained 13 stills. Another, under construction, was
to contain eight finishing stills, while yet another "will contain a
large number of stills; also two six-thousand gallon tanks from which
the oil will be drawn off, and barrelled ready for shipment." There
was a two-story engine house and a "large boiler room with a
chimney one hundred and thirty feet high; here are placed two steam
boilers forty-two inches in diameter and sixty feet long." Coal oil
was indeed a booming business.

Capacity

Time and again in history, researchers working independently of
each other have arrived almost simultaneously at the same results. So
it was with the distillation of coal into oils. While Gesner's work was
barely started, others were experimenting with the distillation of
coal, obtaining patents as much as four years before Gesner obtained

Other research

his U.S. patent for Kerosene manufacture. An important difference, however, was this: the others concentrated on lubricating oils, and not until well after the North American Kerosene Gas Light Company was in production and selling its products did they turn to manufacturing illuminating oil. By contrast, Gesner's efforts from the outset were directed primarily at the market for illuminating oils – the biggest, most important market.

James Young

Chief among Gesner's contemporaries were James Young in Scotland, and the United States Chemical Manufacturing Company, controlled by Samuel Downer, one of Boston's largest producers of whale and sperm oil and sperm candles.

A trained chemist, Young in 1847 (a year after Gesner's first public demonstrations of his illuminating oil) began experiments on the lubricating quality of oil from a petroleum spring which oozed some 300 gallons a day from a coal mine in Derbyshire. Young figured that the oil was actually coal which had been transformed by pressure and heat into a fluid. To enlarge his supply of oil, Young set about to duplicate what he thought was nature's process, and tried distilling oil from coal. His basic theory was all wrong – oil is not transformed coal – but his results were eminently satisfactory. Young obtained patents for his process in England in 1850 and in the United States in 1852, soon had a refinery at Bathgate, Scotland, and a thriving business marketing his "paraffin oil," a far superior lubricant that under-sold existing vegetable oils at five shillings a gallon, versus eight to nine shillings for the rancid vegetable oils.

Coal tar experiment

The United States Chemical Manufacturing Company, meanwhile, began experiments in 1852 aimed at producing lubricating oils from coal tar, a by-product of gas manufacture. By 1855 they had succeeded in producing lubricating oils "from nearly all the known sources, and many varieties of coals and shales." Almost by a fluke, chemists from Downer's firm discovered, on a trip to Scotland, that they could re-distill Young's lubricating oil to produce a good quality burning oil. Downer, with his established interest in whale oil, at first rejected this idea of his chemists. "Our business is lubricating oil," he stated. "Illuminating oils don't amount to anything. You can never replace the large or whale oil lamp; they are the articles for illuminating purposes."

But, possibly impressed with the success of North American Kerosene Gas and Light Company, Downer soon changed his mind, and by 1857 both James Young in Scotland and U.S. Chemical in the United States were also busy manufacturing coal oil.

They weren't the only ones to follow Gesner's lead. By the end of 1860 – less than a year and a half after Drake's discovery – Gesner estimated that there were about 70 U.S. plants manufacturing coal oil. And there was something else too. Seemingly overnight at least 15 other plants had sprung up to manufacture essentially the same product by essentially the same methods, but using crude oil exclusively. The days of the coal oil era were numbered, just as before them had been the days of the whale oilers.

Crude oil enters the picture

In existence less than a decade, the coal oil era left behind it a valuable legacy for the fledgling oil producing industry. It bequeathed a built-up market for illuminating oils, an established chain of distribution and retail outlets, a manufacturing technology capable of turning crude oil into saleable products, a string of operating plants quickly capable of converting from coal to oil, and a product name that still endures, kerosene.

Most of the coal oil refineries survived the switch from coal to crude oil, but none more successfully than the Newton Creek works of the North American Kerosene Gas Light Company. After a series of successive changes in ownership it passed in 1876 into the hands of John D. Rockefeller's Standard Oil Company, and later to Standard Oil Company of New York, now Mobil Oil Corporation. It operated for nearly a century, until it was finally shut down in May, 1951, and later sold to a junk dealer.

Legacy of coal oil

Fate dealt less kindly with Abraham Gesner. Like many another inventor who sold his patents, Gesner saw others reap the big rewards from his achievements. With his assignment of the patents to the company, Gesner was little more than a salaried employee, and even that terminated sometime between 1856 and 1859 when he was succeeded by Luther Atwood (formerly of the U.S. Chemical and Manufacturing Company) as chief chemist. In the end, Gesner's patents did not hold up in the courts because of Young's prior filing, and North American Kerosene, Downer's firm, and other coal oil manufacturers, were obliged to pay royalties to Young. In 1860, Gesner published an authoritative manual for the new refineries that were springing up all over North America, A Practical Treatise on Coal, Petroleum and Other Distilled Oils. For a few years after this

Gesner goes back to medicine

he returned to his practice of medicine, this time working in New York. He retired to his native Nova Scotia, settling in Halifax, and on April 29, 1864, he died, in his sixty-seventh year.

Contribution often overlooked

Gesner's vital contribution to the early development of North America's petroleum industry has been completely overlooked by most oil historians, with the exception of Kendall Beaton of the Shell Oil Company. Referring to Gesner's initial plans in 1853 for the first coal oil refinery by North American Kerosene, Kendall wrote:

"From engineers' drawings of the plant which have survived, we can appreciate Dr. Gesner's very real ability as a practical manufacturing chemist. His plant was laid out in orderly fashion and the individual pieces of equipment, shown in detail drawings, were well planned and well-constructed, differing very little from similar pieces of refinery equipment being built as late as the time of the First World War. For all his self-education, Gesner was far better grounded in the theoretical aspects of his business than were the long stream of 'practical' refiners who would follow him and dominate the American oil refining business for the next half century."

Of Gesner's Practical Treatise on Coal, Petroleum and Other Distilled Oils, Beaton had this to say: "This book, 134 pages with illustrations, is remarkable for the sound scientific knowledge the author displayed and for the accuracy of his predictions on the future course the refining business would take. If he had done nothing else, Gesner's Practical Treatise would entitle him to a major niche in the early history of petroleum technology."

One of the very few to fully recognize the importance of Gesner's work was Imperial Oil which, in 1933 erected a monument over his grave at Camp Hill Cemetery, Halifax, and inscribed on the granite shaft these words: "Erected as a token of appreciation for his important contribution to the oil industry."

Gesner's valedictory

Gesner himself was loath to claim the credit he had so richly earned. Writing on the development of the coal oil refining industry – or, more properly, the hydrocarbon refining industry – he claimed only this: "The progress of discovery in this case, as in others, has been slow and gradual. It has been carried on by the labors, not of one mind, but of many, so as to render it difficult to discover to whom the greatest credit is due."

As his valedictory, so to speak, it was typical Gesner modesty, and typically Canadian.

Chapter Two

Birth of the oil industry

August 28, 1859 is the date recorded in most petroleum histories as the birth of North America's oil producing industry. It was on this date at Titusville, Pennsylvania, near the banks of Oil Creek, that "Colonel" Edwin L. Drake is generally reported to have brought in the first well successfully drilled for oil in North America. The discovery was said by some historians to have proven how sufficient petroleum supplies could be obtained to create the spectacular industry which rapidly followed. Drake's well, drilled to 69 1/2 feet, pumped oil at a rate of eight to ten barrels a day.

So much for myth. In fact, the Colonel's claim is as bogus as his title. And it had been a fancy piece of promotional showmanship. When Drake, a former railway conductor, arrived at Titusville in 1857 to seek oil production at the site of an oil seepage, mail forwarded by his financial associates was awaiting his arrival. To impress the local citizenry, the mail had been addressed to Colonel Drake, and the title stuck for the rest of his life.

Long before Drake had drilled at Titusville, North America's oil producing industry was already well established and operating. The site was less than 150 miles northeast of Titusville, on the other side of Lake Erie, at the "gum beds" of Enniskillen Township in the province of Canada West, later Ontario. Markedly successful, if somewhat unobtrusive, the oil industry of Enniskillen Township

The first oil company

The Colonel's bogus claim

The Great Canadian Oil Patch

Wooden pump
frames a 100-year-old spring pole rig
at Oil Springs, Ontario.

featured the first oil company ever to be incorporated, and an integrated operation which embraced crude oil production, refining, and substantial marketing of illuminating oil, the industry's principal production for half a century. Crude was being pumped at a rate several times as great as the production from Drake's well, from a number of wells which had been dug to shallow depths. And even the first successful drilling for oil — the method attributed to Drake which provided sufficient volumes of oil on which to establish an industry — may also have been carried out at Enniskillen a year or more before Drake's well.

Development of the petroleum operations of Canada lacked only one thing: widespread public attention. It was instead, the later drilling of Drake's tiny pumper that sparked the first, wild, frantic oil boom. As a few years earlier, thousands had scrambled west for the California gold rush, now thousands scrambled east, to Pennsylvania and Enniskillen too, for another gold rush — black, liquid gold. It was instant boom, and from a standing start, petroleum operations constituted a major industry within a year. Never before had such a large and significant industry developed as rapidly.

First wells attracted little attention

But no single, simple, isolated incident at a certain time and place can be so conveniently marked as the start of the oil industry. To find the real start of the oil industry is like tracing the roots of a giant oak tree to find where the tree started growing. And in this case, there was no single acorn. It was instead — as are most really important developments — the culmination of the efforts of many people, in many places, over many years. It included the work of men like Abraham Gesner in establishing the coal oil industry with a new standard of light for the world and a ready market for the later production of crude oil; the salt drillers of West Virginia, Ohio and Pennsylvania, who showed how wells could be drilled to a depth of a thousand feet or more; men like Samuel Kier, with his patented Rock Oil Medicine, who tapped the oil which had contaminated good salt water wells; chemists who analyzed the rock oil and prophetically indicated some of its potential commercial applications; the small band of enterprising men who had established the petroleum operations of Enniskillen Township.

Drake well was catalyst

Drake's well marked neither the origin nor the cause of the oil industry. Rather, it was a catalyst which helped accelerate events already set in motion.

If the Enniskillen oil developments of a century ago escaped the attention of thousands of Canadians, today they have completely escaped the attention of millions. The result is that the early history

31

The Great Canadian Oil Patch

A 100-year old pump in a swampy area near Oil Springs still produces about one barrel of oil per day, despite accumulated rust.

of the oil industry in the United States has been documented with such thoroughness that we know such minutiae as the size of shoes that Colonel Drake wore, while the early history of the oil industry in Canada is sketchily traced with fragmentary records, filled with blank spots and people who are almost unknown. All of the definitive early histories of the oil industry are American-written and their treatments of developments in Canada are either absent or confusing, contradictory and inaccurate.

Depending upon the history you prefer, the first oil production in Enniskillen is reported to have occurred sometime between 1852 and 1862, having been developed by Charles Nelson Tripp, James Miller Williams or a certain Mr. Shaw who has been reported as James Shaw, John Shaw and Hugh Nixon Shaw. Shaw is reported to be either an itinerant American photographer, a "sturdy laborer, muscular and uneducated," or a merchant from Cooksville, Canada West; and who, having been somehow cheated of his fortune, "died broken hearted and quite unknown" at Titusville in 1860, or in "abject poverty" in Petrolia in 1876, or was literally drowned in his own oil. To prove that truth is stranger than fiction, he did indeed drown in his own oil, after having been lowered down into his well to connect a pipe.

Drowned in his own well

What documentation is available on the work of Enniskillen, however, is enough to sketch a fascinating account of the initial

Oil Springs
well drilled in 1858
by James M. Williams,
continues to operate
today outside the
Oil Museum of Canada.

33

development of the petroleum industry in North America.

Early settlers who carved out homesteads from the hardwood forests which covered what is now the southwest finger of Ontario between Lakes Erie and Huron, avoided the tiny township of Enniskillen. Landlocked midway between the two lakes, Enniskillen was a flat, featureless land with an almost impenetrable forest of oak, walnut, elm and black ash, dissected by two small and sluggish streams, Bear Creek and Black Creek. The soil cover was underlain by an impervious layer of blue clay. The flat terrain and a tangle of fallen trees retarded drainage, so that a good rain turned much of the township into a quagmire. It was known as the black swamp. Worst of all were the two gum beds of Enniskillen, composed of a black, tarry substance varying from a few inches to a few feet in thickness, covering several acres of land.

The black swamp

The township covers 86,800 acres. The assessment roll of 1847 showed that 396 1/2 acres were under cultivation, by 37 settlers who owned 34 cows and 16 hogs. Enniskillen boasted a greater population of wild turkeys than people.

There were stories that the Indians and the first settlers had obtained from the gum beds small quantities of oil which were used for medicinal purposes. Charles Robb, a Montreal mining engineer, in a paper delivered in 1861, reported that at Enniskillen, "deers' horns, and pieces of timber bearing the marks of the axe, had been dug up from considerable depths below the surface, in what appear to have been old wells."

Hunt report

A chemist with the Geological Survey of Canada, Sterry Hunt, first pointed out the commercial possibilities of the gum. Hunt analysed some samples and in a report published in 1850 noted that "its consistency is somewhat like the variety known under the name of mineral rubber. The use of this material in England and the continent to build roads, to pave (seal) the bottom of ships, to manufacture gas for lighting, for which it is eminently suited, is sufficient to attach considerable importance to the deposits there are in this country. A careful examination of the locality will be made, having regard to its extent during the next summer. The samples I am holding contain 78 to 81 percent of this combustible and volatile material." Hunt reported that the gum bed deposit from which the samples were taken was "on the 19th lot of the 6th or 7th row of the Enniskillen Township in Upper Canada." This area was later known as the east gum bed.

The Tripps

The Tripp brothers – Henry who lived in Woodstock and Charles Nelson, foreman of a stove foundry in Bath – established the world's

34

first incorporated oil company in an unsuccessful attempt to develop production from this bitumen deposit. They may have been attracted by Hunt's report, or perhaps by a friendly word of advice from Alexander Murray, who farmed near Woodstock and worked part time as a geologist for the Geological Survey.

When Murray conducted a field study of the gum beds the year after Hunt's report was published, he found that the Tripps had probably preceded him to the site. Describing the west gum bed (16th lot, second concession) as a deposit "of nearly pure bitumen" covering half an acre with a maximum thickness of two feet, Murray said it was "underlaid by a very white clay, which I was informed had been bored through in one part for thirty feet ."

West gum bed

Unsuccessful though it was, this could represent the first known attempt to drill for oil in North America, nearly a decade before the completion of the Drake well.

The Tripp brothers set out with high hopes to develop these bituminous deposits. In 1852, according to an early atlas of Lambton County, they "erected buildings and machinery for the manufacture of asphalt, which enterprise did not succeed." That year they also petitioned the Legislative Council of Canada for incorporation of a company, but did not obtain a charter until December, 18, 1854, after they had re-submitted their petition several times. Not all their hopes were pinned on the gum beds, for their final petition to the Legislative Council claimed that Charles Tripp was the "owner in fee of two large asphalt beds in the Western District, one oil and two salt springs in the said district, also one lead vein in the county of Prince Edward, land in the township of Bedford, land in Belmont, lead and copper on Otanaka, and has mining rights, leases and privileges in various other portions of this province ."

Tripps' failure

The charter for the International Mining and Manufacturing Company empowered the firm to "erect works . . . for the purpose of making oils, paints, burning fluids, varnishes and other things of the like from their properties in Enniskillen." Charles Tripp was president and there were six other directors, including four Canadians (including brother Henry) and two Americans from New York. Each director subscribed to 250 shares with a total par value of 1,250 pounds, and total authorized capital was 60,000 pounds – an enormous sum for that day, and indicative of the magnitude of the work envisioned.

Company receives charter

It was the first oil company ever incorporated. Less than two weeks after the International Mining and Manufacturing Company received its charter a group of U.S. entrepreneurs filed at Albany,

New York, a certificate of incorporation for the Pennsylvania Rock Oil Company, organized to develop the oil seepage at Titusville.

Tripp and his associates had not been standing idle for three years awaiting the incorporation of their company. They had purchased extensive holdings covering the gum beds at Enniskillen. They dug the surface deposits of bitumen, boiled it in open cast iron vessels *Boiled* venting the lighter products into the atmosphere, and attempted to produce asphalt for paving roads and sealing the hulls of ships. Tripp *bitumen* sent a large sample of the gum beds for analysis to Thomas Antisell of New York, a consulting and analytical chemist who was one of the experts in the new coal oil refining business. Another sample went to the Hamilton Gas Company for testing in its retorts.

Antisell, in a report to Tripp dated February 19, 1853, described the samples as "a very valuable variety of bitumen suitable for the manufacture of varnishes, naphtha liquids for use as solvents, burning fluids and gas for illuminating purposes ." According to Antisell, "the manufacture of volatile liquids and illuminating gases appears to be its most appropriate use." Two years later the Hamilton Gas Company reported that a sample of 1,450 pounds of Tripp's bitumen produced 4,600 feet of gas in three hours, and that this gas gave 10 to 15 percent more illumination than the gas which the firm was manufacturing from coal.

Tripp Despite these reports, Tripp appeared to continue to concentrate his efforts on the production of asphalt, although some lamp fuel may have also been produced. A sample of the International Mining *fails* and Manufacturing Company's asphalt was included in Canada's exhibits at the Universal Exhibition at Paris in 1855, and won an *to heed* honorable mention.

advice Tripp's efforts were marked by a singular lack of success. Part of Tripp's financial trouble may have stemmed from his decision to concentrate on the production of asphalt rather than the more valuable lamp fuel. It may have been that he lacked knowledge, or more likely capital, to tackle the distillation of the bitumen into its more volatile fractions (components). Transportation was another hurdle – it was 20 miles through dense forest and a quagmire trail from the site of his diggings to water transportation at Sarnia, and the cost of hauling out his asphalt by horse and wagon must have been just about as great as the value of the product. Even with the reports of Antisell and the Hamilton Gas Company, attempts at raising public financing for the International Mining and Manufacturing Company met with little response. By 1856, deeply in debt, Tripp was forced to start selling his gum bed properties.

Enter James Miller Williams, a young (39) dynamic carriage maker from Hamilton, Ont., who succeeded where Tripp had failed, earning the title of "the father of the North American oil industry." Williams was already a most successful businessman when he began what developed into an integrated oil business.

Born of Welsh parents in Camden, New Jersey, Williams left school early to apprentice as a carriage maker, moving with his family to London, then no more than a mere village in Upper Canada, when he was 22. Within two years he had married and was a partner in a prosperous carriage making business. He later sold out and moved to Hamilton, again entering the carriage making business. His wagons were the Cadillacs of the carriage trade; one was described by the Hamilton Spectator as "a splendid new Omnibus . . . surpassing in size and elegance anything of the kind ever before attempted in this country." Before long, Williams had sold out once more and turned to the manufacture of railway cars. He operated plants in Hamilton, Niagara Falls and Brantford. When the railways began making their own rolling stock, he sold out once more, in 1856, and set out to do his thing in the oil business.

Among the numerous debts accumulated by Tripp about this time, according to one widely quoted account, was a sum due to Williams for the purchase of a wagon. To settle the account, according to the story, Tripp offered Williams some of his oil lands. Never one to do anything by half, Williams decided to buy out Tripp's entire holdings, paid 2,000 pounds for 600 acres of potential oil land in Enniskillen, including the two gum beds, and hired Tripp to help in the undertaking.

Williams' operations at Enniskillen were in marked contrast to Tripp's ill-fated endeavors. Where Tripp simply boiled the bitumen to produce asphalt, Williams appears to have set out from the start to produce a burning oil for lamp fuel by the distillation of the bitumen. Where Tripp essentially mined the more or less solid bitumen from the gum beds, Williams was soon pumping crude oil from a reservoir beneath the gum beds. His was the world's first integrated oil company, with production, refining and marketing facilities.

Williams: Father of the industry

Buys out Tripp

First integrated oil firm

37

Williams started his operations at Enniskillen in 1857, according to reports by Charles Robb, a Montreal mining engineer, and by Dr. T. Sterry Hunt, chemist and geologist with the Geological Survey of Canada.

Wrote Robb in 1861: "Ultimately the whole adventure devolved upon Mr. Williams, to whom alone is due the merit of developing this branch of industry in Canada, as well as of pointing out the road to success in the same direction in the United States."

Establishes refinery

Williams established the first petroleum refinery in 1857, on the south bank of Black Creek. It consisted of a simple retort in which bitumen was distilled into an iridescent liquid which was sold as lamp oil. The following year Williams moved his refining operations to Hamilton where he established larger, more sophisticated facilities.

Crude oil in 1857

It is believed to have been that same year that Williams dug beneath the gum beds to successfully produce crude oil – certainly it was long before Drake's well came in at Titusville on August 28, 1859. Hunt reported that Williams and associates "soon found that by sinking wells in the clay beneath, it was possible to obtain greater quantities of the material in a fluid state." Robb wrote: "It was soon discovered, however, on penetrating below the asphalt, that the material could be obtained in large quantities in the fluid state, and consequently much nearer the condition required in the manufacture."

Drills at seepage site

Certainly the first recorded attempt by Williams to dig for petroleum in a fluid state was in 1857 – although it was not a successful endeavor. Assisted by Tripp, then in his employ, Williams first dug at the site of some oil seepages on the banks of the Thames River near Bothwell, some 12 miles southwest of the gum beds in Enniskillen. At a depth of 27 feet the hole filled with oil and water, and in an attempt to reach the "pool of oil" Williams and Tripp tried to drive an iron pipe farther down into the hole. After the pipe had been driven down a "considerable distance" it broke, and the well was abandoned.

One widely quoted report is that Williams and Tripp dug their first successful well that same year on the west gum bed – on lot 16, concession 2, the site described in the GSC report six years earlier by Alexander Murray who said it had even then been "bored" through for 30 feet, probably by Tripp. This time, Tripp and Williams are reported to have dug to a depth of 46 feet where they found oil, and

James Miller
Williams, who
has been called
the Father of
the North American
oil industry.

later drilled an additional 100 feet through rock, finding oil in greater volume. The Toronto Globe and Mail on September 6, 1861, reported that this well was producing an average of 60 barrels of oil a day, and had been in operation for two years.

Another, earlier report of this first well was made by Thomas A. Gale in his book, Rock Oil in Pennsylvania and Elsewhere, published in June 1860, dated the start of production from Williams' well as 1858. Wrote Gale: "Williams and Company's well is 49 feet deep, 7 by 9 feet square, cribbed with small logs and does not extend to the rock; the oil rises within 10 feet of the well which contains 13,724 gallons or 343 barrels of oil, and has been in operation for two years.

The largest amount taken from the well up to the present time was 1,500 gallons or 37 barrels (with hand pump) in 10 hours which reduced the depth of the well three feet."

The Sarnia Observer, on August 26, 1858, reported that "two weeks ago we noticed the discovery, in the Township of Enniskillen, of an abundant supply of mineral oil." The Observer said that when burned the oil emitted, "on account of the impurities, a dense black smoke," but on purification should make "a splendid lamp oil." The produced oil had been "barreled up and sent to Hamilton to be prepared there," where Williams had set up his refining facilities after moving them from Oil Springs.

Sulphur a problem

By September 23, 1859, just 27 days after the completion of Drake's well, Williams' refined kerosene seemed already well established on the market — well enough established to bring the following comments and price complaint from the Sarnia Observer:

"Enniskillen oil — this most superior illuminating oil, can now be had from Mr. W. B. Clark, the agent for Sarnia, at $1.25 per gallon. The article, we have no hesitation in saying, after having given both a fair trial, is superior to the celebrated Albertine oil, being more free of smell, while its illuminating properties are equal if not superior to the latter in all respects. No one who gives it a trial, would ever think of returning to the use of candles, except for transient purposes, the light from the oil being much clearer, while the annoyance of grease from indifferent candles, with which every one is familiar, is altogether avoided. We see the oil is advertised in London at $1 per gallon; if it is really sold there at that price, Mr. Clark ought to obtain his supply from the company on as advantageous terms. The article, it is true, is cheap at $1.25; still there should be little, if any difference between the price here and in London, except the extra freight from Hamilton, whither, we understand, the raw material is sent for the purpose of purification."

Despite the glowing account of The Sarnia Observer, Williams apparently had trouble for several years in removing the obnoxious odor from the sulphurous crude of Oil Springs. His success in overcoming this problem was finally proclaimed in an advertisement on July 4, 1860, in the Hamilton Spectator:

"Those who have any knowledge of the coal oil business are well aware that not a barrel of any of these oils has been manufactured either in Canada or the United States without great difficulties having been experienced and large amounts having been expended in

1862
LONDINI

HONORIS
CAUSA

Medal received by
Williams for
refining of crude
oil in 1858
presented at the
1862 International
Exhibition in
London, England.

order to overcome the offensive odor common to all oils. The odor
has prejudiced many against them, and has hitherto prevented us
from bringing out oils before the public. But recent experiments have
been attended with great success, and have resulted in our obtaining
a process by means of which we can now entirely remove this
disagreeable odor."

The ad offered for sale illuminating oil at a price of 70 cents per
gallon (a sharp drop from a year earlier), machinery oil at 60 cents
per gallon, crude oil at 25 cents in quantities of 1,000 to 4,000
gallons and 16 cents in quantities of 4,000 to 100,000 gallons.

Substantial producing operations had been established at Oil
Springs by this time. Sterry Hunt, following a visit to the site in
December, 1860, reported that nearly 100 wells had been sunk and,
by the following summer, said "many more have since been bored."

Oil Springs rush

41

Charles Robb reported that "Williams has now five wells in more or less successful operation, yielding on an average from 600 to 800 gallons per day."

Transport problem

Volume of production at Oil Springs was held back by the task of moving it to market through the black swamp of Enniskillen. The Great Western Railway by this time had been completed as far as Sarnia, and it was a 12-mile haul from Oil Springs to the railway station at Wyoming. Here the oil was worth 13 cents per gallon, or more than $5 per barrel. Cost of hauling the oil by wagon to Wyoming was four to six cents per gallon – a third to one half of the sales price.

In winter, when the ground was frozen solid and covered with a blanket of snow, a team of horses could haul as many as 16 barrels of oil, more than two tons, over the road to Wyoming. Spring and summer rains quickly changed that, and a team of horses was fortunate to haul out by wagon one barrel at a time. Pot holes on the road, noted the Toronto Globe, were "large enough for horse and wagon to swim in."

Canadian Oil Company

Williams at first operated his oil interests under the name of J. M. Williams & Co. In November, 1860, he incorporated the Canadian Oil Company, into which he put his then substantial oil interests. Canadian Oil Company entered an exhibit at the 1862 International Exhibition in London, England, winning one gold medal as the first to commercially produce crude oil, and another gold medal as the first to refine oils in Canada. Nine years later Canadian Oil Company was defunct and Williams was president of Canadian Carbon Oil Co., an amalgam of several leading Ontario refiners. By 1880 competition from American Oil was driving Canadian oil men to the wall and Williams appears to have disposed of his oil interests and turned his energies in yet another direction. J. M. Williams and Co. became a stamping works, one of the first in Canada to make pressed tinware.

His record as a Liberal member of the Ontario Legislature for 13 years – he was elected as Hamilton's first representative following the confederation of Canada in 1867 – shows that he was a man of few words. His speeches were rare, brief, and to the point. He was a doer, not a talker. A staunch Presbyterian, he was one of the leaders of his church. Also, for several sessions, before he entered political politics, he served on the Hamilton City council. He was a director of the Mutual Life Association of Canada, the Victoria Mutual Fire Insurance Co., the Provident & Loan Society of Hamilton, the

Hamilton & Lake Erie Railway, and the Hamilton & Northwestern Railway. After retiring from the Ontario Legislature he was appointed registrar of Wentworth county in 1879, a largely honorary position which he held until his death at age 72 in 1890.

His obituary in the Hamilton Spectator described him as "a shrewd, sound, practical and experienced businessman" whose services to his city and province "were of the utmost value" and who "was never absent from the post of duty." The Toronto Mail said: "As a businessman he was shrewd and successful and as a public citizen, zealous and enterprising. He was a genial and lovable man . . . "

A careful winner

Williams was "a careful man, simple in his taste, retiring of disposition, practical to a degree and always dependable," one of his contemporaries has written. "He never drilled a gusher or won or lost a spectacular fortune, but oil men said he was the one man who left the first Oil Springs boom with money in his pocket."

That is probably just about as complete a description of Williams as has been left behind. For all his accomplishment, his position as a leading businessman of the day, a short career as a successful provincial politician, and his importance to the petroleum industry, he remains an obscure personality. He apparently left behind nothing in the way of autobiography, journals or reminiscences, and even photographs of him are rare.

Of the enterprising Charles Nelson Tripp, even less is known. He had been a foreman at a stove foundry in Bath, then in Canada West, and in 1850 had sold his employer a patent application on a stove front. Two years later he made his first application for the incorporation of The International Mining and Manufacturing Co. After the sale of his oil interests he worked for Williams but a brief period, and died in New Orleans in 1860.

The man behind Williams

Behind Williams' success may have been the guiding hand of Abraham Gesner. Historians have not been able to find the documentation which would establish Gesner as the expert adviser to whom Williams turned for technical direction and guidance, but the circumstantial evidence strongly points in this direction. Williams almost certainly had someone to show him how to refine his Enniskillen oil, and a highly successful businessman of his calibre could be expected to turn to the most expert advice available. No one was more expert than Gesner, and he was available. After setting up the coal oil plant for the North American Gas Light Company and losing control of his patents, Gesner left the employment of the company sometime between 1856 and 1859 – shortly after Williams had got started in the oil business. Gesner not only knew about the Enniskillen oil; he was also familiar with problems involved in refining this particular crude. In his Practical Treatise on Coal Petroleum and Other Distilled Oils, dated November, 1860, Gesner wrote of the Enniskillen oil: "It differs very essentially from the bitumens of the West Indies and the oils require careful purification."

Designed by expert

Gesner likely knew about the requirements for "careful purification" of this oil from having designed Williams' refining operations, or at least assisted. A description of Williams' refining operations by T. Sterry Hunt of the Geological Survey of Canada in mid-1861 – which by then had been moved from Oil Springs to Hamilton – disclosed what was for that day a sophisticated operation which could have been designed only by one of the very few experts in the field. The plant employed 16 men and refined about 120 barrels of oil per week, according to the Hamilton City Directory. "The process of refining," wrote Hunt, "consists in rectifying by repeated distillations, by which the oil is separated into a heavier part employed for lubricating machinery, and a lighter oil, which after being purified and deodorized by a peculiar treatment with sulpheric acid, is fit for burning in lamps." Gesner's process used at the plant of North American Gas Light Company also used repeated distillation for purification and deodorization of the kerosene by treatment with sulpheric acid and calcinated lime.

Gesner visits Hamilton

Just when Williams may have turned to Gesner for assistance is difficult to determine. It may have been at the time that Williams established his initial, rather simple refining operations at Oil Springs in 1857, or later when more elaborate refining operations were established in Hamilton. That Gesner was in Hamilton early in 1861 is established by an interview with him published March 11 that year by the Hamilton Spectator. It was likely not his first visit to the area, to consult with Williams.

That Gesner was the instrumental factor in establishment of the world's first commercial coal oil plant in New York in the early 1850's is beyond dispute. He very likely also played a vital role in establishing the world's first commercial crude oil refining operations.

Titusville

While the petroleum industry was being developed in Canada, similar events were rushing ahead also in the United States – about one step behind at each stage. The story of Drake's well has been told so often that it is here repeated in brief only, to compare with the time of events in Canada.

It was an oil spring on the Titusville, Pennsylvania property of the lumber firm of Brewer, Watston & Company which set in motion in 1851 a long chain of events leading to the drilling of the Drake well eight years later. Dr. Francis Beattie Brewer, abandoning his medical profession to join his father's business was highly intrigued with this oil spring, and the reputed medicinal value of its product, as well as other possible uses. Brewer had a series of shallow trenches dug to collect the oil, which was used as a lubricant by the lumber mill, and also burned to illuminate open areas of the mill where the belching black smoke did not matter.

Collected
in trenches

A sample of the oil left at Yale University by Brewer came to the attention of a young New York stock promoter, George H. Bissell, who thought he saw an opportunity for another profitable promotion. Obtaining an agreement to purchase the oil rights at the Titusville property for $5,000, Bissell and his associates filed a certificate of incorporation on December 30, 1854, for the Pennsylvania Rock Oil Company of New York. It was the first incorporated U.S. oil company.

Bissell and his partners ordered an analysis of the oil from Benjamin Silliman, Jr., head of the chemistry department at Yale University. Taking more than a year to prepare his report, Silliman would not release it until Bissell had managed to scrape up the money to pay the fee, $526.08. The report was well worth the cost. It pointed out a number of potential commercial applications, but the most important was that 50 percent of the oil could be distilled into a satisfactory illuminant for camphene lamps. (The Silliman study has been described as "perhaps the most epochal report in petroleum history," but its conclusion that Titusville oil could be distilled into a lamp fuel came more than two years after chemist Thomas Antisell had made a similar finding for Charles Tripp with respect to the bitumen deposit at Enniskillen).

Silliman
report

Despite the encouragement of the Silliman report it was difficult to find investors willing to put their money into the Pennsylvania Rock Oil Company. (Dr. Brewer was warned by his banker father that "you are associated with a set of sharpers, and if they have not already ruined you, they will do so if you are foolish enough to let

Seneca Oil Co.

them do it.") Control of the dormant company was acquired by New Haven banker James Townsend, who formed a new oil company, the Seneca Oil Company, on March 23, 1858. The new firm leased the oil property from the Pennsylvania Rock Oil Company for a royalty of 12 cents per gallon of oil produced.

Townsend's next task was to hire someone who would set about the task of developing the property. Edwin L. Drake, then 38, got the $1,000-a-year job because he was available, and because, as a former railway conductor, he had access to a free railway pass to get to Titusville. Other than this, Drake appeared to have few qualifications and no experience to bring to the task at hand.

It is not known whether it was Bissell, Townsend or Drake who first conceived of the idea of drilling a hole, in the manner of the salt water well drillers, in order to increase the production of oil from the seepage at Titusville. All three laid claim to having first thought of the idea.

Drake arrives

"Colonel" Drake arrived at Titusville to start the operation in May, 1858. It was 15 months later before Drake and his driller, "Uncle" Billy Smith, found oil at a depth of 69 1/2 feet, pumping from eight to 10 barrels a day. It was Sunday, August 28, 1859.

Potential commercial value of crude oil had by this time become well established and widely recognized. As a result, Drake's discovery triggered an immediate boom that rivalled the California gold strike a decade earlier. Within weeks speculators had paid probably more than a million dollars for oil leases purchased from farmers along creek beds in Pennsylvania. Within 15 months of Drake's discovery, according to one report, there were 74 producing wells in Pennsylvania turning out oil at a rate of nearly 1,200 barrels a day, and several times as many dry holes had been drilled.

Drake left the oil regions four years after his discovery, a comparatively affluent man with savings of some $20,000, a substantial sum for those days. But the money did not last. He became a partner of a Wall Street broker in oil stocks, and by 1866 had dissipated his savings in speculations. He spent the rest of his life in ill health, poverty and obscurity. He was awarded an annual pension of $1,500 by the state of Pennsylvania in 1873, and he died in 1880.

Drake's claim as founder of the oil producing industry in North America was as phony as his Colonelcy, but he did greatly accelerate the tempo of activity. Within little more than a year, oil developments in the United States had outstripped the earlier oil developments in Canada, and the U.S. oil industry never looked back.

At first it was known as the gum beds of Enniskillen. Later it was called the Enniskillen Oil Springs. Finally, it became the boom town of Oil Springs. A century and a decade later it was no more than a rural crossroads in southwestern Ontario, a quiet backwash in the rush of the 20th century.

Boom time at Oil Springs

A log cabin, some machinery and a few holes in the ground were about all that marked the future site of Oil Springs when Williams began his oil operations in 1857. At first a few others followed Williams' footsteps to dig oil wells along the banks of Black Creek. Following Drake's discovery, Americans arrived in great numbers, seeking new areas of opportunity.

Williams and three others laid out the village of Oil Springs in 1860. By mid-1861 Oil Springs boasted a population of 1,600, an over-crowded hotel, several small stores and close to 100 producing wells with 300 more being drilled along the banks of Black Creek.

A reporter for the Toronto Globe, with tongue in cheek, noted that the name "Victoria," had been proposed for the new village. But the Americans, "having profound respect for Her Majesty, think the honour would be too great for them to bear, and are therefore unanimous for Oil Springs ."

The village's initial water well had been contaminated by oil. But near the principal hotel ran "a small sluggish flowing stream. In it the diggers, covered with oil, washed their dirty selves after the day's work; swilled the mud off their boots, and quenched the thirst of their horses. From this ditch also was regularly procured the water of which the tea and coffee were made, and in which the fat salt pork, the staple article of food for long months, was boiled."

Beds were in such shortage that hotel guests who retired early were awakened at midnight "so that other gentlemen might take a sleep ." The Globe noted that "undressing was not considered strictly requisite ," but one American "rather overdid things when he went to bed in his boots." For a frontier boom town it was a quiet place — "no rows having taken place; knifings and shootings being entirely unknown."

Crowded quarters

Wells were dug and cribbed to about 50 feet from which depth some produced; others were bored for another 100 feet or more. Contractors charged $2 to $4 a foot to sink a well, depending on the depth, and the average cost of a completed oil well was reported to be in the order of $300. Four-man crews bored holes with the spring pole drilling method. A sharpened iron bit, weighing 300 to 400 pounds, was suspended downhole by cable from the thick, ash spring pole. Drillers stood on a small platform attached by rope to the end of the spring pole. With the shifting weight of the drillers on the platform, the pole sprang up and down a foot or so, raising and dropping the heavy bit which slowly banged its way through the rock.

Shaw's gusher

The greatest gusher the world had seen was drilled at Oil Springs in 1862 by Hugh Nixon Shaw, an Irishman who had operated a general store at Cooksville before drilling for oil, and about whom so many conflicting stories have been recorded.

After an unsuccessful partnership venture at Oil Springs, Shaw set out on his own to drill on his one-acre plot, backed by $50 in working capital. Starting in July, 1861, and working by himself, it took Shaw more than six months to complete his well. Shaw's $50 capital was soon exhausted, and so was his credit within a 20-mile radius of Oil Springs, but he stuck to his task. He dug his well four by five feet, through 50 feet of clay, then with his spring pole, bored through another 158 feet of rock.

A broke, tired, and discouraged 50-year-old man, Shaw by the end of that year faced his drilling task each day on a "just one more day" basis. The final day was January 16, 1862. "Today he has the prospect of being the wealthiest man in Canada," wrote the correspondent for the Toronto Globe.

The oil rushed up Shaw's three-inch hole, filled the four-by-five-foot well dug through 50 feet of clay, and overflowed at the surface, a great, black, bubbling and gurgling spring of oil.

Controlled with flax seed

To bring the well under control, Shaw first lowered a 2 1/2 inch pipe down into the hole. A 12-foot long bag, filled with flax seed, was wrapped around the lower part of the pipe. The seed swelled to create a tight packing between the pipe and the hole, forcing the oil to rise up inside the pipe. Up in the air it shot, a black plume of oil more than 20 feet high, flowing at a rate greater than 2,000 barrels a day and covering the ground for acres around.

A second pipe, three-quarters of an inch in diameter and also wrapped with flax seed, was lowered down inside the 2 1/2 inch pipe. Now the rate of the oil flow was choked back through this three-quarter inch pipe. Shaw connected his flowing oil with four large storage tanks, each capable of holding 120 barrels, and hoses from these were used to fill the 40-gallon oak barrels. "I timed the filling of these barrels," wrote the Globe reporter, "and found that in

48

Hugh Nixon
Shaw.

one minute and forty-five seconds each barrel was filled . . . The tanks are always overflowing, although they are constantly drawing it off into barrels."

A writer for the Christian Guardian, London, England, reported that "all the wells of Enniskillen are overshadowed by the wonderful well of Mr. Shaw."

"This gentleman — everyone calls him a gentleman now, though many failed to discover the attributes of the gentleman, though really they were there, until Providence rewarded his indomitable energy with a fortune no one could tell the full extent of – this gentleman, I say, had commenced to sink a well in another quarter, and spent a good deal of time and money, fruitlessly."

Shaw's bags of flax seed managed to tame the well for no more than a few days. "On Friday last, another freak was played," reported the Christian Guardian. "So tremendous was the force beneath that the sandbag was driven upward into the air, and a great column of oil, some four inches in diameter, and 20 feet in height, played away for nearly three days and nights, wasting an even larger quantity of oil than on the first occasion. Many thousands of barrels of oil have flowed over the adjoining lands, the road and the adjacent

Well goes wild

49

creek. I measured the oil in the creek and found that it was from three to four inches deep on the ice of the creek. This continued for a long distance down the creek."

Thirty follow-ups

Another 30 gushers were drilled that year within a square mile area surrounding Shaw's discovery. At least half a dozen of them flowed at even greater rates – one at 7,500 barrels a day. Four hundred teams of horses hauled the oil to the railway at Wyoming, over a new, oak-planked road. There were 10 refineries operating at Oil Springs, plus five at Toronto, three at Wyoming, two each at Sarnia, London and Hamilton, and one each at Petrolia, Ingersoll, Woodstock, Port Credit, Brantford and Bothwell. Use of kerosene for lighting had become general throughout Ontario by 1863, and demand was growing rapidly.

Era marked by waste

"The great flowing wells of Oil Springs," as they were called, typified conditions during the first two decades of the oil industry in both Canada and the United States: tremendous waste, alternating oil shortages and glutted markets, and wildly gyrating prices. From $4 to $6 a barrel in 1861, the price of oil at Oil Springs fell to $2 at the beginning of 1873 and 40 cents by the end of the year. (Some reports have suggested a figure as low as 10 cents.)

". . . there is no quarter of the world where the production has attained such prodigious dimensions as in 1862 upon Oil Creek, in the township of Enniskillen, Ontario," professor Alexander Winchell of the University of Michigan wrote in his book, Sketches of Creation, in 1870. The waste production of oil, said Winchell, "was the mere pastime of full-grown boys. It floated on the water of Black Creek to the depth of six inches, and formed a film upon the surface of Lake Erie. At length the stream of oil became ignited, and the column of flame raged down the windings of the creek in a style of such fearful grandeur as to admonish the Canadian squatter of the danger, no less than the inutility and wastefulness of his oleaginous pastimes." Winchell estimated the amount of oil spilled down Black Creek at more than five million barrels – probably an over-estimate, but still enough to represent "a national fortune, totally wasted."

Spectacular, if somewhat brief, was the oil career of Hugh Nixon Shaw. He was probably the first oil man who had ever drowned in his own oil; on February 11, 1863, little more than a year after he had completed the world's largest oil gusher of that era. The event was succinctly recorded in Shaw's obituary in the Cooksville paper:

"His death was occasioned by suffocation from inhaling obnoxious gases while in an oil well, into which he had descended for the purpose of pulling up a piece of gas pipe. Was within about fifteen

Early drilling rigs
at Petrolia, Ont.

feet of the surface; was heard to be breathing heavily, when he fell back into the oil, and disappeared. Mr. Shaw had long been in the enjoyment of religion . . ."

Even shorter were the spectacular performances of the great gushers of Oil Springs. Wells that at first flowed thousands of barrels a day, within a few months had to be pumped, yielding oil at rates of five to 20 barrels per day. With the decline in production and continued growth in demand, the crude prices at Oil Springs were gradually restored, to $4 per barrel in 1864 and more than $11 per barrel by late 1865.

With the return of better prices, the boom at Oil Springs was on again. More wells were drilled, and if there were no more gushers, there were at least a lot of profitable pumpers. The jerker rod system of oil well pumping was developed for the Oil Springs wells. A single steam engine, fired by wood or by gas from the oil wells, slowly rotated huge, horizontal iron wheels a few degrees back and forth.

51

A year to hit bottom

Iron rods, up to several hundred feet in length, fanned out like spokes from the central wheel to connect with the pumping wells, jerked back and forth along the ground with the rotation of the wheel, and pumped steady streams of oil. One hundred or more wells could be connected by a single jerker system; several thousand wells in the field produced a modest but steady flow of oil.

Oil Springs reached its apex in 1866, with a population of more than 4,000. There were nine hotels, a dozen general stores, as many bars, a weekly newspaper (The Oil Springs Chronicle, Canada's first oil publication), two banks and a board of trade. The main street was planked for a mile and a half with a double width of white oak, proudly proclaimed the finest paved street in Canada. Horse-drawn buses ran the length of the town at five minute intervals. There was a stage service four times a day over a 20-mile planked road to Sarnia. Oil Springs' largest edifice was a 108-room hotel, just completed by a Chicago firm and said to be the largest frame structure building in Canada. At night, Oil Springs was a blazing marvel with three miles of kerosene lamps set on ornamental posts along both sides of the main street.

Petrolia emerges

It took Oil Springs less than a year to hit the bottom. Two things in 1866 brought a sudden halt to the town's boom. There was the development of the larger field at Petrolia, eight miles to the northwest. Oil had been produced in small quantity at Petrolia for half a dozen years, but in 1866 they started bringing in the flowing wells. At from 100 to about 500 barrels a day the Petrolia gushers were not as big as the first ones at Oil Springs, but there were more of them, and it seemed that they would have greater staying power. Eventually the field at Petrolia embraced some 20 square miles. The one at Oil Springs covered only two square miles. Just as at Oil Springs four years earlier, the new wells of Petrolia brought a glut of oil and declining prices, dropping in two years from $11 to 50 cents per barrel.

The second thing to hurt Oil Springs that year was the first of the Fenian Raids against Fort Erie, by U.S. Irishmen. For a time it looked like war between Canada and the United States, and the Americans at Oil Springs figured it was time to head home. Before the end of the year, the population of Oil Springs had shrunk to 300.

While Oil Springs shrank, Petrolia prospered. In one year it grew from a collection of a dozen shacks on a tiny clearing in the forest to a boom town of 2,300 people. Eventually close to 6,000 wells were drilled in the field, and population hit more than 5,000.

Petrolia
circa 1874.

An objectionable odor of the kerosene distilled from the sulphurous crudes of Petrolia and Oil Springs compounded the continual
marketing problem, while the sulphur-free "sweet" oil from Pennsylvania produced a cleaner, generally odorless and superior product.
Williams, in his advertising as early as 1860, claimed that he had
developed refining processes which produced a clean, odorless lamp
fuel. If he had, it was a secret that other Canadian refiners lacked for
years. It was not until about 1868 that Canadian refiners were able
to produce a clean enough product to enable them to capture a share
of the European market. And even then, the problem was not
completely solved for another 20 years until Herman Frasch, working for Imperial Oil, developed a new refining process using oxides of
copper, lead and iron to effectively remove the sulphur compounds.

*Frasch
process*

After crude prices hit 50 cents per barrel in 1867, Petrolia producers began looking for export markets. By establishing a two-price
system with lower prices for exports, Canadian producers from 1870
to 1873 were able to export 60 percent of their production to
European markets. Discovery of far more prolific reserves of sweet
crude in Pennsylvania and elsewhere abruptly shut off the export

market, however, and from then on Canadian producers were limited to the domestic market, protected by a duty on U.S. imports. It was only a matter of time before the growing Canadian demand required far more oil than the modest production from Ontario was able to supply.

It was Canada that set the foundations for establishment of the petroleum industry, and for a very brief period it held the spotlight in the world of oil. It was soon left shamefully far behind. Starting with Williams in 1857, Ontario oil production rose to about 10,000 barrels in 1860, and peaked at less than 900,000 barrels in 1894. By contrast, U.S. oil production starting with Drake in 1859 skyrocketed to somewhere between 250,000 and 500,000 barrels the following year, more than two million barrels in 1861, and 11 million barrels by 1874.

Oil Springs still producing

Perhaps the most amazing thing about the tiny Oil Springs field is that in 1969, riddled with 10,000 holes and 112 years after its discovery the field was still producing oil, at a rate of about 40,000 barrels per year. Thirteen operators were pumping from several hundred wells. The jerker rod system, now equipped with five-horsepower electric motors, was still in use, with up to 50 pumping wells on each system. A good well in 1970 was producing oil at a rate of about 10 barrels per month.

In a century and a decade following Williams' first well, the oil fields of southwestern Ontario had produced less than 50 million barrels of oil — an amount that represented less than two months production from western Canada in 1969.

But volume was not what made Ontario important to the petroleum industry. It is the fact that this is where it all began.

Chapter Three

The billion-dollar blowout

Anyone visiting Calgary in mid-May of 1914 would have concluded, according to the Calgary News Telegram, that the city "had a
population of 80,000 people, mostly lunatics ."

*A town
of
lunatics*

This Stampede town "never saw such a Saturday night," observed
the Calgary Albertan. "It was the wildest, most delirious, most
uproarious, most exciting time that had ever entered into human
imagination to conceive."

Cause of the excitement was oil. For more than a year, an oil fever
had gripped Calgarians as they followed the plodding progress of a
drilling rig nestled in the foothills of nearby Turner Valley, its
timbers shaking and its boiler hissing steam while the steel bit banged
and clunked its way through hundreds of feet of rock. In late
September and early October the well had encountered at a shallow
depth a flow of natural gas that bore with it a spray of light gravity
oil, variously described as condensate, naphtha and natural gasoline.

For months the newspapers had been full of conflicting reports as
to whether or not a commercial discovery had been made. Stock-
brokers' offices displayed samples of the oil to convince Calgarians
that it really did exist. Several cars had used it for fuel, and actually
ran. "Experts" had been freely predicting that "Calgary will soon be
in the throes of one of the greatest oil excitements ever known."
Hundreds of thousands of acres of oil leases had been filed with the

55

federal government, and the value of these leases was skyrocketing. There were riots in the Dominion Land Office as eager speculators lined up to file on anything available – even the municipal Bowness Park. Dozens of new oil companies had been formed, hopefully to drill on those leases, and shares were sold in the hundreds of thousands to Calgarians thirsting to get in on the ground floor and eager to part with their savings.

". . . many Calgarians are suffering from a mild form of insanity," said the News Telegram in October, while The Albertan concluded simply that "the city is oil mad ."

But the excitement was nothing compared with what happened after word reached Calgary on the night of Thursday, May 14, 1914, that this time the Dingman well had hit it for certain: oil.

"If the city was oil crazy on Friday," said the Albertan, "on Saturday it was demented." The Herald noted that the stock pro-moters had "struck a financial gusher ," which made the discovery well "look like a lawn sprinkler."

"All day and all night the crowds fought and struggled for prece-dence in the offices of the most prominent oil companies, and clamored for shares and yet more shares. Relays of policemen barely kept a clear passageway and there was never a moment when the would-be purchasers were not lined up three deep in front of the counters, buying, buying, buying."

Within a few months Calgarians woke up from that monumental speculative spree with such a hangover that more than half a century later the city still remembers the event as the wildest boom that ever hit the west. More than 500 companies had been formed within a few months, holding half a million acres of oil leases and with authorized capital totalling an estimated $400 million. Less than 50 companies actually started drilling, and few of those found any oil. Calgarians, wiped clean of more than a million dollars of savings, were left holding thousands of share certificates worth less than wallpaper. Several homes, and the lobby of one hotel, actually were wallpapered with share certificates.

During the next ten years the new Turner Valley field produced only 65,945 barrels of oil, an average rate of less than 20 barrels a day, together with some natural gas, most of which was flared. Ten years after the discovery only nine wells had been successfully completed. Seldom had there been so much excitement generated over so little oil.

But still it rates as a milestone. It was the nation's first commercial oil discovery in half a century, and the first ever in western Canada.

The oil boom
in Calgary
1914.

Beneath the shallow oil and gas bearing sands discovered at Turner Valley in 1914 lay deeper porous rocks containing immense petroleum reserves that would be discovered only in stages during the next 22 years. Calgarians did recover from the hangover of Alberta's first oil boom and came back — a little wiser and somewhat more successfully — to share in other Alberta oil booms.

Herron

The man most responsible for that "wildest, most delirious, most uproarious, most exciting time" was William Stewart Herron —

farmer, rancher, lumberman, railway contractor, real estate specu-
lator, prospector and oil man.

Herron was 31 when he hit the foothills city in 1901, a small,
slight man who channelled the energy of a steam engine and the
resilience of an incurable optimist into a habitual 16-hour work day.
One of a family of 13 children, Herron was born in Gelert, Ontario in
1870, started work as a cook in a northern Ontario lumber camp

Worked in Penn- sylvania

when he was 16, and later worked briefly in the oil fields of
Pennsylvania near Bradford where he gained a smattering of knowledge about oil. Before he was 20 he had his own lumbering operation
in northern Ontario, employing 150 men. He married the camp cook,
and contracted for grade building work on construction of the
Ontario Northland Railway. Lumbering and railway building were
not enough to keep Herron busy. He had an active interest in geology
and a dream of wealth, and prospected in the northern Ontario
country where the railway was being built, filing a large number of
claims.

Just what happened to Herron's Ontario interests — his lumbering,
contracting and mineral claims — is not known, but it appears to

Purchase of Okotoks farm

have been the first cycle of his boom and bust life. In any event,
when he arrived in Calgary in 1901 it was to make a new start. He
purchased a 960-acre farm at Okotoks, south of Calgary near Turner
Valley, returned to Ontario to wind up his business affairs, and in
1903 or 1904 settled down with his family on the Okotoks farm.
Years later Herron claimed, with a certain bitterness, that he had
been unable to hold onto his mineral claims because he did not have
enough money to develop them, and because the government of the
day "wanted my leases to give them to their friends and push
development."

Fred LaRose

Legend has it that a blacksmith, Fred LaRose, working on construction of the Ontario Northland Railway, in September 1903
threw his hammer at what he thought were a fox's eyes but hit a
silver mine — the world's richest. LaRose sold his claim for $30,000
and by 1905 miners and prospectors were pouring into the area that
had been named Cobalt in one of the greatest mining stampedes of
history. Fifty mines were put into production and in 10 years Cobalt
produced more than $300 million worth of metal — most of it from
ground which Herron claimed he had staked and lost.

Before he had been on his 960-acre Okotoks farm very long,
Herron must have been aware that there were oil and gas prospects in

Alberta. Natural gas was already in use in some areas, several oil shows had been found, numerous oil promotions had been floated, and as early as 1892 R. G. McConnell, a geologist with the Dominion Geological Survey, reported that the Athabasca tar sands in northeastern Alberta "evidence an up-swelling of petroleum unequalled elsewhere in the world."

Alberta's first homesteader, John George (Kootenai) Brown, in 1886 had tapped an oil seepage on Cameron Creek in southwestern Alberta in what is now the Waterton National Park. His Indian friends had shown him the oil seepage, and Brown, together with William Aldridge, dug pits and trenches and skimmed up the oil which they sold to nearby ranchers as lubricating oil at a dollar a gallon. Aldridge in 1899 obtained the first Dominion government oil leases issued in Alberta and in 1902 the Rocky Mountain Development Company had been formed by John Lineham, an Okotoks rancher, and A. P. Patrick, a land surveyor, to test for oil near Kootenai Brown's seepage. At a shallow depth, their well hit oil with a reported flow of 300 barrels per day, but within a few years it petered out while several nearby followup wells were failures.

Kootenai Brown

Canadian Pacific Railway, drilling for a water supply for its locomotives found natural gas at Langevin in southern Alberta in 1883, and again in 1890, this time drilling for coal, found gas at Medicine Hat. This latter developed into one of Canada's largest natural gas fields, supplying Medicine Hat and the nearby town of Redcliff with a prolific source of very cheap fuel, and moved Rudyard Kipling to describe the town as "the city with all hell for a basement." Still drilling for water, the CPR kept finding more gas – at Brooks, Bassano, Dunmore and (in 1909) at Bow Island.

CPR finds gas

Two other Ontario entrepreneurs who hit Alberta shortly after Herron were Archibald Wayne Dingman, and Eugene Marius Coste.

Dingman was born in Greenbush, Prince Edward County, Ontario in 1849, gained some oil field experience in Pennsylvania as a youth, and later turned his hand to a variety of activities in Toronto. He worked for the Scarborough Electric Railway where he was the first to install electric street lights in Toronto; was a partner in a firm manufacturing coaster brakes for bicycles; and then was a partner in the firm of Pugsley, Dingman and Co., which manufactured Comfort soap until its factory was destroyed by fire, about 1900. Dingman

Dingman and Coste

moved to Edmonton in 1902, and then to Calgary where he organized the Calgary Natural Gas Company in 1905. Dingman's firm drilled two wells. The first, on the Sarcee Indian reserve west of Calgary, was completed at 3,400 feet in 1908, the deepest in western Canada to that date, but failed to find gas. The second well found gas on the estate of Col. James Walker within the Calgary city limits in 1909, providing a modest gas supply for nearly 40 years, initially for street lighting and for a nearby brewery.

Eugene Coste

Eugene Coste was the son of Napoleon Alexandre Coste, a Frenchman from a well-to-do Marseilles family who was educated as an engineer but somehow, in his late teens, wound up as a deck hand on a Great Lakes schooner until he jumped ship and swam ashore near Amherstburg, Ont. There he found shelter with a French-Canadian farm family. Napoleon became a school teacher and a local politician, married the farmer's daughter and in 1863, at the age of 28 and with a family of four children, returned to Marseilles. Napoleon worked as a sub-contractor on construction of the Suez Canal, in 1869 piloted the first ship through the big ditch, while Eugene, his two brothers and one sister, were educated in France.

Eugene in 1876 received a Bachelor of Science Degree from the Academie de Paris, spent another three years at the Ecole Polytechnique, and in 1883 graduated from the Ecole National Superieure des Mines as a mining engineer. Napoleon brought his family back to Canada in 1882, to Amherstburg, where he had first jumped ship. He went back into politics, setting up his son Denis as publisher and editor of an unsuccessful weekly newspaper. Eugene joined the Geological Survey of Canada, but left after five years to explore for oil and gas on his own, convinced that oil originated from "volcanic" or Precambrian rocks..

Volcanic theory

Eugene clung tenaciously all his life to his mistaken theory about the volcanic origin of petroleum and natural gas, but that did not stop him from making the discoveries that laid the foundation for Ontario's natural gas industry. In 1888, with backing from his father, he drilled Ontario's first big gas discovery in Essex county (where he had been born) on the shore of Lake Erie, completing the well with an open flow potential of 10 million cubic feet of gas daily. The following year, with his brother Denis, he drilled a second wildcat 200 miles away, discovering more gas in the Niagara Falls area. The Essex field was rapidly exploited, supplying gas markets in southern Ontario and exporting to Detroit. Within 12 years its reserves were

60

Eugene
Coste

depleted, but meantime dozens of other small gas fields had been opened up and a host of companies were aggressively competing for gas supplies and franchise markets. The Coste interests organized the Volcanic Oil and Gas Co. in 1906, and in 1911 it was the senior company of several firms that merged to form the present Union Gas Company of Canada Ltd.

Eugene, meanwhile, had left for the west, retained by the Canadian Pacific Railway to develop the gas it had found while drilling for water, and to find more gas. Coste in 1909 brought in the Bow Island discovery on CPR land, flowing at a rate of 8.5 million cubic feet per day. He talked the CPR into leasing to him the gas rights so that he could build a pipeline from Bow Island to Calgary. In 1910 he organized the Prairie Gas Fuel Company, and in 1911 re-organized this into the Canadian Western Natural Gas, Light, Heat and Power Company, acquiring the properties of Dingman's Calgary Natural Gas Company, and the Calgary Gas Company. The latter served 2,500 customers with manufactured gas. By August, 1912, Coste's company had completed 170 miles of 16-inch line from Bow Island to Calgary, at the time the longest natural gas transmission pipeline in the world.

Herron on the farm

Back on the ranch, meanwhile, Herron was a busy man. Farming left some slack time in the winter months, so he filled it by lumbering, breaking horses for nearby ranches, and hauling coal from Black Diamond and Turner Valley to supply a power plant at Okotoks. For every three horses he broke in, Herron got to keep one. He would hitch a couple of broncos between a quiet team and by the time they had helped pull a few wagon loads of coal to Okotoks, they were well broken.

Samples from gas seep

Waiting for his wagon to be loaded with coal one day, Herron wandered up Sheep Creek where he found a gas seep bubbling up on the banks of the stream. Herron dug a hole and capped the gas seep with a wooden barrel, and then with a rubber hose collected samples of the wet gas in a pair of one-gallon jugs. These he sent off to be analysed at the University of California and the University of Pennsylvania. The analysis confirmed what Herron had suspected and hoped. This was petroleum, not marsh gas.

Herron was determined that a fortune would not slip through his fingers this time, as he believed it had at Cobalt. He needed money to secure oil leases at Turner Valley. Herron sold his Okotoks farm early in 1910, then bought property in Calgary and other farm land west of Calgary. It was a dry year with poor crops, and land prices were depressed. Herron is quoted in a newspaper article as saying he paid $20,000 for his Calgary property and $15 an acre for farm land west of the city. With good crops in 1911 and 1912, land prices went up. Herron sold the farm land for $35 to $40 an acre, and his city property for $48,000. He now had money to pick up potential Turner Valley oil property.

"I knew – or at least I thought I knew, which amounts to the same thing – that there was oil in the Valley," Herron was quoted as saying.

Mineral rights

After 1887, the government of Canada retained all mineral rights on crown lands that were sold or homesteaded. After about 1902, the railways did the same with land which they let go. Thus at Turner Valley in 1910, some of the farmers owned only the surface rights, while others held the mineral rights as well. One of the farmers who held mineral rights to his land was Michael Stoos, and Herron in 1911 purchased his two-section (1,280-acre) farm, adjacent to the gas seep, for $18,000. He purchased other farms in Turner Valley, and filed on some 7,000 acres of oil leases with the federal government for an annual rental fee of 25 cents per acre.

With his leases in his pocket, Herron approached Coste seeking financing to drill, but somehow or other the foothills failed to fit in with Coste's concept of "the volcanic origin of petroleum and natural gas." Herron's proposal was turned down. Herron next approached Calgary city council hoping the city would back him, but was again rebuffed. Finally, he was able to complete a deal with Dingman which resulted in the formation of Calgary Petroleum Products Company, with Dingman as managing director. Directors of the new firm included some of Calgary's most prominent businessmen and a rising young Calgary lawyer who was later better known as Prime Minister R. B. Bennett.

Under an agreement dated July 26, 1912, Calgary Petroleum Products paid $22,000 for a 55 percent interest in some of the Turner Valley leases held by Herron, and agreed to spend $50,000 to drill a well. In another agreement 10 days later, Herron assigned 20 percent interest in the leases to Dingman "for his services in forming a syndicate or company" to finance development. Thus the interest in the well was held 55 percent by Calgary Petroleum Products, 25 percent by Herron and 20 percent by Dingman.

The golden age of oil had just dawned when Calgary Petroleum Products Company was formed. For more than half a century, oil had been produced in North America to make lubricants and lamp oil. Now the age of kerosene was ending and the era of petroleum fuel had just started. In 1903, Henry Ford, who had twice before gone broke trying to make automobiles, turned out his first Model A, and in one year had sold 658 of them at $750 each. Imperial Oil had opened Canada's first service station in Vancouver in 1905, with a rubber garden hose connected to a kitchen hot water tank that was filled with gasoline. There were 565 automobiles registered in Canada. Ten years later there were 60,688. Oil companies were feverishly building new refineries to keep pace with the demand for gasoline, previously a dangerous and unwanted by-product of kerosene. Imperial had one refinery in Canada in 1905, with a capacity of 900 barrels of crude oil per day. By 1920 it had five refineries with a capacity of 23,000 barrels a day. Just as feverishly, oil companies were looking for new oil supply sources. Imperial in 1913 launched its first exploration program, and in a few years its search extended from the Arctic Circle of the Northwest Territories to the steaming jungles of Peru. In 1912, the magic word for wealth was "oil ."

In August that year Dingman headed for Pittsburgh to buy drilling machinery while Herron cut timber for the rig and started hauling it to the drilling site. By October, the drillers started building the

Common ordinary millionaires

Archibald
Wayne
Dingman

wooden derrick and assembling the machinery. On January 25, 1914, Calgary Petroleum Products Well No. 1 spudded in and the heavy steel bit started pounding its way slowly through the rock.

From the start the hole generated a frenzy of excitement. At 467 feet it entered a series of thin sands that yielded small volumes of natural gas with vapors of condensate – enough gas at least to fuel the rig's boiler, and enough condensate to fuel the speculative spree.

Excitement grows

Almost daily, melodramatic reports in the Calgary newspapers fanned the excitement. The News Telegram reported on July 13: "Oil men are generally agreed that oil will be 'struck' in this well inside of the next 30 days." Multiplying the possible facts several fold, it reported that gas at the well was being wasted at a rate of three million cubic feet per day and added that "the company is after oil and a mere matter of one thousand or two thousand dollars worth of gas a day is not considered of sufficient importance to bother with by the future Calgary oil kings."

Dingman
discovery well
blowing in.

By October 9, the Herald reported that "a first class quality of oil
has been struck at the well" and although "no gusher has yet been
brought in, about one hundred gallons of high-grade oil (condensate)
was brought to the surface in a bailer, and samples are now in the
city." The well by that time had reached 1,562 feet. The News
Telegram on October 13 declared that reports from the well "seem
to be more encouraging every day and all are of the opinion that
within a short time it will be shown to the world that there exists in
southern Alberta an oilfield second to none in North America."

65

Everyone an investor

The boom was on, and "crowds swarmed the streets Saturday, filled the hotel rotundas and the sole topic of conversation was oil, oil, oil." Big plans were afoot, according to an "oil broker from Montana" who told the News Telegram that "there is no doubt but that hundreds of companies will commence drilling operations if the flow in the Dingman well turns out to be a permanent one." New companies were already formed to peddle stock on the basis of the leases "in the oil fields." By October 16, reported the Herald, "in the neighborhood of two dozen companies have been organized to sell stock . . . but most of them are awaiting news that a 'gusher' has been struck."

And still the well kept teasing. In November, the News Telegram reported that wet gas containing three gallons of condensate to every 1,000 cubic feet of gas was "blowing off" at the well at a rate of three million cubic feet a day. The Albertan once more assured its readers that "it is only a matter of drilling now before a large quantity of oil is struck at the Discovery well."

Calgarians were in no mood to listen to words of caution. On November 25 the Herald published a letter from Dingman in which he protested "against some of the absolutely irresponsible and ridiculous statements" that were being published. "At the present time and under the present conditions our gas cannot be utilized for the production of gasoline, but later on, under the proper conditions and character of product, we feel confident of being able to extract what gasoline nature has left in the gas." Crude oil had not yet been discovered, but "we are all hoping, and some of us working, to determine if possible the presence of commercial oil in Alberta." On Monday morning the Albertan published this reply: "Dingman's article in the Knocker (Herald) last Saturday makes us think that when he makes his big strike he will be a regular Rockefeller and establish Sunday schools and endow churches."

Some Calgarians, at least, managed to maintain a sense of humor. "The trouble with this oil situation at this formulative stage," wrote Bob Edwards in his Calgary Eye Opener, "is that you are never sure whether the man you meet on the street is a multi-millionaire, or just an ordinary, common millionaire."

And from a reader, the Albertan published this get-rich quick formula:

Cat farm

"Being readers of your valuable paper and knowing you to be fair in your criticism of new companies being organized in Alberta when the prospectus is sent you, and seeing by the Albertan that there is not going to be oil stock enough to go around to all the investors,

Investors
line up in
Calgary,
May 15, 1914.

perhaps some of those having money to invest in a profitable undertaking would be pleased to know of our company.

"We expect to operate a large cat ranch near Sedgewick, Alberta,
where the best farming land in the province can be bought, at least
the surface rights, which will be all we need, for less than the oil
barons would ask for the mineral rights.

"Now to start we will collect, say, 100,000 cats, each cat will
average 12 kittens a year which will mean 1,200,000 skins. The skins
will sell from 10 to 15 cents for the white ones and 75 cents for the
jet black ones, making an average price of 30 cents apiece, thus
making our revenue about $10,000.00 a day gross. A man can skin

67

50 cats a day and he will charge $2.00 for his labor. It will take 100 men to operate the ranch, therefore our profit will be about $9,800 per day.

"We will feed the cats on rats and will start a rat ranch adjoining the cat ranch. The rats will multiply four times as fast as the cats so if we start with say 1,000,000 rats we will have four rats a day for each cat, which is plenty. We will feed the cats on the rats and in turn will feed the rats on the stripped carcasses of the cats, thus giving each rat one-fourth of a cat. It will be seen by these figures that the business will be self acting and automatic. The cats will eat the rats and the rats will eat the cats and we will get the skins."

The promoters

Perhaps no one actually called the stock promoters "rats", but they certainly managed to skin Calgarians. The method was more fool-proof than a cat ranch, and even simpler. The promoter would file on a lease for mineral rights with the Calgary office of the Dominion Land Agent, paying a filing fee of $5 for each lease and a first-year rental of 25 cents per acre. A one-section lease (640 acres) could thus be picked up for $165; a quarter section lease for $45. The promoter would then organize a company to which he would sell his leases for cash and/or stock at a price which in November, 1913, according to the Herald, "usually runs from $10 to more than $25 per acre," or from 40 to 100 times the initial cost. Shares would then be offered to the public.

The Magnet Oil Company, Ltd., according to its prospectus dated June 17, 1914, issued shares with a par value of $350,000 to one Frank Frankel for 8,840 acres of leases that had cost $2,215 to acquire by filing. "Undoubtedly large bodies of oil will be found on the holdings of this company," consulting geologist G. E. Hayes advised in the prospectus. "After looking over your holdings I must say that you have a very strong proposition to put before the public." The prospectus noted that "fortunes made in oil by comparatively poor people in the oil fields of Ohio, Oklahoma, Texas, California and Calgary have been numerous," pointing out that "$25.00 invested in the stock of the Home Oil Company returned $105.00." Rex Oil Company contracted to pay $15,000 in cash and $50,000 in stock for its sole lease holdings of 960 acres acquired for $290, boasting that "there is probably no industry in the world which yields such enormous profits as money invested in oil," and adding that "the element of chance is practically eliminated." (It certainly was eliminated; since it never drilled, the company had no chance of finding oil.)

The News Telegram in June reported that Herron sold 20 acres (which subsequently proved non-productive) "for $24,000 to the Alberta Petroleum Company, which then opened an office on First Street West and started selling shares at 10 cents each."

In a series of articles in November on "The Flotation of Oil Companies," The Herald attempted to dampen the speculative fever in an expose of the promoters' methods and profits. "One has only to take a stroll through the business section of the city at the present time to observe the traps being laid for the unwary by the numerous oil concerns that have sprung up like a crop of overnight mushrooms," said the Herald.

Flotation of companies

"One thing that strikes a person in viewing these displays is the inevitable sample of oil from the Dingman well. . . . some of these samples are of a dark brown color, strangely like linseed oil; others are of a light shade, similar to sewing machine lubricant; others still are difficult to see clearly because of the stains smeared on the outside of the bottles. One can only conclude that 'age cannot wither nor custom stale the infinite variety' of the product of the Dingman well."

The inevitable sample

"A lot of the money that will be lost in oil stocks will go right out of Calgary into the pockets of men who know how to float oil companies and get the public crazy about the 'profits' so vividly portrayed," warned the Herald. "Those who either through the press or by example or inducement are inciting the public of Calgary to gamble in oil stocks are doing a great and irreparable injury, not only to the individual affected, but to the moral tone of the city and to its public and business interests."

The Herald series, retorted the Albertan, is merely an attempt "to keep out the small investor . . . until the big profits, if there are to be big profits, are all made by the more wealthy people." It described the Herald and its series in such terms as "evil work . . . venomous hatchet . . . this disloyal alien," and concluded that "if companies will be unable to develop these areas, it will be because this unpatriotic newspaper wafted the damp breath throughout the country in its attempt to kill this promising undertaking." Investors appeared to agree with the Albertan that "for a man who can afford to take a chance with the money, it is a good speculation."

The venomous hatchet

"The flotation of oil companies," as the Herald described it, was only half of the action in 1913 and 1914; the other half took place in the second floor quarters of the Dominion Land Office where speculators could file on a lease for a fee of only $5.00. Until the regulations were changed on February 28, 1914, the first year's rental of 25 cents per acre did not have to be paid until 30 days after the lease was filed. Since quite a few of the filers did not get around to paying the 25 cents per acre rental, there was a continual supply of dropped leases available for re-filing.

Would-be-leaseholders camped overnight in front of the building in order to be first in line when the office doors opened at nine in the morning. Men were hired by syndicates to hold down positions in the line, working on a rotation basis. When the front doors opened there was a wild melee as men raced, shoved and fought up the steps and along the corridor to reach the land titles office. Violence frequently broke out, office windows were smashed, and eventually the police were called to maintain order.

Leasing rush

The leasing rush was well underway by August 2 when the Herald reported how a pair of ranchers from Cardston beat out representatives of the law firm of Lougheed, Bennett and McLaws for first place in line for filing on a lapsed 640-acre lease three miles from the Dingman well. "It was easy," reported the Herald. "The athletic countrymen, assisted by a husky 300-pound friend who is engaged in the piano moving business, repeatedly handed their opponents off the steps by their linen collars, and when they were out-numbered they occasionally managed to pick up a couple at once and deposit them carelessly over the railing of the land office stairs." The ranchers later reportedly turned down an offer of $15,000 for their leases.

On October 10, the News Telegram reported that "from Thursday afternoon until noon Friday no less than 75 oil leases were filed on, amounting to approximately 48,000 acres." Leases which had been lapsed for some time were thrown open for filing on that Friday. One of the successful filers was a J. W. Travers, who "had two men stationed on the land office steps for two weeks." The Albertan reported that "800,000 acres of land have already been filed on, and still the craze for filing is in no way abated." In November, the Herald reported on a group of speculators who had "employed something like two dozen men, some of whom are employed regularly at $15 a week," to maintain positions on a rotational basis "on the steps of the land office throughout the 24 hours of the day ... at night the men are permitted to rig up a cover of canvas over the steps with cushions, blankets and a coal oil stove ."By December, however, "cooler weather and the recent regulations as to loitering on the land office steps has effectively put a stop to the all-night vigils in front of the door." Police replaced the shoving system among would-be filers by organizing a lottery. "Numbers are put into a hat and every filer draws one."

The events throughout 1913 and early 1914 were building up to the climax that arrived on the night of Thursday, May 14, when the word reached Calgary that Dingman's well had struck oil.

"On Friday, every available motor vehicle in Calgary was forced into service carrying hundreds of men to the foothills to the Dingman well," the Herald later reported. Enough was seen to enable the pilgrims from Calgary to return home with the most optimistic reports of the discovery and stimulated with determination to make Calgary the greatest industrial city on the map.

"Then came the wild scramble after shares of stock. New companies were organized every day. Every spare bit of space in stores and offices forming the main business streets of Calgary was hired by the selling end of some new oil company. The whole downtown district was really swathed in cotton streams bearing the names and prices of new issues of stock.

"The main street where the oil companies had established themselves were the scene of the wildest and most irresponsible kind of delirium. All day long men and women crowded and jostled each other in an attempt to gain entrance to the oil brokers offices where shares might be purchased. Shares sold all the way from 10 cents to $1.25 each.

"In the ticket office of the railway company, an oil company had succeeded in renting a small space for stock-selling purposes. People were lined up for yards outside the door trying to get in to spend their money. One of the railway company's office inspectors from Winnipeg happened to arrive in Calgary just at the height of the excitement ... The selling of railway tickets had been side-tracked entirely. Wastepaper baskets stood about the floor conspicuously filled with cheques and paper money. The entire staff was receiving money from the crazy mob which merely demanded shares and receipts for its money.

"The inspector soon found himself engaged in the same popular business. Afterwards he told of one old lady who had finally succeeded in getting close to the share counter eagerly demanding 'some

"Some stock ... any stock"

oil stock.' She had one hundred dollars to invest. The inspector said he didn't know anything about the stock being sold and didn't even know the name of it. 'Oh, that doesn't matter,' she exclaimed, 'anything will do so long as I get some stock'."

Calgary's paper oil companies maintained their brisk sales of shares for a couple of months, but as one by one the promoters folded up their corporate tents and left with bulging pockets, Calgarians soon suspected that they had been had. By September Canada had entered the great world war and the men who had lined up to buy oil stocks were now lining up to enlist. Calgary's oil stampede was over.

Rise and fall of Turner Valley

By 1920, only nine wells had been successfully completed along a narrow trend at Turner Valley, turning out a miserably small trickle of oil that in 10 years totalled less than 66,000 barrels. Calgary Petroleum Products Company itself soon ran into difficulties. It had completed two producing wells and was drilling a third when, in October, 1920 fire destroyed the company's small absorption plant which had been built to extract some 500 gallons a day of condensate light-gravity oil from the natural gas as well as treat a small volume of crude oil production. Lacking funds to re-build their $50,000 plant, directors sold controlling interest in the company to Imperial Oil Limited and Calgary Petroleum Products was re-organized as Royalite Oil Company, which agreed to re-build the plant and complete two more wells.

The Turner Valley story was far from over. The discovery well of 1914 had tapped a series of shallow sands in the Cretaceous formation, completing two years later at a total depth of 3,924 feet. Less than 100 feet below this lay a great prolific reservoir of oil and gas in the Mississippian formation. It took another 22 years during which a billion dollars worth of oil and gas was wasted before oil men were to realize that this was Canada's first major oil field.

The fourth well to be drilled on the 4,820 acres of leases that Calgary Petroleum Products had acquired from Herron was Royalite No. 4, and it marked the second major stage in Turner Valley's long development history. Royalite No. 4 was started in 1922, and in November 1924 at a depth of 3,740 feet, it blew in, flowing gas at a rate of 20 million cubic feet per day and condensate at 600 barrels per day. Before the well was abandoned it had produced 911,313 barrels of condensate and large amounts of natural gas.

Dingman wells
No. 1 and No. 2.

Another oil boom was on in Turner Valley, and in the next 12 years 114 wells were completed to extract the condensate from the rich and prolific gas of the Mississippian. By 1932 condensate production at Turner Valley had reached a record rate of nearly 4,000 barrels per day while the residue natural gas that was left over was flared at rates up to 600 million cubic feet per day. Orange flames licked the skies from the giant flares and Calgarians used to boast that on a summer's evening they could sit on their front porches and read the newspapers by the light of the Turner Valley flares 30 miles away.

What the Turner Valley producers did not know was that an even greater prize — a vast accumulation of crude oil — also lay trapped in the Mississippian formation. At Turner Valley the producing lime-stone rocks of the Mississippian lay at a tilted angle, dipping steeply to the west. Along the crest of this structure, the rocks contained gas and condensate, while downdip on the west flank, the rocks contained an estimated one billion barrels of crude oil. Gas that was being

73

Oil Column discovered

flared from the crest of this structure was robbing pressure from the reservoir – pressure which would later be required to help recover the oil.

The unsuspected oil column was ultimately discovered by the optimism and persistence of three men: Robert A. Brown, an electrical engineer who had built hydro-electric plants in western Canada and at the time was manager of Calgary's electric light department and electric street car system; George Melrose Bell, publisher of the Calgary Albertan newspaper, and J. W. Moyer, a Calgary lawyer.

Bell and Brown had correctly suspected that an oil column lay downdip from the gas reservoir on the flank of the Turner Valley field. The theory ran contrary to accepted geological thinking of the day, which held that only a large water table lay below the gas cap on the flank of the structure. Brown and Bell envisioned the reservoir as containing gas at the crest, followed by the oil column, and then the water table, and figured that if a well were located correctly on the structure between the gas and the water, that it would find oil. To test this theory would require the drilling of the deepest, most expensive well ever undertaken in Canada to that time.

Brown, Bell and Moyer

On January 20, 1934, Bell and Brown obtained a sub-lease on 60 acres on the west flank of the field from R. W. Brown of Gleichen. Three days later they had formed Turner Valley Royalties with Bell and Brown each holding 9,500 shares and Moyer holding 998 shares.

It was the worst of all possible times to try and finance a wildcat. It was in the depth of the depression and money was difficult to find; investors who had not lost all their money had lost all their confidence in Turner Valley promoters who had pulled too many fast deals too many times; and in any event, no one believed in their crazy geological theory.

But they were determined promoters, and if investors had lost all confidence in common stock, they had devised another way of raising money: by selling royalty interests in the proposed well. A trust deed was set up under which 70 percent of any production was to be paid to the royalty owners, and an offering was made at a rate of $1,500 for each one percent royalty interest. It was slow selling, but enough money was raised to start drilling by April 16, 1934.

Seven times drilling was stopped when the company ran out of money. Seven times Bell and Brown went out and sold more royalties. Late in 1935 – when it looked as though the well would never

One of many unsuccessful wild cats drilled in the 1920's near the Turner Valley field.

be finished – British American Oil advanced a loan of $30,000, Imperial Oil came through with $22,500 worth of drilling equipment in return for a 7.5 percent gross royalty, and Spooner Oils and Calmont Oils each contributed $7,500 for five percent royalty interests. In the meantime, Brown had mortgaged everything he owned – his house, his insurance, his car – to help raise money for the well. Bell, too, was deeply in debt, partly to finance this and earlier unsuccessful wildcat ventures, and also because he was losing money on his newspapers. He was more than half a million dollars in debt. It took $100,000 and two years to complete the well.

Bell, who had been the first president of Turner Valley Royalties, never lived to see the well completed. He died in March, 1936 – three months before it struck oil.

It was on June 16, 1936 at a depth of 8,282 feet that Turner Valley Royalties No. 1 blew in with a roar which was heard throughout the valley, and soon echoed around the world.

"The strike was made late Tuesday afternoon when accumulated gas pressure forced thousands of feet of heavy rotary drilling fluid up the hole and scattered crude oil over a wide area in the vicinity of the derrick," reported the Calgary Herald the following day. "It is the first time in Canada's history that anything approaching a crude oil gusher has been struck. Turner Valley Royalties is believed by oil men to prove the existence of a huge crude oil reservoir."

Hundreds of wells were drilled to extend the oil producing area following this discovery, and Turner Valley became the largest oil field in what was then still called the British Empire, the only significant oil field in Canada for the next 11 years. During the second world war, production rose to a peak rate of 27,000 barrels a day in 1942.

1.8 billion cubic feet of gas flared

By the time the Turner Valley Royalties well discovered the oil column, the damage had already been done. An estimated 1.8 trillion cubic feet of natural gas had been wasted by flaring, and had robbed the reservoir of much of the natural pressure which was required to recover the oil. Turner Valley was still producing nominal amounts of oil in 1969, and engineers estimate that as much as 120 million barrels might be recovered by the time the last well is abandoned. Except for the depletion of the reservoir pressure by the gas flaring, however, more than half a billion barrels of oil might have been produced at Turner Valley. Value of the oil reserves which were lost and the gas which was wasted amounted to more than a billion dollars.

No lasting reward

For Bill Herron, the diminutive dynamo, Turner Valley brought no great, lasting rewards. The man who sought his fortune from the silver-rich rocks of Ontario's Cobalt area to the Caribou gold fields of British Columbia, found that wealth kept slipping through his fingers. The 1914 discovery well and his land dealing gave Herron some brief and modest wealth, but his funds were soon drained by the annual 25-cents-per-acre rental payments on the thousands of Turner Valley leases to which he clung tenaciously. Herron went back briefly to farming and freighting in Turner Valley, but when the Royalite No. 4 discovery hit pay in 1924, Herron and his family were chasing the elusive bonanza with a placer gold mining operation near Barkerville, B.C.

With Turner Valley activity revived by the Royalite No. 4 discovery, Herron organized Okalta Oils Limited in 1926 to develop the Turner Valley leases he had so long held on to. Okalta shared well in Turner Valley development, and Herron was soon a millionaire — at

Flaring gas
at Turner Valley
in the 1920's.

least on paper. But the stock market crash in 1929 and the depression which followed again wiped out his fortune, as the price of Okalta shares dropped from $4.00 to 2.5 cents. When Herron died in 1939 he was, says his son Bill, "damn poor".

"Carry on, we want and need more oil," was the motto attributed to Archibald Dingman, the man who actually brought in the 1914 discovery as managing director of Calgary Petroleum Products. Dingman organized several more small though prosperous Turner Valley companies, but did not live quite long enough to see his motto bear fruit. At the age of 85, he died March 7, 1936 — three months before Turner Valley's big oil pool was discovered.

Much larger oil fields have been found in western Canada and many more will be discovered. But none will likely stir as much excitement as Turner Valley. It was a billion-dollar blowout.

Discovery
at Norman
Wells, 1920.

Chapter Four

Norman Wells and the Canol project

Much of the Norman Wells oil field lies under the broad Mackenzie River, a thousand miles north of Edmonton, 75 miles south of the Arctic Circle. For decades it was too remote to be of economic significance. It took an investment of $134 million to prove the point – a war-time investment in roads, pipelines and a refinery, all of which were shut down and abandoned less than a year after they had been completed.

Exploring in the Sub-Arctic

One of the most northerly oil fields in the world, Norman Wells covers some 4,400 acres within which more than 60 wells have been drilled to tap reserves which lie at a shallow depth in a large Devonian reef. The field in 1970 was still capable of producing perhaps 30,000 barrels of oil a day, yet has never produced more than 3,000 barrels a day. It was discovered nearly half a century ago but less than 20 percent of the estimated 60 million barrels of recoverable oil had been produced by 1970.

Norman Wells was the key factor in the war-time Canol project, designed to provide Alaska with military fuel requirements in the face of possible Japanese submarine attacks which threatened tanker supply movements along the west coast. The project involved construction of a string of 10 northern airfields, more than 2,000 miles

Canol

79

of wilderness roads, 1,600 miles of pipelines and a refinery scraped together from second hand pieces collected from throughout North America.

Triumph
or
blunder?

Canol has been described by its builders as "the greatest construction job since the Panama Canal," and by others as "the most colossal blunder" of the second world war. It may have been both. Certainly any validity the project ever possessed had ceased to exist by the time it was completed. It took 20 months to build, and 11 months later it was shut down and abandoned. Of the $134 million it cost, only $1 million was ever recovered.

The Norman Wells story starts in 1911 when J. K. Cornwall of the Northern Trading Company noted evidence of oil floating along the banks of the Mackenzie River below Fort Norman. Cornwall hired an Indian, Karkesee, who located several small pools of oil from which the oil slicks had originated. Samples of the oil were analysed by the Barber Asphalt Company of Pittsburgh, which reported it to be similar to Pennsylvania oil.

Two years later Calgary was already building up to the oil fever that gripped the city with the completion of Bill Herron's Turner Valley discovery in 1914. Everyone in Calgary, it seemed, was forming an oil syndicate in 1913. One syndicate of Calgary businessmen, however, was looking not at the Alberta foothills, but at Cornwall's oil seeps, 1,200 miles north. They hired an English geologist, Dr. T. O. Bosworth who reportedly just "happened to be in Calgary on his way back to England from South America where he had been employed by the Shell Oil Company." Bosworth examined the properties, later reported that, "It was the remarkable character of the Fort Creek shales and Beavertail limestone, rather than the seepages, which led to a favourable view of the prospects of this field."

In 1914, the world turned topsy-turvy. The Turner Valley discovery, which in May to Calgarians had seemed like the biggest oil strike ever made, by Fall was nothing but a tiny trickle of oil. Thousands of Calgarians who had earlier lined up to buy shares in hastily formed oil companies, now lined up to enlist for the Great War. Cornwall joined them, shipping overseas as a Colonel in the English Army.

Imperial

Imperial Oil Limited, a product of the early oil fields of Ontario, was in 1914 already well established as Canada's largest oil concern and a subsidiary of John D. Rockefeller's Standard Oil. That year, faced with a growing need for oil supplies, it established an exploration and production department and was soon exploring from the sub-Arctic of northern Canada to the tropics of Peru. Imperial in 1914 hired Dr. Bosworth as its chief geologist and purchased the Norman Wells properties from the Calgary syndicate.

With closer prospects to drill first (all of which were "dry"), it took Imperial a few years to get around to Norman Wells. In July, 1919, a cable tool drilling rig with ancillary supplies and equipment, eight men and an ox, set out from Edmonton 300 miles by rail to Peace River and from there 1,600 miles by winding rivers to Norman Wells, the country that brought summer mosquitoes "big enough to shoot with a rifle" and winter temperatures of 60 below. Under the direction of a young geologist, Ted Link (later Imperial's chief geologist), their mission was to set up drilling operations and conduct further geological study. The route lay down the Peace River by scow to the Slave River at Lake Athabasca, down the Slave to Fort Resolution on Great Slave Lake, 100 miles across the lake, and a thousand miles down the mighty Mackenzie River. There was a four-mile portage on the Peace River and a 16-mile portage that took 15 days to accomplish at Smith Rapids on the Slave River.

Eight men and an ox

Alexander Mackenzie first led the canoes of the Northwest Company down the river to the shores of the Arctic Ocean in 1789. Ever since, the Mackenzie River system has been the highway of the north, first for the frail birch-bark canoes of the fur traders, then the wood-burning paddle-wheelers of the Hudson's Bay Company, finally the diesel tugs with the shallow-draft barges. Second largest river in North America, the Mackenzie is from four to ten miles wide, a placid stream of clear, cold water that lumbers on at five miles an hour and dumps half a million cubic feet of water per second into the Arctic Ocean.

Transport

This was the first drilling equipment to travel down the Mackenzie River system. Two decades later, thousands of tons of equipment – pipe, graders, tractors, drilling rigs, camp facilities – were moved along much of the same waterway to Norman Wells for the Canol project. Today, transportation for drilling in the far north is augmented by helicopters, giant cargo aircraft, muskeg vehicles with 40-ton loads that tread over the treacherous bogs with a footstep lighter than a man's, and tractor trains. But the Mackenzie is still the highway of the north.

Imperial's Norman Wells party reached its destination in early September. Their ox, Old Nig, was put to work. "There was a cabin to build, a derrick to erect, the boiler and engine to get up the hill, storehouses and a stable to erect and . . . a tremendous pile of wood to be stacked up against the 60 below of January and February," reported the Imperial Oil Review. Timber for the derrick and buildings was cut along the steep banks of the river, hauled by Old Nig, the ox, and the job was "nearing completion just as the river steamer came on her upward trip back to civilization." Five of the party returned with the steamer; the other three remained at Norman Wells. Isolated for the next 10 months as the long winter night set in, their squat log cabin "marked an exclamation point in two thousand miles of frozen silence," while behind them the river swept on, "sheathed in a 10-foot coat of ice." They were assigned the tasks of northern watchmen and "getting the hole started before the bottom dropped out of the thermometer." By Christmas, Old Nig was being served as stew.

Plagued by mishaps

Ted Link, with another party of seven and 20 tons of equipment in two scows and a motor boat, left Peace River again the following May for the 1,600-mile trip to Norman Wells. One scow was wrecked and lost in shooting the rapids on the Peace River. The whole party was very nearly lost in the Smith rapids on the Slave River. Several times the motor boat was grounded on sand bars, and freed only by men working up to their waists in icy water. By the time they reached Fort Resolution, the remaining scow, stripped to an essential 16 tons of equipment, was nearly 100 percent over-loaded and leaking badly. Ahead of them lay 100 miles of open water on Great Slave Lake before they even reached the Mackenzie. Somehow, by July 8, they managed to reach the drilling site at Norman Wells. And none too soon for the men who had wintered there — for the past month they had lived on nothing but fish and flour.

The discovery

The new party took over the operations. Four of them carried out the drilling while Link, with two others, continued his field work in the area. "Geological work was confined to a study of the formations along the river and tributaries," Link wrote later. "Plane-table and traverses were made and not without difficulty. Mosquitoes and black flies, although not as bad as last year, made life miserable nevertheless. Inland trips had to be made with bedding, grub, plane-table, alidade, tripod and rod on our backs. Tents were eliminated as excess, and many times we got a good soaking from the rain. Too much food is also a hindrance to inland trips. Hardtack and bacon grease are the staples."

"On August 23, 1920," reported the Imperial Oil Review, "when the drill was at a depth of seven hundred feet, word was brought to Mr. Link that oil was standing in the casing pipe within a few feet of the surface. 'Don't bother me again until it over-flows,' said the

Ted Link
in the
Northwest
Territories

geologist, busy at his work." Four days later, a breathless driller again rushed up one of the tributaries of the Mackenzie to find Link – the well was now at 783 feet, and this time the oil was flowing over the top. Link returned to the well, and for 40 minutes they watched as a fountain of oil shot 70 feet into the air, before the flow was shut-in and the well capped.

During the next 20 years, Imperial drilled only half a dozen holes at Norman Wells, completing five oil producers. In 1939 the company built a small refinery which initially operated only in the summer to provide the limited demand for petroleum in the far north, mostly aviation fuel for the bush planes. By 1940, production at Norman Wells had averaged no more than 100 barrels a day throughout any one year.

Five producers

83

White Elephant of Whitehorse

The second world war brought two of the biggest northern projects ever completed; the 1,600-mile Alaska highway punched through from Dawson Creek, B.C., to Fairbanks, Alaska by 10,000 troops of the U. S. Army Engineer Corps, and the Canol project. By the time they were both completed, the Canol project resulted in more miles of road construction than the Alaska highway.

Alaska, in the Spring of 1942, looked like the soft under-belly of North America. The Japanese had severely crippled the U.S. Pacific fleet at Pearl Harbor, over-run the Islands of the South Pacific, and gained a toe-hold in the Aleutian Islands which stretch from Alaska like a series of stepping stones toward Japan. Japanese submarines cruised the west coast waters and posed a threat to coastal shipping.

Alaska was strategic. Lend lease planes en route to Russia landed here for fueling. For the United States, it was a potential launching base for an offensive against Japan. For the Japanese it offered a possible base for an offensive against North America, if the Japanese could manage to scramble over the Aleutians. Alaska was isolated. Its military bases were few and inadequate. With no road or rail connection with the rest of North America, it was dependent on air and sea for all its military supplies.

In March, the United States decided that, with Canadian help, it would build a supply line to Alaska – the Alaska highway. Over this it could drive an army into Alaska, swiftly, safely, surely.

The highway could deliver an army – but could it deliver enough petroleum to fuel that army, as well as the vital Alaskan air bases? The trucks themselves would consume prodigious amounts of gasoline on that long run between Dawson Creek and Fairbanks. If coastal shipping were ever cut off it would require literally hundreds of trucks, perhaps as many as a thousand, in continuous service to supply Alaska's military petroleum needs. The Alaska highway could become clogged just with tank-wagon trucks.

The answer was Canol, named after Canadian oil. The plan was to build a 600-mile pipeline from Norman Wells across the unexplored Mackenzie Mountains to Whitehorse where a refinery would be built to supply petroleum products at a rate of more than 100,000 gallons a day. From the Whitehorse refinery, other lines would fan out to move the products – one 600 miles northeast to Fairbanks, another 265 miles southeast along the route of the proposed Alaska highway to Watson Lake, and a third line 110 miles southwest to Skagway on the coast. The project was conceived by a civilian technical adviser, Dean James H. Graham of the University of Kentucky School of Engineering. It was authorized in April, 1942, by Lieutenant General

B. B. Sommervell, chief of the Army Service Forces, on the basis of a one-page memorandum from Graham. The schedule called for completion of Canol that Fall.

"I knew that the time schedule was very optimistic," Sommervell later told a U.S. Senate investigating committee headed by Senator Harry S. Truman. "In fact, I knew it couldn't be done." Sommervell also told the committee that "from an economic standpoint the whole project was cockeyed from the beginning ."

Canol was thus embroiled in controversy from the start. Contracts for the project were awarded on May 4. Work was underway before the end of the month. On October 26, 1943 – 17 months later – Canol was finally approved by the U.S. Joint Chiefs of Staff. In November, hearings opened before the Truman committee, and it seemed as though Canol might be abandoned even before it was completed.

Contracts awarded

The threat to Alaska, so real in the Spring of 1942, no longer seemed to exist by the Fall of 1943. The Japanese had been driven from the Aleutians, were in retreat – slowly but surely – in the South Pacific, and their submarines no longer menaced west coast shipping, which was, in fact, being used to supply material including petroleum products for Canol. "Conclusion of witnesses for all agencies except the Army was that Canol has no war or postwar value to justify its $134 million cost," reported Life magazine. But the Army was adamant.

Sommervell urged that Canol not only be completed, but expanded. Under Secretary of War Robert P. Patterson testified that success of Canol might well determine the "size and extent" of an air offensive against Japan. The U.S. Congress might well have scrapped the project except for the fact that it was already 75 percent completed.

Canol may indeed have been "the sorriest chapter of the American war effort on the home front," as The Nation magazine later claimed. If it really was – and it didn't seem so in 1942 – that was the fault of the Generals who ordered it. No one could question the accomplishment of the men who carried out the order. Folly or not, it was possibly the greatest engineering and construction achievement of the entire war.

"Fault" of generals?

Three of the world's largest pipeline construction firms – W. A. Bechtel Co., H. C. Price Co. and W. E. Callahan Construction Co. –

The Great Canadian Oil Patch

Contractor partnership formed a partnership called Bechtel-Price-Callahan to build Canol. Imperial Oil contracted, for one dollar plus costs and a royalty on production, to develop the Norman Wells field in order to provide 3,000 barrels of oil a day. Ted Link returned to Norman Wells to supervise the development for Imperial and to conduct further exploration work in the area. A subsidiary of Standard Oil of California was awarded the contract to operate the pipeline and refinery once they were in operation. The civilian contractors were to work on the project with the U.S. Army Corps of Engineers.

Canol presented two major challenges. One was the task of laying a pipeline across the unexplored Mackenzie Mountains. Even more difficult, however, was the task of freighting in the thousands of tons of supplies and equipment to the site of the project.

Getting there was toughest The task of simply getting there was the toughest part of the Canol project. In late May of 1942, some 2,500 U.S. Army Engineer troops passed through Edmonton to tackle the task of delivering the freight. Their plan was to follow much of the same route that Imperial had used 23 years earlier in reaching Norman Wells with an eight-man crew, a cable tool outfit and an ox. Only this time a lot more freight had to be moved in — more than 200,000 tons. Before it was completed they had to turn to a variety of routes. Everything for Canol was funnelled through Edmonton. From here, Canol's supply lines eventually stretched by rail, road and water over routes that totalled more than 9,000 miles.

Joining the army engineers were more than 2,000 civilian employees. In their employment offices from Edmonton to Dallas, and from New York to San Francisco, Bechtel-Price-Callahan posted copies of a notice which warned: "THIS IS NO PICNIC. Working and living conditions on this job are as difficult as those encountered on any construction job ever done in the United States or foreign territory. Men hired for this job will be required to work and live under the most extreme conditions imaginable. Temperatures will range from 90 degrees above zero to 70 degrees below zero. Men will have to fight swamps, rivers, ice and cold. Mosquitoes, flies and gnats will not only be annoying but will cause bodily harm. If you are not prepared to work under these and similar conditions, do not apply."

Route The initial route, in early 1942, lay 285 miles by the Northern Alberta Railway to Waterways at the end of steel near Fort McMurray; from there 1,100 miles down the Athabasca River (with the

86

Workers on
the Canol
Project.

16-mile portage at Smith Rapids), across Great Slave Lake, and down
the Mackenzie River. At Waterways, the army built freight staging
facilities and assembled large barges. Military camps were established
along the route, at Waterways, Fort Fitzgerald, Fort Smith, the Slave
Delta, Fort Resolution, Hay River, Wrigley Harbor, Fort Providence,
Fort Simpson, Fort Wrigley and Norman Wells.

Additional personnel, mail and supplies were brought in by air,
and the army established a string of 10 airfields between Edmonton

Trucking
pipe for the
Canol line.

and Norman Wells. River tugs were brought in by rail from as far as Missouri. They joined the tugs and barges of the Northern Transportation Company, and the wood-burning paddle wheelers of the Hudson's Bay Company. Almost anything that would float was used to carry the freight north. Tractors, fuel, machinery, repair parts, knocked-down camp buildings, lumber, drilling equipment and thousands of tons of pipe — four inches in diameter, 22 feet in length, each weighing 230 pounds — were floated down the inland waterway to Norman Wells. It was the strangest looking armada the northern rivers had ever seen.

Hazards

The route was not without hazards; sand bars, areas of shallow waters, areas of swift waters, and sudden storms on Great Slave Lake.

Several loads of pipe were dropped into Great Slave Lake, while half a dozen tractors and a couple of graders were lost in Great Slave Lake.

By September, less than 20,000 tons of freight had passed through Waterways, far short of the amount required to maintain winter operations. The last two barges to be towed across Great Slave Lake that season "rose on the crest of colossal waves, then plunged unmercifully out of sight in their troughs," veteran oil writer C. V. Myers recorded in his booklet on the Canol project, Oil to Alaska. "The men in the tug-boat ahead saw that their cargo was doomed, and cut loose the cable. The barges capsized, spilling forth their contents into the hungry waters. Now the vital supplies could never be shipped in time." With winter about to grip the north country in a vise, the waterways supply route was closed for nine months.

When Canol was built there were two ways to move freight in the far north. In the summer, when the rivers were open, vast muskeg barriers prevented use of overland transportation. In the winter, when the rivers closed, the muskeg froze and tractor trains could haul heavy loads over the snow of winter roads. There were hazards in both the summer and winter routes. Canol had already found out about the summer hazards on the lakes and rivers of the Mackenzie system. They would find out too, about the winter hazards – the task of keeping machinery moving in sub-Arctic temperatures, battling through long stretches of mud where chinook winds had suddenly thawed the snow cover, sleeping on the open road in temperatures of 60 below, the task of just staying alive.

Winter problems

With the route from Waterways closed, the Canol contractors devised another means to move an additional 9,000 tons of freight before the Spring thaw. From Edmonton, freight would be moved by rail to Peace River rather than to Waterways. From Peace River they would build 1,000 miles of winter road to Canol. The new route was ordered on October 3 and hundreds of men plus equipment started pouring into a new base camp at Peace River: 130 more tractors, 600 pairs of freight sleds, 23,000 drums of diesel fuel, warehouses, bunkhouses, mess halls, repair centres, hospital facilities. All of this was in addition to the 9,000 tons to be moved to Canol.

"The camp was one problem; building the road was another," Myers wrote. "To complete it in time to move the freight before the spring thaw would require progress at the rate of ten miles per day.

The road

Road crew No. 1 was finding it impossible to meet more than half of this objective. Crew after crew was dispatched to overtake its predecessor, to assist, and to carry on. On December 18th, the thermometer sank to 65 below. On that record day of cold, Road Crew No. 5 ventured forth beneath a cloud of steam and smoke. Not one tractor train had yet left Peace River."

Tractor trains

Road crews worked north from Peace River and south from Norman Wells. Eventually they met halfway, and the first tractor train left Peace River on December 23, only to find that the north had dealt yet one more trick. There was virtually no snow cover. "Huge Caterpillars strained over bare earth in places, almost pulling the runners from beneath the sleds," Myers reported. ". . . it had become apparent that tractor trains could never do the job. Snow had been delayed too long. It might be delayed longer." They decided to use trucks as well as the tractor trains. The winter road had never been built for trucks, but somehow they managed to get through. It was tough going. A cook on one of the tractor trains decided to "quit for the eleventh time when the butt end of a tree came smashing up through the floor of the caboose, hit the stove smack in the middle and went through the rear wall." The last freight train left Peace River on April 4 and when it reached Canol, 10 million ton-miles of freight had been moved over the winter road.

Great Slave Lake

There were other tractor trains busy that winter. When shipping closed on the Mackenzie system, 8,000 tons of four-inch pipe had been stock-piled on the south shore of Great Slave Lake. The ice on the Mackenzie River breaks up in May, but on Great Slave Lake it lingers until July. If the pipe could be moved 150 miles across the lake in winter, then the following summer they could start barging it down the Mackenzie River at least six weeks earlier.

The ice on Great Slave Lake buckles and forms huge ridges which run for miles like a line of low hills. At the crest of these ridges, there are great cracks in the ice, some extending all the way down to the water. The tractor trains hauling the pipe had to detour as much as 50 miles around the ice ridges, following meandering and shifting routes across the lake. The most furious blizzards in the sub-Arctic sweep unimpeded across Great Slave Lake, cutting visibility to a few feet. One tractor train got caught on the lake in a blizzard, unable to find its way around the ice ridges and unable to cut across them with its train of sleds and pipe. The pipe was abandoned and the tractor and caboose were able to make it back to Hay River, but it had been

90

a narrow escape. The solution was found by a road and bridge crew which cut through the ridges and built plank bridges across the ice cracks to maintain a constant route. So Canol used not only a winter road over land but also a winter road over 150 miles of ice.

The 1,100-mile Mackenzie River system from Waterways and the 1,000-mile winter road from Peace River brought in freight for the eastern end of the Canol project at Norman Wells. Freight was also brought in by two other routes to tackle the western end of Canol, working east from Whitehorse. One route was across Alberta and British Columbia by rail to tidewater at Prince Rupert; up the inside passage of the coast by ocean barge 500 miles to Skagway, Alaska, and then up the steep, narrow-gauge track of the historic White Pass and Yukon Railway for 110 miles to Whitehorse. By late Fall of 1942 the Alaska highway had been punched through as far as Whitehorse and − at least until the Spring thaw − supplies could be moved in by truck from Dawson Creek, which was also connected to Edmonton by rail.

Freight routes

While the freight was moving in, the Canol builders faced their other major hurdle, the Mackenzie Mountains which cut across the 577-mile Norman Wells-to-Whitehorse route, a stone wall barrier with the rocks piled 9,000 feet high, cut by swift streams and vertical 400-foot canyons, pock-marked by unknown lakes and glaciers. Only one man had ever crossed that section of the Mackenzie Mountains and recorded anything about the country. Joseph Keele, a geologist with the Geological Survey of Canada, following a trip in 1907 − 08, had described the Mackenzie Mountain range as even more rugged than the Rocky Mountains. But Keele had not come within a hundred miles of Norman Wells. Most of the route was completely unknown, and for more than 300 miles there was no human habitation. The task would be to find a pass, then find a route across the pass, build a road along the route, and then lay a pipeline along the side of the road.

The mountains

Starting in June, bush pilots flew a series of reconnaissance flights across the Mackenzie − Yukon divide in search of a route. But more than aerial surveys were needed, and in late October Guy Blanchet, a Bechtel-Price-Callahan employee, set out from Norman Wells with three Indian guides and their dog teams to complete the survey of the route across the mountains. They made rafts to cross swift, half-frozen rivers, skirted unmapped lakes, lived off game − sheep, caribou, moose and ptarmigan − fought off an attack by a pair of

Bush flights

91

timber wolves, and battled their way through. Blanchet badly sprained his ankle and hobbled nearly half the trip on improvised splints. When they reached Macmillan Pass it was easy going down the long, gentle slopes on the western side of the divide, and it was clear that the eastern end of the pipeline route would be by far the toughest part.

Blanchet's obstacles

A month after they started, Blanchet and his party completed their 250-mile trip at a lonely cabin near a lake where a cache of food and supplies awaited them. On December 22, the first road building party left Norman Wells to start the road across the mountains; 23 men, tractors, and a train of cabooses which served for bunkhouses, store room and maintenance shop. Their obstacles were described in Myers' booklet.

"Diesel fuel froze to the consistency of vaseline, and would not pour. Light machine oil became as hard as cup grease. The best grade of antifreeze froze solid in the tins."

"Sometimes tractors stopped as often as every 15 minutes . . . In 70 below zero temperatures mechanics had to get out and clear the (fuel) lines. The cold rendered the sleigh runners as brittle as cast. Time after time they broke. Welders and mechanics repaired them, and again the snail pace continued. Motors had to be kept running 24 hours a day. To stop a motor once and let it get cold meant stopping it for good."

Hot springs

"In Dodo Canyon underground hot springs kept the ice thin and treacherous. Twenty-ton Caterpillar monsters would drop through the ice and have to be hauled out by other Caterpillars. Fuel sleighs overturned on steep grades."

On January 3 the temperature was 35 below at 11 a.m. By noon it had risen to 35 above. Four days later it was 39 above. Then as suddenly as it had risen it dropped to 15 below, followed by a blizzard so intense that the party didn't move an inch for two days.

Throughout 1943 the tempo accelerated as thousands of men attacked the Canol project in different ways. As the road crew from Norman Wells worked its way slowly west, 1,500 army engineers were working east from Whitehorse. Welders followed the road builders and a ribbon of four-inch steel started snaking its way across the mountains. (Because of its light viscosity, oil from the Norman Wells field would flow at temperatures down to 70 below, thus the line could be laid on the surface, eliminating the need for ditch digging). Imperial Oil drilled more than 40 additional oil wells in the

Burning out
a discovery
at Norman Wells

Norman Wells field. Supplies were pouring in from Skagway over the White Pass & Yukon railway, and in summer freight was again moving to Norman Wells down the Mackenzie River system from Waterways. The branch pipelines were built radiating out from Whitehorse, 110 miles southwest to Skagway, 600 miles northwest to Fairbanks, and 265 miles southwest to Watson Lake on the Alaska highway.

At Whitehorse, construction was underway on the 3,000 barrels a day refinery that would produce gasoline, diesel fuel and other products from the Norman Wells oil. It was a refinery built of bits and pieces collected from more than 2,000 suppliers from throughout North America. Major refining equipment came from a shut-in refinery of Corpus Christi, Texas. The boilers came from an old power plant at Hamilton, Ontario, while the turbine and generators were from an idle mill at Penedale, California. It was probably the most traveled refinery in the world, and its journey was not yet over. Whitehorse proved to be only a five-year stop.

The Canol road was completed on December 31, 1943. Trucks could now move supplies freely between Whitehorse and Norman Wells. The final weld on the pipeline was made on February 16,

Whitehorse refinery

93

1944, just 20 months and four days after the first reconnaissance flight across the Mackenzie-Yukon divide. By April, Norman Wells crude oil was surging through the pipeline to the Whitehorse refinery.

It was too late to be of any significance to the outcome of the war. The tide had already turned and the Japanese had long since fled the Aleutian Islands. Plans for an Alaskan-based offensive against Japan were dropped. The refinery operated on Norman Wells crude for 11 months and by March, 1945, it had processed 976,764 barrels of oil. Then it was all shut in – the pipeline, the refinery, the roads, the airfields and most of the wells in the Norman Wells field. Canol, said Newsweek magazine, was "the white elephant of Whitehorse."

Rusting away

For more than two years, the $134 million Canol project was literally rusting away. The U.S. Foreign Liquidation Commission vainly looked for a buyer who would at least salvage the refinery, but when the best bid it could get amounted to only $151,133 it turned the offer down. It was the discovery of the Leduc field near Edmonton by Imperial Oil in February, 1947 that resulted in the salvage of at least the refinery. Imperial soon discovered it had a major oil field at Leduc, and needed a refinery at Edmonton to process the crude. It bid $1 million for the refinery in August, 1947 (just six months after the Leduc discovery), and spent another $6 million to tear it apart and move the 7,000 tons of pieces 1,300 miles by truck and train to Edmonton. It was re-assembled the following year and placed on stream less than 18 months after the Leduc discovery, the first refinery at Edmonton. Nearly two decades later, some of the pipe was salvaged from the pipeline.

In 1970

In 1970, Norman Wells was still beyond the range of economic supply, except for a limited northern market. But tomorrow may be different. North America is moving rapidly farther north for its oil supplies. Big-inch pipelines from the Rainbow and Zama Lake fields – just 50 miles from the Northwest Territories, 500 miles from Norman Wells – move oil southwest to refineries as far as Vancouver, southeast across half a continent to Chicago, Minneapolis, Detroit

and Toronto. The barges of the Mackenzie River are again moving drilling rigs into the far north. So are the giant helicopters, the huge cargo aircraft, the muskeg vehicles, and the new roads and railways that have been built to develop the north. Oil men are spending tens of millions of dollars to find northern oil fields like Norman Wells, and they are confident they will find many of them.

The north is still wild, vast beyond the imagination and held in the grip of Canada's sub-Arctic. But it is no longer isolated, inaccessible

Laying the
Canol line.

or impenetrable. Oil men and their equipment now roam the north
wherever they want, whenever they want, in operations that have
almost become routine. Oil men have conquered the north, and it
was Norman Wells and Canol that showed them how to do it, that
pointed the way to North America's storehouse of petroleum for
tomorrow.

95

The Great Canadian Oil Patch

First look
at the Leduc
discovery, 1947.

Chapter Five

An accident at Leduc

The discovery of Leduc was, in part at least, an accident – the most fortunate accident that has ever happened to Canada.

By the end of the second world war, oil men were starting to despair of ever finding large oil reserves in western Canada. Tens of millions of dollars had been spent and hundreds of wildcats had been drilled in the search for oil fields throughout the prairie provinces and far into the north country during the previous 30 years. And what was there to show for it? A few natural gas fields, the Turner Valley oil field west of Calgary where production was already in an advanced stage of decline, and the Norman Wells field on the fringe of the Arctic Circle, which had a colorful but short career as the supply source for the second world war Canol project. There were, of course, the vast reserves of Alberta's Athabasca tar sands, but one yet had been able to devise a method of economically extracting the 300 billion barrels of oil locked in these sands.

It seemed incredible that a sedimentary basin as gigantic as that which covered most of western Canada would yield only two oil fields. But now, oil men were starting to wonder if that just might not be the case. And even if there were more, just how much could you afford to spend to find them?

The need for a significant new source of oil was becoming desperate. Canada, in 1946, was consuming petroleum at a rate of 221,000

Dry years on the prairies

barrels a day – and importing 200,000 barrels a day at an annual cost of more than half a billion dollars in foreign exchange funds. For a nation the size of Canada, it was a heavy economic burden.

On the prairies, the need for an indigenous supply source was even more imperative. Imports of foreign oil, because of the distance they had to be shipped, were prohibitively expensive; Turner Valley, the only local supply source was dwindling rapidly. The major oil reserves at Turner Valley had been discovered in 1936, and under the stimulus of war-time demand, production had reached a peak of 28,000 barrels a day in 1942. By 1946, it had declined to 20,000 barrels a day (Ontario accounted for most of the remaining Canadian oil production).

Turner Valley in the war years

Turner Valley, during the war years, supplied the oil needs for refineries not only in Alberta, but throughout the prairies. But in the Spring of 1946, Imperial Oil president Henry H. Hewetson commented: "Turner Valley is not exhausted but production for the whole area is down. I don't think there will be any oil shipped out of Alberta after the end of this year."

Before Turner Valley, Montana oil fields had supplied the demand of the prairie provinces. But now Montana production had dropped to a fraction of its war-time rate, and there was no surplus available for export. Prairie refineries had to turn to crude shipped by rail from as far as Texas and Oklahoma, at a cost laid down in Regina that amounted to $1.93 per barrel just for the transportation.

There were more than a dozen firms, large and small, still searching for oil in western Canada, and the most active and persistent of these was Imperial Oil. It had been on the scene for a long time – since 1914. Imperial's first Alberta wildcat had been drilled in 1917, and by the end of 1946 it had a string of 133 dry holes and just one oil discovery, Norman Wells. Even that was too remote to be produced. Its total exploration expenditures in western Canada amounted to $23 million, of which more than half had been spent in the 1939-1946 period.

Stolberg well

It was a relentless, unrewarding search, financially disastrous for many of the smaller firms, and even for the majors it was a bitter, personal frustration for management, geologists, drillers. Typical of the frustrated efforts was a deep test in the foothills belt, called Imperial-Shell Stolberg, which the Imperial Oil Review described as "another of the bitter climaxes which must accompany Canadian oil industry efforts to find new reserves for an oil-hungry nation."

"The foothills of Alberta are one of the world's most heartbreaking hunting grounds for oil," said the Review. With formations "folded back and forth like a Chinese fan ," it is also one of the most difficult drilling areas. Twisted formations can "hold the drill pipe in a vise-like grip thousands of feet below the surface;" rocks tough enough to scratch glass like a diamond can wear out a drilling bit in just a few inches of hole so that "drillers must start the laborious pulling of thousands of feet of pipe to change them;" slanted and convoluted rocks can twist off a drilling pipe causing lengthy and expensive "fishing" operations to retrieve the lost pipe. The Stolberg well encountered all these problems.

The well was spudded (drilling began) on March 29, 1945. It took nearly two years to drill and cost more than a million dollars. Twice the pipe was stuck in the hole, once for 16 days until the bit was blasted into tiny pieces with a time bomb and five quarts of nitro-glycerine. At 12,170 feet the drill stem twisted off leaving a jagged end sticking above the 368 feet of pipe sitting on the bottom, which had to be caught and lifted up more than two miles out of the hole. When the hole reached its total depth of 13,747 feet, a final test yielded a tiny puff of gas and a copious flow of salt water. The drilling crew started the task of tearing down the rig and moving it over 70 miles of mountain and muskeg trail that had been hacked through to the site of yet another deep foothills test, and another dry hole.

Two years to drill

"Despite this present rather gloomy picture the prairies, which are today at an economic disadvantage in regard to oil supply, give some indication that they may, ultimately, develop into one of the world's great oil producing areas," commented the Review of 1946. "The petroleum industry, as a whole, is today engaged upon the greatest search for oil in Canada that our nation has ever seen, and has concentrated on the western plain." Then, with a hollow-sounding optimism that must have been born of despair, it added that "the future of oil exploration in western Canada is bright."

But just in case this bright future failed to provide new oil reserves, Imperial was considering the manufacture of synthetic petroleum fuels from natural gas, and had conducted extensive experimental work. A process for producing synthetic liquid hydrocarbon fuels from coal had been developed in Germany during the thirties and had provided Germany with much of its petroleum requirements during the war. The process involved heating coal to convert it to coke, passing steam through the hot coke to produce a

Optimistic outlook

"water gas" consisting of carbon monoxide and hydrogen, and then passing this gas over a catalyst at elevated temperatures and pressures to yield a liquid hydrocarbon.

Oil from gas

The process could be adapted to produce a synthetic crude oil from natural gas more economically than from coal. The synthetic oil could be refined, noted the Imperial Oil Review, by "a process whereby a very high octane fuel called polymere gasoline is made. The gasoline produced in the synthesis process is not of very good quality, but by further treating and by adding cracked gasoline and polymere gasoline a good yield of high grade fuel is obtained."

The Review estimated that it would require 11,000 cubic feet of natural gas to make one barrel of gasoline, and that a plant to make 5,000 barrels a day of gasoline would cost, in 1946 values, "roughly 25 million dollars." At that rate, it would take five billion dollars of investment in plant facilities to synthesize from natural gas Canada's 1970 gasoline requirements, plus untold billions more in exploration, development and treating facilities to produce and remove impurities from the natural gas. It would require a supply of some 11 billion cubic feet of natural gas every day and about 100 trillion cubic feet of natural gas reserves — three times the volume of natural gas discovered in Canada to 1969. It was not a very attractive alternative to crude oil, but a possible necessity.

"Imperial Oil has embarked upon an extensive program of exploratory drilling to locate natural gas in quantities great enough to warrant construction of a synthesis plant if synthetic production costs can be brought down to economically practical levels," the Review stated. "If an adequate supply of gas is assured and improved processing methods become available it is possible that a synthetic fuel industry may serve the west . . . It is necessary to proceed cautiously at present, since the discovery of further adequate crude oil fields in this part of the country would seriously jeopardize such a huge plant investment."

One last attempt

Before taking the final, irrevocable step of committing itself to a multi-million dollar synthesis project — and thereby admitting defeat in its search for western Canadian oil — Imperial reviewed the entire exploration scene. It wanted to determine whether or not there remained an oil play with reasonable prospects of success which could forestall the gas synthesis project. Eighteen senior advisers, including top geologists from the parent Standard Oil of New Jersey, met in a series of several exhausting sessions. They reviewed the geological prospects from the U.S. border to the Arctic circle, from Hudson Bay to Vancouver Island. Finally, they decided on one last play focused on a geological feature known then as the "hinge belt" in the western Canada sedimentary basin.

Hinge belt

As it turned out, Imperial decided on a play for reasons that were geologically all wrong, but found oil anyway.

Geological knowledge of the western Canada Sedimentary basin at that time was limited; a few hundred wildcats scattered over such a vast area simply had not provided enough information for a complete picture. The geologists knew that the basin was wedge-shaped, the sedimentary rocks 20,000 or more feet thick in the deepest portion along the foothills of the Rocky Mountains, thinning in a northeastern direction until they petered out against the edge of the Precambrian shield. The various sedimentary formations, or rock layers, tilted downward in a southwest direction toward the deeper basin areas. The hinge belt theory held that along the shallow northeastern flank of the basin these beds tilted at a gentle incline, and that deeper in the basin they tilted at a steeper angle, much like a board with a hinge in the middle of it. The point where the beds dipped more steeply formed the hinge line, which stretches throughout the basin almost 2,000 miles from the southeast corner of Saskatchewan to the Arctic Ocean. Geologists reasoned that subsurface formations might pinch out along this hinge belt, forming traps in which oil might be accumulated. It was imaginative geological thinking (and that is what finds oil), but later knowledge of the basin has largely demolished the theory.

A second error was in selecting rocks of the Mesozoic era (75 million to 225 million years ago) instead of rocks of the Paleozoic era (225 million to 600 million years ago) as the most likely source of oil on the Alberta plains. One of the geologic theories of that time held that the western Canada plains during most of the Paleozoic era was a vast desert. Oil is formed from prehistoric plant and vegetation life, and there is not much life on a desert. Ergo, there would not be much oil found in the Paleozoic rocks of the western prairies. It might be merely an aphoristic story, but one of the top geologists of Standard Oil of New Jersey at that time is reputed to have recklessly claimed that he would "drink all the Paleozoic oil found in western Canada plains ." As it subsequently developed, it was the Paleozoic

Wrong era chosen

which produced the Leduc discovery, and 80 percent of all the oil found in western Canada during the next 20 years.

Having selected the hinge belt as a likely geologic feature and the Mesozoic as the most likely oil bearing rocks, Imperial zeroed in on a large area in central Alberta as a likely locale, and picked up several million acres of government reservations and freehold mineral rights. Geologists had made their regional studies. Now it was up to the geophysicists to help pin-point possible drilling sites with their seismic surveys, their instruments tracing the energy waves set off by dynamite explosions to measure the buried rock formations.

The seismic surveys revealed a number of anomalies, possible structures in the rock layers where oil might be trapped. None of them looked exceptional; dozens of others had been mapped before in seismic surveys, but when drilled had yielded no oil. Still, there was always a chance.

Location chosen

A well location was picked to test one of the seismic anomalies that had been mapped near the village of Leduc, 18 miles southwest of Edmonton. It was not necessarily the most attractive of the seismic anomalies that had been mapped, but it did offer certain advantages. It was located west of the large Viking-Kinsella gas field where Imperial had been developing gas reserves in the Viking sand for its possible gas synthesis project, and there was a reasonable chance that if the Leduc test failed to find oil it might find more Viking gas. If a gas synthesis project were required there would be certain advantages to a gas supply located at this site, close to the North Saskatchewan River which could provide a large water supply for plant cooling, and close to Edmonton.

So the well location was picked, on the farm of Mike Turta, for Imperial Leduc No. 1, a test for oil in shallow rocks above where the big reserves lay, at a site where the discovery of natural gas would at least be a convenient second-choice.

Spudded 1946

The well spudded in on November 20, 1946, and at a depth of 3,550 feet it encountered the Viking sand, where a test produced only a small flow of gas, a trace of oil, and salt water. A test bottomed at 3,999 feet gave another show of oil, but again, just a teaser. Finally, in a sand at the base of the Lower Cretaceous formation a test was taken of the 10-foot interval below 4,286 feet, flowing natural gas at a rate of nearly two million cubic feet per day, together with oil. The next test covering a lower interval of the sand yielded generous amounts of salt water.

This Lower Cretaceous sand yielded no gusher, but it was certainly encouraging. Admittedly, the pay section was thin, part of the sand was gas bearing, part oil bearing, and part water bearing. But with a lot of skill and some luck it just might be possible to coax enough oil out of this sand to make an oil well. On the other hand, if the well were deepened further the drilling mud which is pumped down the hole and up the sides of the well to bring the drill cuttings to the surface, could mud-off the pay section so badly that any chance of completing an oil well might be lost. And below this sand lay the rocks of the Paleozoic formations where, some geologists argued, there lay no hope of finding oil.

The discovery

The company had to make a decision: attempt to complete a small oil well from the Lower Cretaceous — a puny reward after a string of 133 dry holes — or go for broke by deepening the well to see what lay below. Imperial decided to go for broke.

At a depth of 5,085 feet in the Devonian formation — well into rocks of Paleozoic age — the well encountered a porous limestone, and cores showed unmistakable oil staining. On the first test of this limestone formation, the oil rose 840 feet up the drill pipe, a good recovery of oil. On February 3, another test produced a plume of oil that shot up in the air half the height of the 136-foot drilling derrick, and drenched the rig and crew with oil. The next day the final test, from a total depth of 5,066 feet, yielded an even better flow of oil. Imperial, by this time, knew it had western Canada's first oil discovery in 11 years.

Coming-in party

Imperial threw a "coming in" party for Leduc No. 1, with some 500 Edmontonians standing on the grain field of farmer Mike Turta on the afternoon of February 13, thoroughly chilled in the −14 degree temperature, to watch the well placed on production. It was a long wait. They started arriving shortly after noon, but it was 2 p.m. before repairs had been completed on the swab — a kind of valve that operates like a plunger on a water pump and is lowered down the well tubing on a wire line. At 4 p.m. after the fourth swab had been pulled from 4,000 feet, great gurgling, gushing surges of oil, water and drilling mud spewed forth into the flare pit, 200 yards from the rig. A match was set to some oil-soaked sacking at the end of a rope, and tossed into the flare pit. "There was a roar and a whoosh as the flare pipe caught fire, and flames leaped 50 feet high, burning off the first flow of oil mixed with gas, water and contaminating mud," the

Review reported. "Dense black smoke spiralled far into the sky. Some of the crowd applauded as if they had just witnessed a feat of magic, but the sound of their clapping was lost in the roar of the flare."

For two hours, intermittent surges of oil, water, gas and mud spewed forth while 5,000 feet below the well was purging itself. Finally, at 6:10 p.m., Alberta minister of lands and mines, Nathan E. Tanner, spun a valve and a steady flow of clean oil was directed to the storage tanks. Leduc No. 1 was on production.

The best, however, was yet to come, two months later at Leduc No. 2, a mile and a half southwest of the No. 1 well. It uncovered still another and far more prolific pay section than the No. 1 well.

Leduc Number Two

The decision to drill the number two well had been made on the basis of the oil found in the Lower Cretaceous sand at the first well. Rigging up for the second test started on January 29 and the well was spudded February 12, the day before the No. 1 was placed on production. It was only a light rig with a shallow depth capacity that had been moved in for the second test, enough depth capacity to test the Lower Cretaceous sand at 4,300 feet. But before drilling had started, of course, the No. 1 well had found the deeper and more prolific production in the Devonian limestone.

The No. 2 well found a thin oil and gas sand in the Lower Cretaceous, no better than at the first well, and continued down in search of the deeper limestone production. But here the limestone gave only a show of oil, definitely not enough to make a well. It was a great disappointment. It looked as though Leduc might turn out to be only a minor oil field. Drilling had already extended beyond the rated depth capacity of the rig, but a decision was made to drill 50 feet into the dense shale section beneath the limestone before giving up on the number two well. At a depth 5,370 feet the bit broke through the shale and into a dolomite section, a sponge-like rock with holes big enough to stick your finger in, a sponge filled with oil. It was the best pay section that had yet been found in Canada.

It took a lot of time and the drilling of many wells before the geological picture at Leduc began to emerge. Even now, details of that picture are still being filled in. About 400 million years ago the oceans of the Devonian era advanced from the north into western Canada. As the oceans advanced, tiny living organisms, seldom more than a millimeter long, built giant reefs near the advancing shorelines.

As the waters grew deeper, the reefs grew higher — some of them to a thickness of more than a thousand feet.

As the prehistoric oceans advanced and retreated, depositing sediments in their wake, the successive rock section was gradually built up, layer by layer. A blanket of impervious shale covered the reefs. On top of this, another layer of porous limestone was draped in big arches over the thick reefs. Under immense pressure and over great time, the living matter in these reefs became converted into oil and natural gas, which was trapped in the reef by the over-lying layer of dense shale, or cap rock. Oil and gas migrated also through the higher, porous limestone section, and became trapped in the arches where these rocks lay draped over the reefs.

It was this draped layer of limestone rock, later called the Devonian D-2 or Nisku, where the Leduc No. 1 well had found its oil. In the No. 2 well, there was little oil in the D-2, and the drill bit churned on to punch into the reef, later called the Leduc or D-3 formation.

Reef exploration picks up

Devonian reef production in western Canada had first been discovered in 1920 at Norman Wells, but it was not until several years after Leduc that geologists came to recognize this reef production for what it really was. No one had ever thought of reefs in western Canada as storehouses of petroleum; no one even knew that they existed here. Once geologists and geophysicists realized what they were looking for, the reefs became much easier to find.

In the 20 years after Leduc, dozens of productive Devonian reefs were discovered, some of them with pay sections nearly a thousand feet thick, some of them up to 30 miles long, with reserves in individual reefs that ranged up to a billion barrels of oil. Oil bearing reefs have been found from a point mid-way between Calgary and Edmonton to more than a thousand miles north at Norman Wells. To 1969, more than seven billion barrels of recoverable oil reserves — 60 percent of all the oil found in western Canada — plus several trillion cubic feet of natural gas, had been discovered in Devonian reefs. Value of these reserves was in the neighborhood of 20 billion dollars.

In no other area of the world have reefs produced as much oil as in Alberta. And their discovery was the result of the accident at Leduc.

Chapter Six

Discovery of Pembina

A nightmare that haunts the wildcatter is the thought that the drilling bit might grind right through an unsuspected oil zone. The abandoned and supposedly dry hole could leave behind, unknown and untouched for years or even decades, a major oil field worth perhaps hundreds of millions of dollars.

It can happen easily; and has, in fact, happened many times, particularly in the early days of exploration when oil men lacked today's sophisticated methods of measuring the characteristics of rocks buried a mile or more below the ground. Not all oil zones, when penetrated by the bit, release a great surge of oil. Oil trapped in the tiny pores of many rocks is yielded only after great coaxing. Rock cuttings, ground up by the drilling bit and carried to the surface by the circulating stream of drilling fluid, may give little hint of the presence of oil.

Arne Nielsen

It might well have happened at the discovery well of Canada's largest oil field but for the alertness of a young geologist, an Alberta farm boy just three years out of University.

Arne Nielsen as a youth had assumed that he would be a farmer, and probably someday would have his own spread not far from the farm on which he was born, near the village of Standard in southern Alberta. But now, in January, 1953, he sat in his new Edmonton office and marvelled a little at the swift course of events that had led instead to his position, at age 27, as central Alberta district geologist with a major international oil firm, the Socony Vacuum Exploration Company.

Arne had the stamp of an Alberta farm boy, short but stocky and powerful build; the large, strong hands; the broad features and blue eyes that hinted of his Danish ancestry. His father, Aksel, had immigrated to Iowa as a boy of 17, unable to speak a word of English, and two years later joined a group of 32 Danes who took up farming on CPR lands in the Standard area. Aksel returned to Denmark to marry his childhood sweetheart, and had brought her to Alberta.

Arne was raised on the farm, attended the small school at Standard, and in 1943 had found himself the only boy in the entire grade 12 class. Most of his friends had enlisted in the armed forces to serve in the second world war. Like many Alberta farm boys, Arne was a crack rifle shot, and he too itched to join up for the great adventure. It was only at his father's insistence that he had completed high school before enlisting in the army at 17, still a year younger than the legal age limit.

He served as a rifle and mapping instructor with an armed corps in Ontario, eagerly awaiting the opportunity to ship overseas and see some of the action, and some of the world. He was on his way to Halifax and embarkation overseas when the war in Europe ended. He volunteered for service in the Pacific, but again, Japan had surrendered, the war was over, and 19-year-old Private Arne Nielsen returned to civilian life, a frustrated home-front veteran.

Two and a half years in the army brought an abrupt change in the direction of Nielsen's life. With the financial help of veterans' credits, he could consider the possibility of university.

On the farm at Standard, Arne and his father had gathered a small but intriguing collection of fossils and sea shells, turned up from the rich prairie soil by the plow. Sea shells on a land-locked prairie — moved thousands of miles from what are now the Arctic Islands and deposited more than 30,000 years ago by North America's last retreating ice age — had long intrigued the farm boy. This, and his mapping experience with the army, led him to decide on a study of geology.

A new excitement

Petroleum exploration was almost dormant in western Canada when Nielsen began studying geology at the University of Alberta early in 1946, and the mining industry seemed to offer a more likely career. Leduc changed that, as it set off a surge of exploration which quickly confirmed the vast petroleum potential of western Canada. Even at university, Nielsen caught the sense of drama and excitement of this petroleum search, which was radically altering the post-war economy of the prairie provinces. During the summer months he worked as a student geologist with field parties, first with the Geological Survey of Canada and later with oil companies, working in the Alberta foothills and the virgin wilderness areas of the Yukon and Northwest Territories.

In 1950, his diploma as Master of Science in geology still uncrinkled, Nielsen joined the Canadian division of the Socony Vacuum Organization, now Mobil Oil, working in the quiet and serious manner that has characterized his career. Less than three years later, in January, 1953, he was named to head Socony's new four-man district exploration office in Edmonton (Canadian divisional office remained in Calgary).

In a large oil company, the pursuit of oil is a co-operative undertaking of geologist, geophysicist, economist, exploration manager, and top management, which makes the ultimate selection of proposed exploration and drilling programs. It was in this manner that Nielsen participated in a rank wildcat, Socony-Seaboard Pembina No. 1, 70 miles southwest of Edmonton in a wilderness of pine, spruce and muskeg, pockmarked by a few isolated farms. It was one of the first ventures for Nielsen's new Edmonton district — and it could easily have missed becoming the discovery well for Canada's biggest oil field.

Pembina venture   The venture involved a farmout of 100,000 acres of government petroleum reservation rights from the Seaboard Oil Company of Delaware. In return for drilling a deep wildcat well to an estimated depth of 9,400 feet, Socony would earn a half interest in the reservation. The proposed wellsite was on a suspected anomaly which had been mapped by seismic exploration, 16 miles from the nearest previously drilled well. It was a $200,000 gamble in which the odds — as with any wildcat — were at least ten to one against an oil discovery.

Final decision to drill the well was made at Socony's head offices in New York, based on the recommendations of the Calgary and Edmonton offices. Nielsen had participated in the farmout negotiations with Seaboard, had recommended drilling the well, and had prepared the geological prognosis.

A geological prognosis is a guide prepared for the drilling of every wildcat. It attempts to blueprint unknown rock conditions thousands of feet below the surface, based upon the best available geological and geophysical knowledge, deduction, intuition and guesswork. The prognosis outlines the rock formations expected to be penetrated in the hole, the estimated depth at which each will be penetrated, and characteristics of the formations. It indicates which formations should be drilled through, and from which formations cores should be recovered for detailed study. Without a geological prognosis, a wildcat would be no more than a shot in the dark.

In the six years following the Leduc discovery, exploration had yielded a string of prolific Devonian reef discoveries in Alberta: Redwater, Bonnie Glen, Golden Spike, Wizard Lake, Stettler, and several others. From Edmonton, the major pipeline systems were already carrying Alberta oil across most of the continent: east across the prairies to Ontario and south into the United States; southwest across British Columbia to Vancouver and the U.S. Pacific northwest. west.

Comparatively few tests, however, had been drilled in the deeper part of the Alberta basin west of Edmonton where exploration costs were high due to almost impenetrable muskeg and forest, as well as the greater drilling depths to the Devonian reefs.

Devonian reef discoveries

Pembina No. 1 was to evaluate all prospective zones down to the Devonian Leduc reef. The major oil prospects were considered to lie in the Devonian, and farther up-hole in the Mississippian. Above that, secondary oil prospects were considered possible in the sandstones of the Lower Cretaceous, Jurassic, Viking and Cardium formations.

Few wells had penetrated the Cardium sandstone, and little was known about it. Along the Rocky Mountain foothills southwest of Edmonton, the Cardium outcropped at the surface, but at wells drilled in the Edmonton area it was not present. Somewhere between Edmonton and the foothills the wedge-shaped sand must pinch out, and near the point where it pinched out there was a possibility of an oil accumulation, trapped by an impervious layer of shale. The Pembina No. 1 well might be near that pinch-out line, and thus Nielsen's prognosis listed the Cardium as one of the secondary oil prospects. Top of the Cardium sandstone was projected at 5,240 feet, and Nielsen's prognosis called for no cores to be taken from this formation "unless samples show good porosity or oil stain."

The well was spudded in on February 23, and as the drilling bit ground toward its objective nearly two miles below the surface, the wellsite geologist examined the rock cuttings returned to the surface in the circulating drilling mud, looking for the changes in rock types

Pembina Number One

which would signify the progression from one formation to the next, and for indications of oil staining which might hint at the presence of an oil accumulation.

Cardium test

The first prospective zone was the Cardium. It wasn't easy to pick the top of this sandstone from the rock cuttings, since the formation was not widely known or easily recognized. From oil stained rock cuttings, the wellsite geologist picked the top of the Cardium sandstone at 5,330 feet, and a drillstem test was ordered to determine whether or not the formation contained oil in commercial quantity.

A drillstem test allows formation fluids, such as oil or water, or gas, from the interval being tested to rise up the drill pipe, propelled by the formation pressure. On tests of a high-pressure, prolific oil bearing zone, such as a Devonian reef, oil will rush up the drilling pipe and flow at the surface at a rate of several hundred or even several thousand barrels a day. On tests of less permeable and lower pressure zones, the formation fluid may rise only a few hundred feet toward the surface, and is then trapped in the drill pipe by a valve. The string of drill pipe, in 90-foot stands, is pulled to the surface to find out what, if anything, has risen in the pipe during the test period.

Nothing flowed to the surface during the test of the Cardium sand. When the valve was closed and the pipe pulled, it was found that the bottom 110 feet of the drill string contained a mixture of drilling mud and formation oil.

It was the first indication of oil that had been found in Socony's new regional district, but there was nothing to indicate a commercial discovery. It looked just like thousands of other oil shows that had been found throughout western Canada, teasers which eventually produced little or no oil.

Nielsen decides to press on

Still, there was always a chance that this could be the exception. In Nielsen's opinion the oil found in the drillstem test warranted further evaluation of the formation, if not immediately, then at least after the well had reached its final contracted total depth, another 4,000 feet down. In a wire March 27 to Socony's Calgary office, Nielsen recommended obtaining sidewall cores and running electric logs over the Cardium sand. "We did not obtain a core from the Cardium and it would be very useful to have some for porosity, permeability and fluid content analysis," Nielsen wired. "This would be very useful in deciding future program for Cardium."

An electric log of a drilled hole looks something like a cardiogram chart of your heart. Electric impulses measure the characteristics of the rock sequences penetrated, indicating the top of each and giving some hints as to which formations might contain oil or gas. The log of the Pembina well indicated that the top of the Cardium sand was actually 16 feet higher than had been established by the wellsite geologist on the basis of the drilling samples. As a result, the interval covered by the drillstem test might have missed the best part of the sand.

"In view of the result of the microlog and sidewall coring, we feel that further testing of the Cardium sand is imperative before the well is completed," Nielsen advised the Calgary office. He recommended that a string of seven-inch casing be cemented in the hole from the surface to a depth of 5,428 feet, and that the hole then be deepened to its projected depth of 9,400 feet. This casing would protect the Cardium sandstone from being plugged up by drilling mud while the hole was being deepened. Later, the Cardium could be further tested through perforations shot through the seven-inch casing.

The string of intermediate casing was set and drilling resumed, but not without difficulties. On April 6, Nielsen wired Calgary: "Unfortunately yesterday a one-foot wrench was dropped into the hole . . . what do you propose? " The wrench was fished out by a powerful fishing magnet lowered down the hole on a wire line. The Spring thaw turned roads in the Pembina area into quagmires and severely hampered the movement of drilling mud and supplies to the wellsite.

In May, the well reached its total depth of 9,425 feet without encountering further shows of oil, and was plugged back for more tests to further evaluate the Cardium. A perforating gun was lowered down the hole, and one-inch holes were shot through the casing into the Cardium sandstone. Tests of the formation yielded only very small amounts of oil, far from enough to make a producing oil well. It still looked as though the well was no more than a teaser.

Total depth reached

At this point, Nielsen and Jim Warke of Socony's producing department, who had been in charge of drilling operations at the well, decided that a hydrafracing treatment might open up oil production from the tight Cardium sandstone.

In hydrafracing (meaning hydraulic fracturing), a mixture of oil and sand is pumped down the hole and into the potential oil producing formation under considerable pressure, resulting in hairline fractures of the rock formation. The grains of sand keep the fractures propped open, and oil is thus allowed to flow through the fractures

Hydra-fracing attempted

111

into the wellbore. The method had been developed only a few years previously in the United States, and had never before been successfully applied in Canada. But Warke, who had started in the oil business at Turner valley and later worked in the oil fields of the Persian Gulf, had seen the method work and urged that it be applied at the Pembina well. Nielsen agreed.

"A lack of permeability would appear to be the cause of the low oil recovery," Nielsen wrote in a memo to management at Socony's Calgary office. "It is conceivable that a hydrafrac treatment might substantially increase the oil output . . . I wish to express my strong support of a complete and thorough testing of the Cardium sand in the Pembina well. It is our opinion that the Cardium sand may become a major reservoir and a complete knowledge of the potentialities of this sand at the Pembina well will be of invaluable assistance in determining our future exploration in the area."

Wrote one company production engineer: "Nielsen favors hydra-frac treatment of this interval in the hope of substantially increasing oil output. The writer cannot feel any optimism about the possibility of obtaining oil at commercial rates . . . but in the interest of a full evaluation . . . would concur with the recommendation."

"I sure hope you bring that well in," Warke told Nielsen. "I've spent $13,000 without company approval to gravel this road so we can keep this job going. And if you don't bring in a discovery, I may be out of work."

A mixture of diesel oil and 3,000 pounds of sand were pumped down the hole and into the Cardium formation at a pressure of 1,800 pounds per square inch. The pressure cracked the tight Cardium sandstone, and the oil started flowing into the wellbore. The well was completed on July 1 after tests had indicated an initial production potential of 72 barrels of oil per day. Heavy summer rains in the area had made roads so impassable that the oil could not be trucked out, and the well was shut in for two months. But on an extended 30-day test in September, the well sustained an oil production rate of better than 200 barrels per day.

First Cardium find

Socony Seaboard Pembina No. 1 marked the first discovery of Cardium oil in Alberta, the first large stratigraphic oil trap in Canada, and the country's biggest oil field – all from a wildcat well which could have so easily been abandoned.

A well with just 30 feet of net pay capable of producing some 200 barrels a day of oil appeared to most of the industry to be no more than a very minor pool, compared with the big Devonian reef fields with 300 feet or more of pay and wells capable of producing several thousands of barrels of oil per day.

What was not generally appreciated was the type of oil accumulation that had been discovered at Pembina. At all the other large oil fields in Canada, structural features had provided the trap in which oil had accumulated, predominantly in the Devonian reef structures. At Pembina, there was no structure. Instead, there was a comparatively thin and relatively impermeable sandstone, spread over a very large area. The wedge-shaped sandstone lay tilted at an angle, the porosity pinching out into impervious shale at the up-dig edge. Oil had migrated through this sandstone until it had become trapped by the shale, forming what geologists call a stratigraphic pinchout trap. There is only a modest amount of oil beneath each square mile of the Pembina field, but the entire producing area covers 1,000 square miles — in area, the largest oil field in North America. But who could know this at the time the first well was completed?

A new kind of structure

Following the Pembina discovery, Socony drilled a second well 12 miles to the northeast. Here the Cardium formation was mostly shale, with the rock slightly oil stained, and the well was abandoned. A third test was drilled midway between the discovery and the abandonment, and from the Cardium sandstone flowed oil at a rate of 240 barrels a day. Only then did the significance of the Pembina discovery start to become apparent. Oil companies rushed into the area to buy land and drill as quickly as they could.

Others rush in

Under Alberta regulations, Socony and Seaboard had to convert their 100,000-acre reservation into 50,000 acres of checkerboard leases; the 50,000 acres reverting to the government were offered to the industry bit by bit at competitive lease sales. First such sale on January 26, 1954 "exploded Pembina possibilities to the world," Warke later wrote. Leases of 160 acres in the proven area sold for prices as high as $500,000, and a pair of reservations of 100,000 acres each brought in a total of $24 million.

The reservations were the big prize at the sale. Socony, and other companies, drilled as close as possible to these reservations to acquire information on which to base their bids. Daily reports from these key wells were highly secret, and although scouts from competing oil companies kept the wells under the constant surveillance of their field glasses, they learned little. At his home in Edmonton, Nielsen

The Reservation sale

113

had installed a powerful radio transmitter and receiver. Daily reports were radioed to Nielsen's home, in code. From there, the information was relayed to Calgary and New York.

On the day of the sale, H. R. Moorman, the head of Socony's Canadian operations, arrived in Edmonton with a $7 million cheque for the reservation block closest to production.

Texaco wins

"No one had ever paid that much at an Alberta sale before, and we were confident that we would get the parcel," Nielsen later recalled. But when the sealed tenders were opened that day in the offices of the provincial Department of Mines and Minerals, the high bidder for the parcel was Texaco Exploration with a cheque for $13 million. The second reservation was purchased by Imperial Oil for $11 million. Imperial subsequently drilled a series of dry holes on its block, and eventually abandoned the entire acreage without finding a drop of oil. Imperial's block lay just off the edge of the big field.

During the next four years, Pembina accounted for nearly half of all oilwell drilling in western Canada. Drayton Valley, in the centre of the field, blossomed from a tiny, isolated village with a population of less than 100 to a model community with a population of more than 2,000.

5,000 wells drilled

Close to one billion dollars was spent to develop the Pembina oil field, and more than 5,000 oil wells were drilled. Fifteen years after the discovery well, the field had produced nearly half a billion barrels of oil. Geologists estimated that close to eight billion barrels of oil had been trapped in the sandstone reservoir, of which about 1.7 billion barrels might be economically recovered with the aid of hydrafracing and secondary recovery techniques. The Alberta government reaped close to a quarter of a billion dollars from competitive sales of oil and gas rights and lease rental fees. With an added royalty on each barrel of oil produced, total revenue for the Alberta government from the Pembina field will approach one billion dollars by the time the last barrel of oil is produced.

From geologist to president

Nielsen wasn't too involved in the subsequent development of the field. A year after the discovery well was completed he was transferred to Regina as district geologist for southern Saskatchewan, and later became exploration manager of the company's U.S. Gulf Coast division. In 1967, at 41, he was the first Canadian to become president of Mobil Oil Canada Ltd. As head of one of the principal

Arne
Nielsen.

subsidiaries of the giant U.S. parent, Nielsen took over the reins of a
firm with 800 employees, more than $60 million a year in oil and gas
sales, and an aggressive exploration program which spanned Canada
from the U.S. border to the Arctic Islands; from British Columbia to
the continental shelf offshore from Nova Scotia.

For an Alberta farm boy who had never expected to leave the
farm, and still had more than half of his career ahead of him, it was a
good start.

The Great Canadian Oil Patch

Exploratory drilling in Rainbow area in 1967.

Chapter Seven

Prize at the end of the Rainbow

Few investors in Canadian oil have been more successful than the government of France. It owns 51 percent of Societe Nationale des Petroles d'Aquitaine. Within five years, starting in 1964, SNPA parlayed an investment of $26 million in Canadian oil exploration into reserves and assets worth more than $350 million, annual earnings of $5 million, and a tremendous growth potential. The government of France also holds a 90 percent interest in Elf Oil Exploration and Production (Canada) Ltd., with large holdings of petroleum exploration rights from the government of Canada in the Arctic and off the Atlantic coast.

Between SNPA and Elf, the government of France in 1969 held interest in petroleum exploration rights in Canada covering 164,000 square miles, an area equal to 80 percent the size of France.

The entry of SNPA into Canadian exploration appears to have been marked by almost effortless and instant success. Behind the facade, however, lay years of tenacious effort and struggle by a small, independent wildcatting firm. Guided by the determination of a young Canadian geologist, it held to the wildcatter's faith in its quest for a big discovery at a time when its fate appeared to be almost certain oblivion. It was the French SNPA which finally backed this exploration faith with substantial hard cash. The almost immediate result was one of Canada's most important oil discoveries, in a re-

French government interest

117

mote corner of northern Alberta where most companies had given up hoping of finding large oil reserves. The discovery was made in an area known, appropriately enough, as Rainbow.

The long journey to the pot of black gold at Rainbow started in 1950 on the golf course of the posh Banff Springs Hotel in Banff National Park. The initial flush of excitement still pervaded the industry. Leduc was 3 1/2 years old, and a rapid sequence of other prolific discoveries – Redwater, Golden Spike, Joseph Lake, Acheson, Excelsior and Stettler – had confirmed Alberta as a major new oil area – one of North America's most promising. U.S. investor interest in the new Canadian oil fields was at a high pitch.

Among the golfers at Banff that year were Leon G. Ruth, a stockbroker from Buffalo, New York, specializing in oils and Canadian investments; and Dr. Theodore A. Link, former chief geologist with Imperial Oil, who had just established a geological petroleum consulting practice in partnership with Dr. Arthur W. Nauss. Neither Ruth nor Link were adverse to combining a little business with their relaxation – Ruth was ever alert to new investment opportunities in Canadian oil, and Link was equally alert to any attractive opportunities for his new consulting business.

The deal made by Ruth and Link on the golf course at Banff was that they would organize an oil company. Ruth was to raise the capital from his Buffalo associates, while Link and Nauss were to provide the firm with geological and operating services under a contract fee. Inspired by the grandeur of the surrounding Rocky Mountains, and perhaps hopeful of equally spectacular results from their new enterprise, they named the proposed firm Banff Oil.

Founding of Banff Oil

Banff Oil came into existence the following March, with Ruth as president and an initial capital of $175,000 received from the sale of 350,000 shares at 50 cents each. Proceeds were used to acquire a 10 percent interest in 960 acres of leases in the Redwater and Big Valley fields. During the following year, Banff issued an additional 875,000 shares for cash and properties, and by mid-1952 had developed more than a million barrels of producing oil reserves and had acquired interests in nearly 2 1/2 million acres of exploration holdings in Alberta. In September, 1952, Banff became a public company with the sale through U.S. and Canadian underwriters of one million treasury shares at approximately $2.50 per share. Walton H. Hohag, Jr., former Canadian exploration manager for Socony Vacuum Oil Company, was hired as general manager, replacing the services provided under contract by Link and Nauss. With public financing, an operating staff, modest oil reserves and revenues, and a large spread of exploration holdings, Banff Oil by late 1952 had emerged as a hopeful wildcatter. It took 13 years to find the real payoff, and it was only because of the dogged determination of a young geologist, John Rudolph, that Banff even survived that long.

A native Calgarian, Rudolph wound up in the oil business because his first career choice seemed too dull for the tall, active youth with a love of the outdoors. Two years of articling with a chartered accounting firm, after he had completed high school, had earned him top marks in Alberta on his primary exams in accounting. "I just couldn't face the thought of sitting on my bottom, cooped up in an office, and looking at accounting figures for the rest of my life," Rudolph later recalled. In 1943, then 19, Rudolph abandoned his accounting career to join the Canadian Army, took a year's engineering studies at the University of British Columbia under a potential officers training course, and was shipped overseas.

John Rudolph

"It was the tail end of the war, and while I got to see a lot of Europe, I didn't get to see any action," Rudolph has said. It was not an outstanding military career, either. "I shipped out as a corporal, and came back a private."

Rudolph arrived back in Calgary on the day that Japan surrendered, and soon headed back to the University of British Columbia. He obtained a bachelor of science degree in geological engineering in 1948, the year after the Leduc discovery.

During the summers of 1946 and 1947, Rudolph worked for Socony Vacuum (which later became Mobil Oil) as a surveyor with field geological parties in western Canada. In charge of Socony's Canadian exploration at the time was Hohag, subsequently Banff's first general manager, and later its president.

After graduating, Rudolph joined the Canadian geological staff of Stanolind Oil and Gas, a subsidiary of Standard Oil Company of Indiana. It was not long, however, before he was itching for greater opportunity and challenge than he felt he could find with a large, major oil company. His opportunity came in 1954, when Hohag invited him to join Banff Oil as head of the geological department. In fact, Rudolph *was* the geological department. Banff's staff at that time totalled five.

One-man geological department

Hohag resigned from Banff late in 1959 to head another independent exploration firm, this time searching for oil and gas in Spain.

Elected president

Rudolph stepped up from the one-man geological department to become general manager, and the following year was elected president.

Wildcat strategy

There are two basic approaches which a new, independent oil company may adopt in its quest for success. It may devote its initial capital resources to acquisition of proven or semi-proven oil reserves in the hope that these will provide a sustained flow of cash with which to carry out further development and exploration. Or it may explore for new oil and gas fields. The wildcatter approach is riskier, but the potential rewards are greater. From its conception, Banff Oil set out as a wildcatter. To stretch its limited resources, it sought participation by others in the exploration plays it developed.

Early problems

Exploration success requires several things, Everette DeGolyer, one of the world's most renowned oil explorers, once noted: land, know-how, money and luck. "I'll take luck," was DeGolyer's quoted comment. Banff's earliest acquisitions soon gave it a strong land spread. It had top-flight exploratory know-how, a very modest amount of money, and average luck. The rewards pretty well matched this pool of resources, and were barely adequate to maintain a corporate existence.

Banff's difficulties during its first decade and a half didn't really stem from a lack of exploratory success. Its discovery record, in fact, had been excellent. None of these early discoveries were giants, but several were fair-sized, and together they represented a substantial volume of oil and gas reserves. The problem was that Banff's cash resources were soon so thin that the interest it wound up with in each of its discoveries was a very small percentage.

It was at best a shaky company when Rudolph took over as general manager in 1960. Working capital by the end of that year had been depleted to only $100,000, little more than enough to drill a shallow wildcat. Sales of oil and gas were less than a quarter of a million dollars, and Banff's net loss amounted to more than $100,000. Ownership of the 3.5 million shares outstanding was widely spread among some 200,000 U.S. and Canadian shareholders, none of whom owned as much as five percent. In effect, no one held control of the company, least of all the management group, and Rudolph's task was to try and sustain the company for the benefit of the shareholders, while lacking enough revenue to carry the overhead and conduct exploration work. Banff's entire staff consisted of Rudolph, the company treasurer, and two secretaries.

"Exploration ideas were our stock in trade," Rudolph has said. "That's what kept Banff going. We'd work up plays, sell them to larger companies, and manage to retain perhaps five percent of the action, if we were lucky."

Reserves of natural gas, by-product sulphur and gas liquids, discovered by Banff in 1956, first came into production in 1961 at gradually increasing rates. With this and steadily increasing oil production arising from its stock in trade, exploration ideas, Banff was able to sustain steady growth. By 1964, revenue had tripled to $800,000 per year. Staff was slowly built up. In 1962, Ron White, formerly with Canadian Oil Companies, was hired as chief geologist – Rudolph's position when he had joined the firm in 1954, so that the exploration staff was back where it had been eight years earlier, with two geologists, including the president.

Production started in 1961

Even with this growth, there was still hardly enough revenue to carry a meaningful exploration program. Cash flow generated from operations in 1964 and available for investment in exploration or elsewhere was less than $170,000 (perhaps enough to drill two shallow holes) and the company had $3 million in loans against its future production.

There was another ever-present danger – the possibility of a take-over. With no one, including the entire management group, holding more than five percent of the issued shares, it would have been simple for a larger company to buy control of Banff through purchases of shares on the stock market. And the price would not necessarily have reflected the full value of Banff's assets. The more Banff succeeded in building up reserves and revenues, the greater the take-over risk became. It was just starting to develop enough assets to make it worth taking over.

This was the situation which confronted Banff when Societe Nationale des Petroles d'Aquitaine decided to make its entry into the Canadian oil scene late in 1963. One of the first steps was to form Aquitaine Company of Canada Ltd., a wholly-owned subsidiary. It was a late entry into Canadian exploration, with nearly every major oil company and dozens of independents well established for more

Aquitaine appears

than a decade. Most of the exploratory acreage in western Canada, except "moose pasture" and remote areas in the Yukon and Northwest Territories, appeared to be already under permit. To start from scratch and build an exploration staff familiar with Canadian geology, work up exploration plays and assemble a land portfolio, would take a long time. A quicker way would be to acquire control of an independent which already had land, staff and know-how, but was perhaps short of capital.

But perhaps one not quite as short of money and assets as Banff. In any event, Banff was far from the top of the shopping list when SNPA decided to try and buy a Canadian vehicle. One by one the others on the list were crossed off — either they were not available, or the terms were not acceptable — until, at the beginning of 1964, Banff's name stood at the top.

A new aggressive stance

Banff, however, was ready and willing to make a deal. The resultant agreement was unique and had two principal features. The first was that Aquitaine would acquire effective control of Banff, which was achieved through an offer to Banff shareholders to purchase 1,465,000 shares at a price of $2.50 each. Since Banff shares had been selling in a price range of 90· cents to $1.60 during the preceding year, the offer was quickly taken up by shareholders.

Second part of the agreement involved a joint venture operation in which Banff and Aquitaine would work as partners throughout western Canada. The agreement was subject to periodic review, but initially provided that the two companies would participate 50-50 in exploration throughout southern Alberta, Saskatchewan and Manitoba, in the smaller "bread and butter" plays where the risks were less and the returns more immediate. In more remote areas, such as northern Alberta and the Northwest Territories, where there were prospects for larger finds but where the risks were higher, the costs were greater and possible returns more distant, participation would be 90 percent by Aquitaine and 10 percent by Banff. Banff would act as operator, but Aquitaine would pay its proportionate share of both the direct and overhead costs, which meant that it would pay nearly all the costs.

In effect, the agreement meant that Banff became the Canadian exploration and operating staff for Aquitaine, at least initially. It gave Banff 10 percent of the action in the real wildcatting, 50 percent in the low-budget bread and butter plays, a far larger and more aggressive program than it had previously been able to consider, and for the first time a fully-staffed exploration department. Rudolph at last had the opportunity to show what Banff could really do with its stock in trade, its exploration ideas, and its creative geological imagination.

Decision to head north

The north country — the extreme northern tip of Alberta, northeastern British Columbia and the Northwest Territories — was selected by Banff and Aquitaine for their primary exploration effort, partly because the geological prospects appeared attractive to both partners, and partly because it seemed about the only area left where large land spreads could be acquired at low cost. There was still enough elbow room for wildcatting.

By April, 1964, Banff had expanded its staff in order to handle a major program. Ron White had been promoted from chief geologist to exploration manager, and a brilliant young geologist, Dr. Michael Hriskevich, had been hired from a major oil company and appointed chief geologist. Rudolph and Hriskevich had worked together before, in 1952-54, when they had been on the geological staff of Stanolind. Hriskevich was hired not only because of his ability, but also because of his extensive experience with the geology of the north country.

Hriskevich's play

Hriskevich had a play in mind when he joined Banff. His first assignment was to work this up for presentation to management. Within two months, Hriskevich had completed his studies, prepared an extensive set of geological maps, and was ready to report. His report was presented on the evening of June 23, 1964, at a meeting with Rudolph, Ron White and three Aquitaine directors who were visiting from Paris.

It was an interesting picture that confronted the directors of Banff and Aquitaine that early summer evening. The general area under study was the northwest corner of Alberta, embracing 50,000 square miles, 400 miles northwest of Edmonton. The primary prospects were reefs of Devonian age, the type of structures which had accounted for most of the oil found in Alberta. Other firms had explored sporadically for Devonian reefs throughout the north country during the preceding 15 years. The number of wells drilled was relatively sparse — a total of 165 wildcats or one for every 300 square miles of potential area. The results had been discouraging. A few had found gas, containing also natural gas liquids and sulphur, but these were relatively small pools and too far from pipelines to be economically exploited at that time.

The industry was anything but hot on the area. Several firms had already acquired, explored and dropped holdings in the region, only to have them reacquired, explored and dropped again by a second

123

firm. The exploration manager of one major oil company, outlining Alberta's oil potential at a public hearing before the Alberta Oil and Gas Conservation Board, with a wave of his hand had wiped out oil hopes for the northwest corner of Alberta, describing the region as "gas prone." But there were some who had not given up hope. Among them were Banff and Aquitaine.

Hriskevich zeroes in on Rainbow

Hriskevich's maps narrowed the area of interest to a basin near Rainbow Lake where geologic conditions were such that the tiny living organisms that build reefs might have thrived during Middle Devonian time, building possible traps for oil or gas accumulations.

Finally, Hriskevich outlined two large reservation blocks embracing 161,000 acres south of Rainbow Lake, held by Mobil Oil of Canada. The land had been originally acquired by Imperial Oil which had drilled and dropped it, then acquired by Mobil which had conducted seismic surveys. Mobil was ready to farm the acreage out to another party, and would assign a half interest in the two blocks in return for the drilling of two wells. The year before, Mobil had advised other firms of the availability of a farmout, but had found no takers. One of the firms which had considered the farmout in 1963 was the company for which Hriskevich then worked. He had recommended that his management take the play, but his proposal was rejected. Now he was once more recommending it, this time to the management of Banff and Aquitaine.

There were three specific features of interest in the immediate area: two seismic anomalies on which wells had been drilled earlier by Imperial Oil, and a third seismic anomaly which was still undrilled.

Four strikes against anomaly

One of the two Imperial tests, south of the farmout lands, had found a thick Keg River reef, with 70-feet of condensate-rich gas pay at the top. In such a remote area, the find was considered uneconomic and the well had been abandoned. Twenty miles northeast of this, on the acreage now held by Mobil, the other Imperial well drilled in 1954 had found, instead of a Keg River reef, a salt plug 300 feet thick. Five miles to the east of this salt plug was the third seismic anomaly.

It was this third seismic anomaly which represented the possible drilling prospect. But it had four strikes against it – strikes which had caused others to back off from drilling.

Strike one was the possibility that the anomaly might have been caused by a seismic "ghost" rather than the presence of a structure.

In seismic surveys, the sound waves set off from explosions near the surface are supposed to travel down to various layers of subsurface rocks and then reflect back to the surface. But in some areas the energy waves will bounce back and forth between two or more subsurface rock formations, before reflecting up to the surface. This fouls up the seismic picture and sometimes fools the geophysicists and geologists into thinking there is a structure where none exists. The northwest corner of Alberta was an area known to be spooked by such seismic ghosts.

Seismic ghosts

Strike two was the possibility that the anomaly reflected a subsurface fault structure rather than a reef structure.

The third strike was the possibility that it reflected another salt plug, similar to the one found 10 years earlier at the Imperial well just five miles west, rather than a reef structure.

Fourth strike was the possibility that even if it were a reef structure, there was, of course, no assurance that it would contain hydrocarbons. And past exploration history suggested that if a reef structure were present, and if it did contain hydrocarbons, in all probability it would contain sulphurous natural gas rather than crude oil in this "gas prone" region. There were few firms, indeed, interested in drilling another sulphur-laden gas pool within one hundred miles of the Northwest Territories.

Hriskevich, however, was convinced it was a good prospect. He had previously examined the seismic data with a geophysicist, and based on the latter's interpretation it appeared that the anomaly was more likely a reef than a salt plug. Aquitaine, moreover, was one of the few firms not discouraged at the possibility of finding sulphurous natural gas. Parent firm SNPA has been founded on the discovery of one of the world's largest sulphurous gas fields, at Lacq, France. Development of this field had made SNPA the world's third largest sulphur producer, as well as a substantial producer of natural gas, gas liquids, and petrochemicals. So the prospect of similar reserves in western Canada was not uninviting.

The selling job

Banff by this time had developed into a small group of young, well-trained and enthusiastic specialists, and management meetings, even with the Aquitaine representatives, were characterized by an informal, shirt-sleeve working environment. Those at the meeting that evening were already familiar with most of the background behind Hriskevich's report and his carefully prepared set of geological maps. The meeting lasted only half an hour, but it was long enough to arrive at a decision to proceed with the play. More detailed work was to be prepared and an approach would be made to Mobil to negotiate a farmout of the two reservations.

Farmout

Two days later, Banff made its initial contact with Mobil, expressing an interest in acquiring the farmout. Banff's entire interest was not, of course, focused on this single play, and further work here had to be paced with continuing evaluation of possible plays throughout western Canada. Banff acquired all of Mobil's seismic data at Rainbow, and also made an agreement to acquire the earlier seismic work by Imperial Oil. A painstaking re-interpretation of all the Mobil and Imperial seismic data was undertaken. "The seismic was very poor in the area," Rudolph later stated. "It was a long and arduous task to review the shooting and convince ourselves of what we thought it was trying to show."

Finally, in October, a farmout agreement was completed with Mobil. Banff and Aquitaine could earn a half interest in one of the reservations by drilling the first well, and held an option to earn a half interest in the second reservation by drilling a second well. Costs would be shared 90 percent by Aquitaine and 10 percent by Banff so that the net interests would be divided 50 percent to Mobil, 45 percent to Aquitaine, and 5 percent to Banff. Banff and Aquitaine obtained a further farmout option on 34,000 acres from Central-Del Rio Oils and purchased two blocks of 86,000 acres at a competitive sale held by the Alberta government. Before the end of the year, Banff and Aquitaine had assembled a land spread of more than 280,000 acres at Rainbow.

The discovery

The Banff Aquitaine Rainbow West 7-32 well, five miles east of the Imperial abandonment which had found the thick salt plug, started drilling in January, 1965. Three months later it had been completed as one of the half dozen most important oil discoveries in western Canada. It had found a near-record 686 feet of very prolific pay, including 251 feet of sulphurous gas pay and 435 feet of oil pay.

"The fact that we made a discovery didn't surprise us," Rudolph has said. "After all, that's what we were drilling for. What did amaze us was the size of the discovery."

A few key discoveries have led to nearly all the oil reserves found in western Canada. Each has been the first to find oil in a particular

Rainbow townsite
in early 1967.

formation, leading to an intensive search for more oil pools in the same formation. Imperial's Leduc discovery in 1947 led to the discovery of three billion barrels of recoverable oil in Leduc reefs; Pembina led to two billion barrels in Cardium sands; the Swan Hills discovery led to another two billion barrels in Beaverhill Lake reefs. In the Keg River reefs of northwestern Alberta, about one billion barrels of recoverable oil had been found during the four years following the Rainbow strike, and the full potential had not yet been established.

Key discovery

    The Keg River reefs at Rainbow and Zama grew tall and narrow. "Pinnacle" reefs they are called, and they resemble a city of sky-

127

John C.
Rudolph

scraper buildings, more than a mile below the surface. One Keg River reef at Zama covers only seven acres but the oil section is 326 feet thick, as tall as a 30-storey building. Others have pay sections up to more than 700 feet thick. The largest covers just 4,600 acres, an eighth the size of the Leduc reef which constitutes the giant Redwater field. Some 150 oil and gas bearing Keg River pinnacle reefs had been discovered by 1969, each containing estimated recoverable oil reserves ranging from 5,000 to 150 million barrels.

Sparked by the Rainbow discovery, virtually every oil company active in Canada rushed to join the Keg River play. In four years the number of wells drilled in the 50,000-square-mile northwest corner of Alberta jumped from 165 to more than 1,000. Two major oil pipelines were built to move oil from Rainbow and Zama 400 miles to Edmonton. Prices paid for government oil and gas leases zoomed from about 10 cents per acre to more than $8,000 per acre for the best leases. In four years, the Alberta government collected more than $200 million from the sale of oil and gas leases in the play.

1,000 tests in four years

128

By 1969 Banff had found a total of 29 separate oil and gas bearing Keg River reefs at Rainbow, including most of the larger ones, and several other oil and gas pools in shallower formations. Its interest was only five to ten percent in each of these pools, but that was enough to boost its production revenue from $800,000 in 1964 to nearly $3 million four years later. More dramatic was the effect on Aquitaine. From a standing start in 1964, it had built up annual Canadian production revenue of nearly $11 million with net earnings of $5 million. A $16 million public share offering in Aquitaine Company of Canada Ltd., in 1968 was heavily over-subscribed. In mid-1969 the parent SNPA of Paris held 93 percent interest in Aquitaine of Canada, valued at stock market prices in excess of $350 million. It had been acquired at a cost to SNPA of only $26 million.

Emergence of Aquitaine

A proposal to merge Banff Oil Limited into Aquitaine Company of Canada Ltd. by means of an exchange of 52 Aquitaine shares for each 100 shares of Banff Oil was announced in March, 1970. The effect of the merger would be to reduce the ownership of Aquitaine Company of Canada held by Societe Nationale des Petroles d'Aquitaine of Paris to approximately 71 percent. Prior to the announcement of the planned merger John Rudolph had resigned as president and a director of Banff Oil, and later was appointed president of a new exploration company, General Exploration Company of Canada Ltd.

Banff's Rainbow discovery in the remote, gas prone area of north-western Alberta and the Keg River play which it launched represented one of the major steps in the continuing development of Canada's petroleum resource potential. Other key discoveries will trigger similar major oil plays in the newer exploration regions, the Yukon and Northwest Territories, the Arctic Islands and the continental shelves which lay offshore. They should prove to be just as dramatic, just as exciting, just as rewarding.

Chapter Eight

Ribbons of Oil

Reinforcing the fabric of the nation

The iron tracks of the railways welded Canada together. A century later, the fabric of the nation was reinforced by a mesh of steel pipes.

Oil and gas pipelines are not generally considered the means by which nations were built. Railways are. Civilization rode west on the rails. Railways opened the virgin lands for settlement, moved in people and goods, moved out their produce from fields and farms; created towns and cities.

Pipelines, buried six feet below the ground, are silent, unseen, unknown. Yet there are now more miles of oil and gas pipeline in Canada than railway trackage. They move almost as much freight as the railways, and they move it at a fraction of the cost. Nearly 70,000 miles of oil and gas pipelines girded Canada by 1970, stretching from the extreme northern tip of Alberta east to Toronto, and west to Vancouver. Connected with the network of pipelines in the United States, they move Canadian energy to markets southwest as far as San Francisco, southeast to Chicago and Buffalo, N.Y., and to a wide range of points in between.

Have you ever seen crude oil? Have you ever felt it, or heard it? Most people who work for oil companies actually see crude oil only rarely; some of them, never. It comes up through a pipe in the

Applying protective coating to Interprovincial's 34-inch Chicago line.

ground, goes through a series of valves into a large storage tank, into a pipeline, travels hundreds or thousands of miles underground; then through a series of vessels, pipes, and towers and tanks in a refinery, from which it emerges as gasoline, diesel fuel, furnace oil, lubricating oil and a hundred other things. This entire process can function without anyone actually seeing a drop of crude oil.

You stop to think every time you drive into a service station about how all this is helping to build Canada? Well, hardly. *Moved by pipeline, you say, nearly two thousand miles from a well to a refinery and then trucked to the service station? Why fancy that!* Do you stop to think when you turn on a gas range in a kitchen in Montreal that the flame which pops up is the end delivery point of a pipeline system running 2,500 miles to a natural gas reservoir which lies two miles beneath the rolling surface of the Alberta foothills? No more than you think about where the water comes from when you turn on the bathroom shower. It is just there.

An essential network

The analogy between pipelines and railways in the building of Canada can be extended only so far. Pipelines have neither carried people and goods for the settlement of frontier areas, nor established new towns and cities. They have created new industries and expanded others, but to a lesser extent than the railways. They move freight only one way, and for the most part, only petroleum and natural gas. Railways themselves constitute an industry. Pipelines are only one segment of an industry, albeit a vital link without which Canada's oil and gas industry could not exist on anywhere near the scale which it has attained. The contribution of pipelines to the economic growth and development of Canada cannot be measured separately, but only by the total contribution of the nation's oil and gas producing industry.

Certainly not as dramatic as the effect of the railways a century earlier, yet essential still to the fabric of the nation is this unknown, unglamorous pipeline network. Nothing contributed more to the growth, development and economic prosperity of western Canada in the quarter century post-war period than the oil and gas producing industry. The industry has added more than one million to the population of the prairie provinces, created a higher standard of living, services and opportunity, and generated billions of dollars for the national economy. Without these contributions the regional economic disparities which pulled against national unity would have been vastly greater.

When the possibilities of developing a nation-wide system of oil and gas transmission lines were first seen, politicians were quick to draw the analogy with railway construction 70 years earlier. ". . . oil and iron can form the foundation upon which Canada could become a great world power," Howard Green, Progressive Conservative Member of Parliament for Vancouver-Quadra, told the House of Commons early in 1949.

Many politicians also sought to apply to pipelines the same basic national policies which had guided railway construction. Many history text books report that the railway systems of Canada were built in defiance of natural economic laws. The geography of North America dictates that the principal lines of transportation run north and south. But Canada wanted to build a nation east to west. The railway lines were built east to west, cutting across the grain of geography, at great expense which had to be subsidized by the nation. If this was vital to the nation in the case of railways, the reasoning was, then it would be of the same importance in the case of pipelines.

But oil from the new fields of Alberta could be moved more cheaply by a route through the United States, some people counter-argued. "If that argument is sound, then why did we ever build railroads across Canada? " Progressive Conservative leader George Drew demanded in the House of Commons. "We built railway lines in Canada because we wanted our own transportation system for the opening up of our own area."

"Surely it is in the national interest, regardless of cost," Howard Green declared in the Commons, "that the main pipeline carrying Canadian oil should be laid in Canadian soil." Pipeline routes cutting through the United States, even though achieving lower transport-ation costs, would represent "a great mistake in national policy."

It was this conflict between economics and an interpretation of national policy which set in motion nearly a decade of political debate. It became a raging storm, the great pipeline debate, the major political issue of the day. It helped bring the defeat of the Liberal government after a 22-year term in office.

Pipelines were largely unknown in Canada when Imperial Oil made its Leduc discovery in 1947. There was a crude oil pipeline from Turner Valley to nearby refineries in Calgary, another from Portland, Maine which moved tanker-shipped South American crude to re-fineries in Montreal, and a third small system feeding U.S. oil into

The national interest

A United States route?

Fastest pipe in the west

133

Ontario. The war-time Canol pipeline from Norman Wells to White-horse had been the largest pipeline project ever undertaken in Canada, but it lay abandoned. There was a fairly extensive natural gas transmission and distribution system serving Alberta, while other principal Canadian cities were served by small distribution systems supplying high-cost, manufactured coal gas. In 1947 there were 418 miles of oil pipelines in operation in Canada.

The rising need

With the Leduc discovery and the even larger Redwater discovery the following year, Alberta's oil producers faced a need for a much larger market than that provided in the province. Pipelines were the only economic answer. If enough oil reserves were found, Alberta crude might be moved to markets as far as Ontario. By railway, the cost of moving crude from Edmonton to Sarnia, Canada's largest refining centre, was $3.40 per barrel. Price of U.S. crude laid down in Sarnia was $3.50 per barrel. Railways obviously could not do the job.

First step

As an initial step, Imperial Oil planned a 450-mile oil line from Edmonton southeast to Regina to supply refinery demand there. Later, if enough oil were found, the system could be extended farther east. An engineering group was assigned to prepare design, economic and feasibility studies, working out of Tulsa, Oklahoma. Engineering and economic studies were prepared on the use of varying sizes of pipe, from 16 to 20-inch diameter. Based on the reserves that had been found to that time, the decision was to build a 16-inch line to Regina.

Jurisdiction restrictions

Imperial faced a political problem in Ottawa. Because of the maze of municipal, provincial and federal jurisdictions which would be involved in the construction and operation of pipelines traversing more than one province, such a system would have to operate under federal jurisdiction. Otherwise, construction and operation of such lines could be restricted or even prevented by the legislative action of any province. The federal government had decided that pipeline companies would have to be incorporated by special acts of Parliament, much in the manner that railway charters had been granted. The hang-up was that no enabling legislation existed.

Early in 1949, Imperial applied to the federal government for incorporation of Interprovincial Pipe Line Company. Incorporation of several other firms proposing construction of either oil or gas pipelines was also sought.

Minister of Transport Lionel Chevrier introduced in the House of Commons on April 5, 1949 a bill for the enactment of The Pipe

Lines Act of Canada, closely patterned after the Railway Act. The bill received wide support from all parties in the House, although during the brief debate a slight hint of what was to come was provided by Howard Green when he declared that "this oil and gas should be used to the greatest possible extent within our own country."

Pipe Lines Act

After a brief examination by the House of Commons standing committee on railways, canals and telegraph lines, the bill was passed April 29 and The Pipe Lines Act of Canada became law. The next day, third and final reading was completed on bills to incorporate, by special acts of Parliament, five pipeline companies – Interprovincial Pipe Line, Westcoast Transmission Company, Trans-Northern Pipe Line Company, Western Pipe Lines, and British American Pipe Line Company. The bills were rushed through with about five minutes debate on each and virtually no information presented on the proposed plans of the pipeline companies, as the legislators hurried through their business to concentrate upon a national election. The election, on June 27, returned the Liberals to power under Prime Minister Louis St. Laurent, with 74 percent of elected members.

First line authorized

On June 10, the federal Board of Transport Commissioners, following public hearings, authorized Interprovincial to build its 16-inch, 450-mile pipeline from Edmonton to Regina.

Long before the authorization had been received, before Interprovincial had even been incorporated, Imperial Oil had taken the first step to build the line – that of obtaining the necessary pipe.

Imperial first started looking for a supply of pipe in 1948, in the hope that the line to Regina could be built the following year. The task of finding 450 miles of pipe was not easy. No pipe mills in the United States could deliver in time, and in Canada there were no pipe mills. Page-Hersey Tubes Ltd., was prepared to build Canada's first pipe mill, a $5 million plant at Welland, Ontario, but there was yet another problem – a supply of the special steel plate required to make the pipe. Finally, with some help from federal Trade and Commerce Minister C. D. Howe, Imperial was able to complete arrangements in December to import some 40,000 tons of steel plate from Britain. This steel would not meet the specifications for making the pipe, but it would meet some of the customer requirements of The Steel Company of Canada, thereby freeing capacity in Stelco's Hamilton plants to make the specification plate from which Page-Hersey could roll the pipe.

135

By mid-1949 the problems appeared to have been met to allow construction of the line to Regina the following year. Imperial Oil had obtained, by special act of Parliament, a charter for a pipeline company; the Board of Transport Commissioners had authorized construction of the line; Stelco was preparing to roll the steel plate, and Page-Hersey was building Canada's first pipe mill.

Changing needs

There were further complications. Even while it was proceeding with the plans for a 450-mile line to Regina, Imperial had its engineering group in Tulsa working on design and feasibility studies of a much longer system from Edmonton to the head of Lake Superior. From this point, the crude could be moved by tanker during the summer shipping season to refineries at Sarnia. The rapidly growing oil reserves in Alberta, with the attendant requirement for larger market outlets, appeared to make the longer line feasible. "Extension of the Edmonton-Regina pipeline to the head of the lake in the near future is a development which Imperial Oil is actively pursuing," Imperial chairman H. H. Hewetson stated in May in an address to the Regina Chamber of Commerce.

Decision to build to the Lakehead

By that summer, Imperial had decided on construction of the longer pipeline system, had selected a route 1,140 miles from Edmonton to Superior, Wisconsin, and had completed the preliminary design and engineering studies. In August, Lakehead Pipe Line Company Inc., was incorporated as a wholly-owned U.S. subsidiary of Interprovincial to construct and operate the portion of the pipeline system in the United States. In September, application was made to extend the planned system from Regina to Gretna on the Manitoba – U.S. border; the section from Gretna to Superior would be handled by Lakehead Pipe Line. The application was quickly approved by the Board of Transport Commissioners.

Imperial had selected a route to a U.S. port at the head of Lake Superior rather than a route to Fort William or Port Arthur on the Canadian side for two reasons: The U.S. route was shorter and less costly, and would provide greater access to possible future oil exports to the Chicago region. The route to Superior was some 120 miles shorter than a route to Port Arthur or Fort William, representing a saving of $10 million in construction costs and $1 million per year in operating costs.

Decision to extend the line presented some further engineering problems. Greater deliverability capacity would be required, and this could be more economically provided with a larger diameter pipeline.

136

But the 16-inch pipe had already been ordered, and had to be used somewhere. Greatest deliverability capacity would be required on the section from Edmonton to Regina, where the line would make its initial deliveries to refineries. The system ultimately designed by IPL engineers was for a line consisting of 450 miles of 20-inch diameter pipe from Edmonton to Regina, 340 miles of 16-inch pipe from Regina to Gretna, and 360 miles of 18-inch pipe from Gretna to Superior. Because the Page-Hersey mill was designed to make up to only 16-inch pipe, the 18 and 20-inch pipe was supplied by U.S. mills. ". . . because of steel shortages and because further crude reserves were established during the early planning stage," IPL later explained, "the system has 16-inch pipe between sections of 20-inch and 18-inch. This may seem incongruous but it works, and works well."

Pipe sizes mixed

Cost of the system was estimated at nearly $90 million. Giant-sized steel storage tanks, capable of holding more than 1 1/2 million barrels of oil, would be built at Superior to store oil delivered by the line during the five months of the year that Lake Superior is closed to shipping. Orders were placed with shipyards at Port Arthur and Collingwood, Ontario for two, 15,800-ton tankers costing nearly $8 million, at that time the world's largest lake tankers.

Estimated cost of moving oil from Edmonton to the major Ontario refinery centre at Sarnia was about $1.00 per barrel, compared with $3.40 per barrel by railway.

Approval to build through the U.S.

On September 12, just three months after it had received authority to build its pipeline from Edmonton to Regina, Interprovincial obtained the approval of the Board of Transport Commissioners to extend the proposed system 340 miles to the U.S. border, with its U.S. subsidiary to construct the remaining 360 miles to Superior.

However economically sound it may have been, the decision to terminate the IPL line at Superior rather than at the twin cities of Port Arthur and Fort William in Ontario raised a political storm of protest.

When the first session of the 21st Parliament of Canada assembled that fall, it was not long before the question of the Interprovincial Pipe Line was raised. Progressive Conservative leader George Drew strongly opposed the U.S. route, declaring "our first obligation is to supply our own centres with that vital fluid by means of a pipeline." Other Conservatives picked up the theme, particularly Howard Green

Political storm

with his statement that the main oil line should be entirely within Canada "regardless of cost."

Howe's defence

Howe staunchly defended the decision on the U.S. route, pointing out that the higher cost of the Canadian route would penalize Alberta producers in the form of a lower price for their oil. "Certainly the cost of the pipeline must be paid by the oil it transmits; I know of no other source of income for a pipeline," was Howe's blunt analysis of the obvious.

"I think the plan is to sell a great deal of oil in the United States," blurted Howard Green at one point in the debate.

"Is there anything wrong with that? " asked Howe.

Lakehead opposition

Back in his riding at the twin cities, Howe's stand was anything but popular. Port Arthur Mayor Fred Robinson headed a civic industrial committee organized to fight the issue. The group sent to every member of Parliament and to city councils, chambers of commerce, labor unions and other organizations across Canada, a circular with a strongly-worded nationalist line, emblazoned with the Canadian red ensign and the slogan "Put Canada First."

"This pipeline belongs to Canada," it declared. "American capital has played a part in development and progress of Canada, but at a price. The price is an inferiority complex when it comes to promoting our own welfare . . . Surely, we are not so shortsighted that we will sell our birthright for a few million dollars. . . . It is your fight as a Canadian! You can keep this pipeline in Canada if you are determined to do so."

But Howe, the practical engineer and builder of business, was not one to be moved by histronics. He stood firm by his decision to allow the more economic U.S. route.

Financing

Financing plans for the $90 million pipeline were completed by Imperial late that year. Of the total, $72 million would be borrowed in the form of 3.5 percent first mortgage bonds, and $18 million would be raised in equity capital consisting of common shares and debentures convertible into common shares, at a price of $50 per share. Of the equity, or ownership, capital, Imperial purchased one third; 25 percent was purchased by other oil companies, and 42 percent, or $7.5 million, was offered to the public. Those who subscribed to the public offer found it highly profitable. An investment of $1,000 in 1949, 20 years later — after providing for stock splits and accumulated dividends — was worth approximately $25,000.

IPL has been called "the fastest pipe in the west", with construction of the 1,129 miles of line from Edmonton to Superior completed between the spring and fall of 1950 in 150 days. No other pipeline as long or large as this had been built in so short a time. Preliminary work had been completed well in advance of the actual construction start. The Tulsa-based engineering task force moved its headquarters to Edmonton in November. Aerial photographic surveys provided stereo and mosaic prints and were used in detailed ground survey work in 1949 to locate the exact route. Property was acquired along the right-of-way, which involved dealing with 2,100 landowners in Canada and 400 in the United States.

In March, six pipeline construction crews with a labor force of 1,500 men kicked off the job. The railways hauled 178,000 tons of high-test steel pipe to sidings near the right-of-way. The big ditching machines dug a trench three feet wide and five deep across the prairies. Behind the ditchers came the pipe stringers, the welders who joined the 40-foot sections into a continuous line, the crews and machines that cleaned, coated and lowered the pipe into the trench, backfilled the trench, pressure tested the completed sections; finally came the clean-up crews.

The kick-off

The flat prairies offered relatively easy pipeline construction, but there were tough spots. One involved the crossing of the South Saskatchewan River near Outlook, Saskatchewan. Schedule called for completion of the crossing by the end of March prior to the spring thaw, while the water level was still at its winter low. "A race against time amd the elements is in progress on the ice-bound South Saskatchewan River 10 miles south of Outlook," reported John Howard in the Regina Leader Post. "Construction crews are battling the elements at their worst in their efforts to lay 3,144 feet of the Interprovincial oil pipeline eight feet below the riverbed before the ice breaks up. So far the crews have had to contend with a two-day blizzard, a sandstorm, and biting sub-zero winds."

Plan was to string the pipe in 80-foot lengths across the ice, weld it, coat and wrap it, sheath it with board slats to prevent damage to the pipe, and attach 2,800-pound concrete river clamps every 20 feet. A four-foot swath would be cut through the ice, drag lines would dig a six-foot trench through the river bottom, and the pipe would be rolled off the ice into the trench. But the spring thaw had already started to swell the river and when the ice was cut the water burst through and flooded the operation, forcing the crews to retreat and make a second attempt at a new location. This second attempt was too late. The ice was starting to thaw, and in one day four Caterpillar tractors broke through into six feet of water and had to

Problems

be yarded out. The attempt to cross the river while it was still frozen had to be abandoned, and a new set of engineering plans drawn up to lay the pipe across the open river.

Completion

At a ceremony in Edmonton on October 4, Alberta Premier E. C. Manning turned the valve which started Alberta oil flowing on its two-month journey to refineries across the prairies and into Sarnia. The IPL line, noted C. D. Howe, "will stop a drain on our economy of at least $150 million U.S. dollars a year which we are now spending for foreign crude." He described it as "an essential factor in our preparedness program for the defence of Canada."

Before the line was in operation, however, it was evident that additional capacity was required, and the following year marked the start of two decades of continuous expansion and growth of the IPL system. Work in 1951 and 1952 involved the initial looping of the IPL system, the laying of 100 miles of 16-inch line beside the original line in sections between Regina and the U.S. border crossing at Gretna, and additional pumping horsepower, to increase throughout capacity.

Extension to Sarnia

The system of winter storage of crude at Superior and summer shipments by tanker to Sarnia soon became inadequate to handle the rapidly growing volume of oil. The decision was made to scrap the terminal at Superior and extend the system to Sarnia. In 1953, additonal looping was done along the line between Edmonton and Superior and 645 miles of 30-inch pipe (at the time North America's largest diameter crude oil pipe) was laid from Superior across Wisconsin and Michigan to Sarnia. The extension involved the crossing of the Straits of Mackinac between Lakes Michigan and Huron, the deepest underwater pipeline crossing ever attempted, and one of the world's major pipeline construction feats. At the crossing the Straits are 4 1/2 miles wide and up to 240 feet deep. Two 20-inch lines made of steel one-inch thick were laid across the Straits.

Growing capacity

Looping of the system between Edmonton and Superior continued year by year to provide steadily increasing capacity. In 1956, the line was extended another 156 miles from Sarnia to the outskirts of Toronto where additional refineries could be supplied with western oil. With this extension, the main line of the IPL system stretched 1,930 miles, with an additional 92-mile spur to Buffalo, New York. It was the longest crude oil pipeline in the free world.

140

Installing pipe
in swampy area.

By 1967 IPL required still more delivery capacity for markets east
of Superior. In addition to deliveries to the Ontario refineries, it was
moving a growing volume of crude to U.S. refineries at Buffalo,
Detroit, Toledo and other U.S. points. The 30-inch line east of
Superior was powered with pumping capacity up to the engineering
limit. The line between Superior and Sarnia would have to be looped.

In providing additional capacity east of Superior, IPL faced two
alternatives. It could lay a loop or second line beside its existing
system along the northern edge of Wisconsin, across the Mackinac
Straits, and down through Michigan. Or it could lay a loop around
the southern end, rather than the northern end, of Lake Michigan,
through the Chicago area, and up to Sarnia. This southern route, at
754 miles, was more than 100 miles longer than the route of the
existing line through Mackinac Straits, but there were two advant-

141

ages. It would avoid the expensive underwater crossing of the Straits, offsetting at least part of the cost of the extra length. More importantly, it would make Canadian oil accessible for the first time to the big Chicago refinery centre, which consumed oil at a rate of nearly 700,000 barrels a day. Ever since the IPL line had been conceived in 1948, the Chicago market had been considered a possible outlet for Canadian oil, but not one barrel had yet been sold there.

Chicago proposal

IPL's decision was to build 464 miles of 34-inch pipe from Superior to Chicago and an additional 290 miles of 30-inch line from Chicago to Sarnia. Looping on the original line had already resulted in two complete lines between Edmonton and Superior, and work was well advanced on a third 34-inch line. The plans envisioned one of the world's largest crude oil transmission systems. From Edmonton to Superior it would embrace three separate lines varying from 16 to 34 inches; from Superior east there would be two lines, the 30-inch northern system through Mackinac Straits, and the 34 and 30-inch line through Chicago.

Political roadblock

IPL's plans, however, ran into a political roadblock in Washington. Planned expansion required a U.S. presidential certificate of public convenience and necessity in order to allow a third pipeline crossing of the International boundary. Similar certificates for the first two pipeline crossings had been obtained withoutdifficulty, but this time the going was rough.

U.S. independent oil producers were alarmed at the growing volume of Canadian oil being imported into the United States, and the fact that Canadian crude undersold U.S. crude at refineries in the Great Lakes region by a range of 40 to 60 cents per barrel. IPL's plans for a big inch line to Chicago posed the threat of a further flood of Canadian oil. Led by the politically powerful Independent Petroleum Association of America, U.S. producers strongly opposed the IPL loop through Chicago and further encroachment of Canadian oil in their markets.

Permit granted

An informal agreement between the Canadian and U.S. governments finally resulted in the issuance in January, 1968, of the presidential permit allowing the third pipeline border crossing and construction of IPL's Chicago loop. The Superior-Chicago section was built in 1968. Tied in with smaller, existing lines, it permitted increased deliveries to Ontario and U.S. refineries at Detroit and Toledo. The remaining Chicago-Sarnia section was built in 1969.

Even with its loop, IPL was still unable to immediately deliver crude to Chicago refineries, despite the fact that several Chicago area refineries were eager to buy the lower-priced Canadian oil. Terms of the informal agreement reached between the U.S. and Canadian governments late in 1967 were not disclosed until a year and a half later, and then only after a Chicago refiner, Clark Oil & Refining, filed a suit before the U.S. Interstate Commerce Commission. Clark's suit maintained that IPL's refusal to deliver Canadian crude to its Chicago refinery represented an illegal restraint of trade.

Clark Oil files suit

It was this action by Clark which smoked out the terms of the governmental agreement. Canada's oil producers were both shocked and distressed when they found out the details. In return for the U.S. presidential permit allowing IPL to build the loop, the Canadian government had agreed that it would limit the Canadian oil deliveries to U.S. refineries east of the Rocky Mountains to an annual increase of 27,000 barrels a day during a three-year term, and that no Canadian crude would be delivered into the Chicago area prior to 1970.

Despite any temporary political roadblocks, the system of Interprovincial Pipe Line Company in 1969 was still assured of continued, long-term growth in its task of moving increasingly larger volumes of oil from western and northern Canada to markets in Ontario and the U.S. midwest. It is one of the most efficient crude oil movers in North America. In 1968, it transported 338 billion-barrel-miles of crude oil at an average tariff of three cents to move a barrel of oil 100 miles – half the cost of mailing a one-ounce letter. Including loops and branch lines its system embraced 5,000 miles of pipe by late 1969, built at an investment of nearly $600 million. Its capacity had been expanded to handle more than one million barrels of crude oil per day – 100 times the capacity of the original line constructed in 1949.

While construction crews in 1950 were building the Interprovincial Pipe Line east to the Great Lakes, oil producers in Alberta had already turned their eyes west to possible market outlets in British Columbia and the U.S. Pacific Northwest.

Pipeline to the Pacific

In an area embracing Vancouver, Seattle, Portland and Spokane, demand for petroleum products amounted to a quarter of a million barrels a day, virtually all of it moved into the region by tankers. Refinery capacity amounted to less than 15 percent of this demand, with most of the refinery capacity at Vancouver. Bulk of the demand was supplied by refined products shipped by tanker from California. Studies indicated that by 1960 California reserves would no longer be adequate to supply even that state's oil demand, let alone export to other markets.

Strategic move

The Pacific Northwest was the only major oil consuming area in the United States which was not connected by pipeline to continental petroleum supplies. This region, together with British Columbia, was considered to be in an "exceedingly vulnerable military position." With the second world war over just five years ago and now the United States, Canada and others involved in another war in Korea, military security was regarded with a sense of urgency.

A crude oil pipeline from Alberta to the west coast could alleviate this "exceedingly vulnerable military position." It would also create market outlets for the rapidly growing supplies of Canadian oil. But it was strategic considerations which allowed construction of the line to the west coast during the Korean war years. So important were the military aspects considered that the U.S. Petroleum Administration for Defence and the Canadian Department of National Defence eventually allocated 154,000 tons of steel for construction of the line at a time when steel supplies were tight and urgently required for military needs. Without these steel allocations, construction of the line would have had to wait.

Project takes shape

It was late 1950 when a group of representatives of U.S. and Canadian oil companies approached S. D. Bechtel, head of the Bechtel Corporation, in San Francisco with a request that his firm act as the operating vehicle for companies interested in the possibility of building such a line. The Bechtel organization was one of the world's largest pipeline construction firms, and as part of a consortium of contractors had been involved in the war-time construction of the Canol line.

Bechtel engineers studied two possible routes. One was from Edmonton 275 miles south before turning west to cross the Rocky Mountains over the Crows Nest Pass, to Spokane, Portland, Seattle and Vancouver. The other route crossed the Rockies via the Yellowhead Pass in the Jasper National Park, through Kamloops to Vancouver and south to the Seattle area in Puget Sound. The Yellowhead route was chosen because it was 100 miles shorter and 700 feet lower at its maximum elevation.

Representatives of seven major companies were working with the Bechtel Corporation and investment houses on the preliminary plans for the line by early 1951. A feasibility report on the project prepared that year by the Stanford Research Institute projected Alberta production capacity by 1951 at 325,000 barrels a day, of which some 140,000 barrels a day could be available to the proposed west coast line. By 1954, nearly 200,000 barrels a day of Alberta oil would be available to the line. Application was made to Parliament for incorporation and on March 31, Trans Mountain Oil Pipe Line Company was incorporated by special act of Parliament. Initial shareholders were Imperial Oil and Canadian Bechtel Limited, while other oil companies later joined in.

By late 1951 the project was taking shape. Preliminary survey of the route had been completed, financing had been planned; application for the steel had been filed with the Petroleum Division of the Department of National Defence. Trans Mountain's application for a permit to build the line was heard by the Board of Transport Commissioners in Ottawa on December 10. Four other firms had also applied to build oil lines from Alberta to the west coast, but withdrew their applications. Trans Mountain was the only one in a position to proceed. Three days after the hearing, its permit was issued.

Cost of the 718-mile, 24-inch pipeline was estimated at $82 million. Of this, $65 million would be borrowed by first mortgage bonds and the remaining $17 million raised through the sale of 1.5 million common shares. Twenty oil companies subscribed to 800,000 of the common shares and the remaining 700,000 were offered in a public issue. Design engineering, and detailed aerial and ground route surveys were completed in 1951.

Financing

The route of the Trans Mountain line from Edmonton to its terminal near Vancouver was anything but a pipeliner's dream, crossing 400 miles of rugged mountains filled with canyons, roaring streams, rock slides, avalanches and spring floods. A total of 72 rivers and streams were crossed, the widest being the 2,250-foot crossing of the Fraser River at Port Mann, B.C. Contractors used sections of the 24-inch line pipe, sealed the ends, and made rafts to float trucks, tractors and other machinery across rivers. Much of the route was in isolated, inaccessible areas. It followed the line of the Canadian National Railway for 510 miles as far as Kamloops, then followed the Canadian Pacific Railway line for 55 miles. But the presence of the railway lines, which in some areas took up most of the available space through mountain passes, often proved as much of a hindrance as a help. The right-of-way passed through mountain valleys where the winter snowfall was more than 50 feet, and stands of timber where trees 10 feet in diameter had to be felled and their roots grubbed out.

The route

At Edmonton, the route starts out at an elevation of 2,200 feet and after passing through wheat land and rolling timber, rises to a

*Problems
encountered
at the
Iago
jump-off in
Coquihalla
canyon.*

maximum 3,920 feet in the Jasper Park. The Rocky Mountains are crossed at an elevation of 3,760 feet in the Yellowhead Pass. From here the line drops gently on the western slope of the Rockies to 1,125 feet then rises abruptly to 3,900 feet on a plateau south of Kamloops. The coastal mountains are crossed through the Coquihalla Pass, and the route plunges down the steep-banked Coquihalla Pass to Hope, dropping 3,640 feet in 28 miles.

Challenge of mountain canyons

Working on steep mountain sides, giant tractors several times ran out of control and plunged as far as 600 feet to valley bottoms. In other areas, tractors were buried in sand and rock slides. Miraculously the catskinners managed to escape relatively unscathed. Laying the pipe down the Coquihalla Canyon presented particular problems, described in a company history of the line's construction.

"A 400-foot section of pipe remained to be placed in the 'jump-off' at the top of Coquihalla Canyon. About 700 feet of pipe had yet to be placed at the Iago slide area farther down the canyon. At these two points it was necessary to carve a trench for the pipe down rock inclines so steep that small D-3 bulldozers were let down and dragged up by cable and winch like toy yo-yos on a string. Over the brink of the Coquihalla jump-off the line was then lowered and again over the steep point at Iago. The pipe itself was sheathed in wooden slats to withstand the abrasion of lowering. Where necessary, the trench was

Going was rough at Blue River.

Delivering
pipe
to the site.

heavily sandbagged into steps and terraces, after backfilling, to withstand rockslides, the wash of waters, and the pull of avalanching
snows.

Coating, wrapping, welding and backfilling in Coquihalla were
feats of skill and nerve. At the bottom, the Coquihalla River was
crossed, and this meant trenching under a rushing mountain stream.
Dozers and trucks splashed, bumped, bogged and all but shook themselves like wet dogs as they emerged. Passing railroad crews looked
from their mountainside shelf with awe as they watched catskinners,
welders, and other pipeliners battle it out with nature and gravity.

"Damn fools, but I guess they've built it," a passing trainman is
quoted as having stated.

Construction of the line started in June, 1952, employing up to
2,500 pipeliners, and halted temporarily during the winter when the
mountains filled with snow. Work resumed the following spring, and
on August 23, 1953, the first crude started on its way from Edmon-

149

*Refinery
expansion*

ton, to reach Vancouver two months later. A short lateral was later built to deliver oil to the Puget Sound region.

Refinery expansion quickly followed completion of the Trans Mountain line. In a 15-year period after the line was placed on stream, three refineries with a combined capacity of 200,000 barrels a day were built at Puget Sound while refining capacity at Vancouver was boosted from 27,000 to 100,000 barrels a day. Although the Puget Sound refineries were built initially to operate on Alberta crude supplied by Trans Mountain, subsequent development of oil production in Alaska supplied part of their requirements.

The Trans Mountain and Interprovincial systems, representing close to a billion dollar investment, are the principal arteries in Canada's crude oil delivery system. Small feeder lines from fields as far away as the Northwest Territories, stretch into Edmonton like spokes converging on the hub of a wheel. From here the two principal big-inch lines span the continent delivering three million dollars worth of crude oil every day.

Chapter Nine

Westcoast Transmission and Frank McMahon

The big pipe dream of Francis Murray Patrick McMahon had seemed to explode into nothing as he sat in the barber's chair in the Hotel Pierre in New York in the early afternoon of that black Friday, June 18, 1954.

Black Friday

Every inch a promoter, a gambler, a plunger — and proud of it — Frank McMahon had come a long way since his first job working on a diamond drilling rig near his hometown in the Kootenay Valley of southeastern British Columbia. With his immaculate dress, rugged but patrician features and the slight greying at the temples, McMahon really had been every bit as successful as he looked, and he looked so successful that he had once been asked to pose for one of a "men of distinction" series of advertisements sponsored by Lord Calvert whiskey, an offer he had to decline because he controlled a competing distillery firm. It would have been difficult to imagine that for years he had roamed British Columbia and the Western United States, from Texas to Alaska, as a two-fisted diamond driller, except for the husky build, the large, strong hands, and the broad Irish grin.

Frank McMahon had been successful because he had refused to

recognize defeat and because he was able to sell to others his unshakable conviction that he was certain to come up a big winner. When he turned from diamond drilling to oil well drilling and produced a string of dry holes he promoted more money and kept on drilling until, finally, he parlayed a last $100 plunge into an oil producer at Turner Valley, the foundation of an aggressive, independent oil company. When disaster struck in the form of a wild oil well which blew out of control for months, the most renowned wild well in Alberta's oil history, this adversity too was turned into fortune. Every strike that McMahon made simply provided more chips for the game as he played for increasingly larger stakes.

The big pipe dream

Most of McMahon's chips in 1954 were riding on the gamble that he could pull off this big pipe dream of his, this idea he had had for 20 years that a fortune could be made by building a natural gas pipeline from the Peace River country of northern Alberta and British Columbia nearly a thousand miles south to markets in Vancouver and the U.S. states of Washington and Oregon. It was by far the biggest thing that McMahon had ever tackled, a $200 million project, the first really large natural gas transmission pipeline in Canada.

For nearly six years McMahon had thrown his by then considerable resources into the tough, bitter fight to build his pipeline. He had helped persuade the government of British Columbia to change its laws to allow private capital to explore for oil and gas in the northern part of the province, and had spent $5 million to find and develop B.C.'s first natural gas in commercial-sized volumes. He had persuaded the government of Alberta to authorize the first large volume export of gas from that province. In several years of public hearings before the regulatory authorities of the Alberta and Canadian governments, McMahon's group had won out over two rivals which had proposed to move Canadian gas to the same markets.

McMahon's rivals

One rival group, backed by the large New York investment house of Morgan Stanley and Company, proposed to move gas from southern Alberta into the United States, across Idaho and Washington to Seattle, with a stub line north to Vancouver. This would have left Vancouver gas consumers dangling at the tail-end of the pipeline supply, and left almost all of the rest of the province completely unserved, in contrast to McMahon's proposed line which would snake down the length of British Columbia, vitalizing interior towns and industries with a new, low-cost source of energy. The U.S. consumers would be at the tail end of McMahon's line.

McMahon's other principal rival was U.S. oil man Ray C. Fish of Houston, Texas (whose chief lieutenant was Robert Herring). Fish had proposals for pipelines all over the continent. One proposal essentially duplicated that of the Morgan group with a pipeline from southern Alberta to the U.S. west coast and a branch line north to Vancouver. A variation of this proposed that while gas from southern Alberta was used to supply markets in the U.S. Pacific Northwest, gas from Texas could be used to supply Canadian markets in Ontario and Quebec, thus affecting an international gas swap. Yet another Fish proposal called for a 1,500-mile pipeline from the San Juan gas basin of New Mexico and Texas to the potential markets in the U.S. Pacific northwest and Vancouver.

The two competitors had been eliminated by early 1952 so far as moving Canadian gas was concerned, McMahon's Westcoast Transmission Company being the vehicle approved by the Alberta and Canadian governments to do the job. All that remained was to obtain the approval of the U.S. Federal Power Commission to import the Canadian gas for the Washington and Oregon markets. Without these markets the project was doomed; the line would simply not be economically feasible based only on the more limited potential gas demand in British Columbia.

The case was before the U.S. Federal Power Commission in Washington, D.C. for two years before it was resolved, one of the longest and toughest before a regulatory body renowned for the duration and fierceness of its competitive hearings. It came down to a choice between McMahon's proposal to pipe Peace River gas south to the U.S. Pacific Northwest, and Fish's proposal to pipe San Juan gas north. The prize was the only large U.S. population area not yet supplied by gas, a prize well worth the struggle.

U.S. hearings

McMahon held the trump cards. His Peace River gas was 500 miles closer to the centre of the coveted market area, and thus would be lower priced. Also, McMahon seemed to have the only assured, adequate supply. Ability of the San Juan gas reserves to supply the projected market demand was brought into question during the hearings before the FPC, while gas utility and consumer interests in California were opposed to the Fish plan since they testified they needed the San Juan gas to meet their requirements.

So confident was McMahon that he was offering $5,000 bets to his

U.S. friends on the outcome of the hearings. There were no takers.

That's why black Friday came as such a shock to Frank McMahon as he sat in the barber's chair in the Hotel Pierre in New York that late Spring afternoon. That is where he heard about the decision of the Federal Power Commission which rejected the application of his Westcoast Transmission and approved instead the application of Ray Fish's Pacific Northwest Pipeline Corporation to pipe San Juan gas 1,466 miles to Seattle.

Rejection

U.S. consumers, ruled the FPC, should not be dependent upon gas imports from another country as their sole source of supply "without some inter-governmental agreement guaranteeing a continuous supply. Otherwise, all control over the production, allocation and transportation to our border would be in the hands of agencies of another government whose primary interest would of necessity always be in the needs and advantages of their own people, and whose judgements and actions would be essentially dependent upon public opinion within that country rather than upon the interests of American consumers . . . regardless of any long and cherished friendly relations with any neighbor nation able to supply such area with natural gas," ruled the FPC, "it would not be in the public interest to permit the importation of its gas as the sole source for the consumers in need of uninterruptable supply at a reasonable price, which should always be assured by the commission to the full extent of its powers."

"It's been a setback"

That, as anyone could plainly see, was the end of Francis Murray Patrick McMahon's big pipe dream. His incredulous statements to the press were dismissed out of hand as sheer braggadocio, or, at the very least, pure Irish Blarney. Since the markets in Washington and Oregon were lost, McMahon is quoted as saying, he would export Peace River gas instead to California. "It's been a setback," McMahon graciously admitted. "But we are not too concerned since we have worked on plans for export to California for some time."

Investors did not believe a word of it, and shares of McMahon's companies took a beating. In the final half hour of trading on the American Stock Exchange that Friday, shares in McMahon's principal company, Pacific Petroleums, fell from $12 to $6. On Monday, Canadian Atlantic shares fell from $7 to $3.50 while shares of Inland Natural Gas, the firm headed by Frank's youngest brother, John, which was to distribute to communities in the interior of British Columbia, fell from $4 to 50 cents. "Many individuals and a few brokerage houses were wiped out," Fortune magazine later reported.

Not only had the pipe dream burst at the seams, but the pile of chips which McMahon had accumulated over the years and which he had stacked on Westcoast Transmission seemed to have been lost in this game. McMahon himself, it appeared, might be wiped out.

There was a touch of irony, too, on black Friday. On the same day that the U.S. Federal Power Commission in Washington turned thumbs down on the Westcoast line, in Ottawa the Board of Transport Commissioners completed hearings on an application by Trans-Canada Pipe Lines for construction of a 2,200-mile, $300 million gas pipeline from Alberta to Montreal. In just one day a gas pipeline to the east was approved and a gas pipeline to the west coast was killed.

The trouble with Frank McMahon, however, is that, once again, he refused to recognize defeat. As a result, three years and four months after the FPC decision had been handed down in Washington, Westcoast Transmission had completed construction of 650 miles of 30-inch pipe, which was moving a steady flow of gas down the spine of British Columbia to consumers in Vancouver and the U.S. Pacific northwest. Just how that was accomplished is the story behind Canada's first major natural gas transmission pipeline, and the man who brought it about.

Frank McMahon was born in 1902, in the small mining town of Moyie, British Columbia, the eldest of three brothers and the son of the local hotel owner who had, without any great success, prospected and dabbled in investments in quest of some of the great mineral wealth locked in the rocks of the rugged Kootenay country. It was slightly ironic that Frank's first summer job, at age 14, was working on a diamond drilling rig at the nearby Sullivan mine of Consolidated Mining and Smelting Company at Kimberley, the largest lead, zinc and silver mine in the world. McMahon senior had been a substantial shareholder in the predecessor firm which had owned the Sullivan mine claims, but had sold out a couple of decades before the investment became valuable.

Diamond driller from Moyie

Frank attended school at Whitworth College and Gonzaga University in Spokane, where he was a classmate of movie star Bing Crosby. In his third year of a business administration course, he quit to go hard rock drilling full time as a diamond setter and boss driller, worked first in the Kimberley area and then in the mid-1920's headed south for San Francisco where he worked on the drilling of the footings for the Golden Gate and Bay bridges, earning $7 a day.

After a short stint with Standard Oil of California, where he started out pumping gasoline and graduated to an industrial accounts salesman, McMahon returned north to set up his own contract diamond drilling business in Vancouver in 1927, and for two years operated along the coast from California to Alaska until the 1929 market crash and subsequent depression put him out of business.

First
stab
at gas

It was in 1930, when there was no work for his hard rock drilling business, that McMahon made his first stab at providing a supply of natural gas for Pacific coast markets in British Columbia and the U.S. northwest – a venture which wound up with only enough gas to supply a couple of farm houses in the Fraser Valley. Twenty-seven years later his companies were the major suppliers of gas in British Columbia, Washington and Oregon.

McMahon had picked up a few leases near a small gas seepage in the Fraser Valley, part of the sedimentary basin that fringes the coast in lower British Columbia and the upper part of the state of Washington. At the same time a U.S. promoter had arrived on the scene exploring for gas to supply what looked like a promising market in Seattle and Vancouver. He was C. S. Shippy, builder of what was then the longest natural gas pipeline, the Missouri-Kansas line.

"Shippy had some money and I had the drilling equipment and knew about the gas seepages," McMahon later recalled. "So we made a deal."

McMahon traded in his leases for shares in a new company, converted his hard rock drilling equipment to drill a series of shallow holes for oil and gas, and helped Shippy spend a million dollars. The only two gas wells they found, in the Fraser Valley, were too small to be of any commercial value, so they turned the wells over to the farmers on whose lands they were drilled, helped them hook up their gas stoves, and walked away from the venture.

Second
stab

McMahon returned to Vancouver, and for a while was a door-to-door salesman, selling oil burners. But McMahon's first taste of wildcatting had given him an appetite for it, and if his first venture resulted in failure, well, McMahon did not recognize failure anyway.

With the instinctive optimism of a gambler, he felt convinced that the next venture would succeed. "When a man is exploring for oil, the only reality is the next wildcat, the one that will come in," a historian of U.S. wildcatters, Ruth Sheldon Knowles, once wrote.

156

Chapter Nine/Westcoast Transmission and Frank McMahon

"He lives so completely in his undiscovered wealth that the struggle to pay his bills is what seems like a dream." That is the way it was for Frank McMahon.

His next wildcat venture was in the Flathead Valley of southeastern British Columbia, near his home town of Moyie. McMahon knew of early exploration ventures here near the turn of the century which had created a brief flurry of excitement, and was sure that he could uncover the Flathead Valley's real petroleum wealth. He organized his first oil company, Columbia Oils Ltd., sold shares to a group of wealthy Vancouver citizens, and spent two years and $300,000 drilling his Flathead Valley wildcat. When that turned out a dry hole, he talked his Vancouver backers into a further $200,000 for a pair of wildcats in Montana, with similar results.

More dusters

As fast as he exhausted one play, McMahon came up with another play, a new hope, the next wildcat, the one that would come in. After the Montana dusters it was the rich and fertile Peace River country of northern British Columbia and Alberta which McMahon, who by then had established his wildcatting base in Calgary, visited in the mid-1930's. Imperial Oil had drilled a small gas discovery here in 1921, at Pouce Coupe, just on the Alberta side of the border. Too small and remote to be of any commercial value, the discovery well had been abandoned, but escaping gas had been ignited and for years had produced a flare, sometimes roaring to a height of as much as 75 feet. As he watched the pyrotechnic show, McMahon recalled his first ill-fated quest for natural gas in the coastal basin, the small gas seepages and the two farm gas wells in the Fraser Valley. Here in the Peace River country there was obviously a much greater supply of natural gas, as demonstrated by the flare at the Pouce Coupe well, and McMahon wondered whether or not it might ever be possible to move this gas by pipeline to Vancouver, perhaps even to markets in the United States.

"I'd always had a great yen to get into natural gas," McMahon is quoted as saying years later "I was working as a diamond driller in the States when they started to build the first big pipelines down there. I saw fantastic possibilities. In the first place they seemed to be a hell of a good business deal. And in the second place they were one of the best things I'd ever seen to make living easier."

Pipeline promoter

McMahon approached Vancouver department store owner and entrepreneur Col. Victor Spencer, who had been one of the principal backers of the ventures in the Flathead Valley and in Montana, and sold him on the possibilities of developing large gas supplies in the Peace River and piping it to Vancouver. McMahon and Spencer started preliminary engineering studies on the feasibility of such a line and laid plans for an exploration program. But before they could put their plans in operation, the B.C. government in 1936 reserved all petroleum rights in the northeast corner of the province. The government had decided to explore for oil and gas itself, and later did drill a million dollar dry hole before giving up that idea. In the meantime, McMahon's plans to develop Peace River gas had been blocked.

Spectacular failure

McMahon, by 1936, had been promoting oil and gas exploration for six years, with results that were spectacularly unsuccessful. He had reached the end of his own financial resources and had just about exhausted his creditability with his rich Vancouver backers. That was the year that R. A. Brown and his associates discovered the oil column in the Turner Valley field near Calgary, their Turner Valley Royalties No. 1 bringing in what was then the largest oil field in the British Empire.

Calgary was electrified by the excitement of this biggest Turner Valley discovery. McMahon could feel the winds of fortune blowing all around him, fanning the wildcatter's fever. He had searched for his fortune in vain from Vancouver to the mountain valley of the Flathead, from Montana to the Peace River, and now others were cashing in on a play just 20 miles away. He had no money, no leases, no backers, but somehow he too would have to find a way to grasp the brass ring.

McMahon's luck changes

Poring over maps of the area, McMahon found a lease less than a mile from Brown's discovery well, held by a Canadian Pacific Railway agent who then lived at Abbotsford, near Vancouver. With a stake of $100 to gamble, McMahon hurriedly drove to the coast to seek out the CPR agent, paid the $100 for an option to acquire the lease for $20,000, and set out to raise the balance of the money, again approaching his Vancouver backers. By December 7 McMahon had raised the money to exercise the lease option and had incorporated West Turner Petroleums Limited. It was another eight months before West Turner Petroleums had raised enough money to start drilling, and even then its finances ran out before the well was completed, and arrangements had to be made for assistance from Royalite Oil, a subsidiary of Imperial Oil, to complete the well. It was finally brought in on April 1, 1938, at a rate of 3,500 barrels of oil per day, one of the largest producers in the field. Two more wells were completed on the 80-acre lease that year.

Early the next year West Turner Petroleums was merged with British Pacific Oils Ltd., which also held leases at Turner Valley, resulting in the formation of Pacific Petroleums Ltd., which was to become McMahon's principal vehicle and one of the largest oil and gas producers in Canada.

Norman R. Whithall, Vancouver investment dealer and lumberman who had been one of McMahon's Vancouver backers, was the first president of Pacific Petroleums, while McMahon was managing director.

By 1941, with a small but profitable operation, Pacific's directors were ready to coast, rather than risk their money on further wildcat gambles. But not McMahon. Success at Turner Valley, the way he saw it, merely provided the opportunity to hunt for bigger game. McMahon pulled out of Pacific to form Drillers and Producers Ltd., with contract drilling and producing operations, including three wells drilled on acreage acquired from Pacific. Frank and his younger brother, George, formed other small companies, including Canadian Atlantic Oil Company in 1945, to explore for and develop oil production in Alberta and Montana. But after development of Turner Valley, there were lean and slow years for Alberta wildcatters, until the lid blew off with Imperial Oil's discovery of the Leduc field in 1947.

Still a gambler

Just as McMahon had found a way to get into Turner Valley, he found a way to get into Leduc as well. A Scottish farmer, John Rebus, held an unclear title to a 160-acre lease near the Leduc discovery, which McMahon won with a cash offer of $200,000 plus the normal 12 1/2 percent royalty, double the previous top offer made to Rebus; then he cleared the title by offering Imperial Oil, the possible disputant, 100,000 barrels of oil to be taken out of future production. McMahon put the Rebus lease into Canadian Atlantic, which promptly brought in two good producers, then on the third attempt was hit with an epic wild well.

Into Leduc

From its producing formation a mile below the ground, Atlantic No. 3 blew out of control early in March, 1948, and in a six-month rampage spewed forth an estimated 1 1/4 million barrels of oil and more than 10 billion cubic feet of natural gas. Two and a half days before the escaping flow — some 10,000 barrels of oil and up to 100 million cubic feet of gas per day — was shut off, Atlantic No. 3

Atlantic No. 3

Atlantic No. 3 well spewed forth more than a million barrels of oil and 10 billion cubic feet of natural gas during a 10-month rampage.

caught fire, a ball of flame that shot 800 feet into the sky and a column of smoke that mushroomed up to 7,000 feet and sent a tremendous tailing plume eastward over the prairies for a hundred miles.

When the well first blew out, drillers quickly, if temporarily, cut off the flow by pumping hundreds of tons of mud down the hole. Although it was not known until later, the drill pipe had been broken 2,800 feet from the surface, and thus the mud had not cut off the flow from the source. The gas and oil, driven by tremendous pressure, escaped through the break in the drill pipe. Three days later it had seeped through fissures in the earth and was escaping at the surface.

During the following weeks, more material was pumped down the hole to cut off the flow — feathers, sawdust, cottonseed hulls, shavings, golf balls and 10,000 bags of cement. But still the oil kept spouting up through the ground until in two months there was a 40-acre lake of oil. The oil kept coming as fast as it could be pipe-lined to the railway siding and hauled away by tank trains, or pumped back to the producing formation through nearby wells.

Normally the flow of oil from a well is controlled through a choke

Atlantic No. 3
on fire.

that might be reduced to as little as half an inch. Under normal conditions, six months' production from Atlantic No. 3 would have been choked down to about 36,000 barrels. "But that well," McMahon has said, "was produced through a 40-acre choke."

Tamed by relief wells

Two relief wells were eventually drilled to kill Atlantic No. 3. Located 700 feet away on opposite sides, the relief holes were drilled at angles to intersect the producing hole a mile below the ground and a few feet above the producing formation. Through the relief wells water was pumped at rates up to 1,500 barrels an hour followed by mud and cement to eventually seal off the rogue well.

Risk of fire throughout the entire operation was extreme, and police cordoned off the area to exclude thousands of spectators who wanted to see what was happening. (Ignoring the dozens of "no smoking" signs, one roughneck working not far from the wellsite retired to an outdoor privy for a secret smoke. When he struck his match, the roughneck and privy took off like a space ship, thrown 200 feet by the blast of the explosion. Miraculously the roughneck survived, and even more miraculously no fire resulted).

Just as the relief wells, after months of drilling, seemed on the verge of taming Atlantic No. 3, the 136-foot derrick, undermined by the cratering of the earth, toppled over and continued to sink a little farther each day into the subsiding ground. A spark, perhaps caused by the friction of escaping gas against the metal of the rig, perhaps caused by a rock hurled by the force of the escaping gas, finally ignited Atlantic No. 3, which burned for 60 hours before the relief wells quenched the flow.

Surprisingly, little of the oil had been lost, and the escaped production gave McMahon's Canadian Atlantic a quick million-dollar profit. With extensive international coverage by newspapers, radio and newsreels, it also publicized Canada's new oil discoveries, and McMahon's operations, on a scale which nothing less dramatic could have achieved, and brought millions of dollars into Canadian oil from U.S. and Canadian investors.

McMahon returns to Pacific

Trading his shares of Canadian Atlantic for Pacific stock, McMahon stepped back into Pacific early in 1948. Then, using Pacific as his holding company, he set out on such a series of wildcat projects that all of the more conservative directors of the company resigned, with the exception of Norman Whithall. McMahon, through Pacific Pete and its affiliated companies, in 1947 and 1948 launched a gas exploration program in the north with the incorporation of Peace

River Natural Gas Co.; in partnership with Sunray Oil and others formed Great Bear Oil Co. for a $5 million exploration program on a five-million acre land spread in northeastern Alberta, which failed to produce any commercial discoveries; sold a block of 600,000 Pacific shares to Sunray (which temporarily held control of Pacific); launched an aggressive lease acquisition and drilling program in the new Redwater field; and incorporated Westcoast Transmission to pipe natural gas to Vancouver and the U.S. northwest. Between the Spring of 1948, when he was re-appointed managing director, and by that Fall, Pacific's staff had increased 10-fold to 150. McMahon now was playing in the big league.

McMahon had never forgotten his 1935 idea of piping Peace River gas to Canadian and U.S. Pacific coast markets. Twelve years later, backed by his success at Turner Valley and Leduc, he at last had the resouces to move in and tackle the job.

The political pipeline battle

The B.C. government's blanket withdrawal of petroleum leases from the Peace River country was still an obstacle, but not for long. After spending a million dollars of the taxpayers' money to drill the Commotion Creek No. 1 dry hole, the idea that the province's petroleum resources should be developed and exploited by the government rather than see big profits go to free-wheeling wildcatters, no longer seemed appealing. Largely at McMahon's persuasion, the B.C. Legislature in 1947 passed an act allowing the leasing of provincially-owned petroleum rights to private interests.

On the day that the B.C. oil rights became available for filing, McMahon was on the doorstep of the government office in Victoria when it opened at 8 a.m., and took out B.C. petroleum and natural gas prospecting permits 1, 2 and 3 for his new Peace River Natural Gas, shortly to be controlled by his Pacific Petroleums. (Phillips Petroleum Company of Bartlesville, Oklahoma, which years later was to buy control of Pacific, was next in line, acquiring permits 4, 5 and 6. For the next couple of years, while Pacific explored for B.C. gas, few others even bothered to pick up permits).

Next step was the incorporation of a vehicle to build the pipeline. On April 30, 1949, McMahon's Westcoast Transmission Company was one of the first five pipeline firms to be incorporated by special act of Parliament under the federal government's new Pipe Lines Act. The Pipe Lines Act and the acts incorporating the five firms (the others were Interprovincial Pipe Line, Trans-Northern Pipeline, Western Pipe Line and British American Pipe Line) were quickly

Pipe Lines Act

163

pushed through the House of Commons in the final few days before dissolution of Parliament and national elections. Others who later sought incorporation of pipeline companies by special acts of Parliament were not to have so easy a time of it.

McMahon was now launched on a 10-year battle before his pipeline plan was brought to fruition. It was in fact, not really so much a battle as a war, with half a dozen different battles, many of which were fought at the same time. There was the battle to discover and develop Peace River gas reserves, in both Alberta and British Columbia; the battle to win, against other, larger, competitors, an Alberta permit to export gas from the province; the battle to win approval from the Canadian government; the battle to win approval from the U.S. government, and a few other political and financial skirmishes.

Reserve
levels
concern
Canadians

McMahon's idea to pipe natural gas to Pacific coast markets may have been visionary in the mid-1930's but by 1947 the merits of such a scheme were readily apparent to others. During and immediately following the second world war there were dramatic developments in natural gas in the United States. Long distance gas transmission lines now crossed the United States like a spider's web. Competition between big pipeline companies for the right to serve new market areas was intense, and often bitter. The phenomenal demand growth for natural gas, which would soon supply one third of all U.S. energy requirements, was well under way.

In Canada, natural gas supplied less than two percent of the nation's energy needs, and virtually all of that in Alberta. But with recent large gas discoveries in Alberta and an enormous supply potential, the U.S. developments clearly foreshadowed what was about to happen in Canada. By 1947, there were plans to pipe Alberta gas southwest to U.S. markets in Washington and Oregon, as well as east to Winnipeg then south to U.S. midwest markets.

There was considerable concern, however, that export to U.S. markets would result in a deficiency in supply to meet potential Canadian requirements. Dr. G. S. Hume, director of the Geological Survey of Canada, was appointed by the federal government to assess the potential Alberta gas supplies, and in early 1948 reported that the estimated proved reserves amounted to 1.4 trillion cubic feet with an additional 2.2 trillion cubic feet of probable reserves. A second report by Hume in 1950 had boosted this to 2.8 trillion cubic feet proven, plus 4.2 trillion cubic feet probable.

Chapter Nine/Westcoast Transmission and Frank McMahon

Faced with pending applications to export gas from the province and the need to formulate a policy, the Alberta government appointed an inquiry commission headed by Robert J. Dinning. Many Albertans feared gas export on the grounds that it would (1) result in higher gas prices as others sought to purchase a commodity then in surplus supply; (2) deplete supplies required to meet Alberta's needs, and (3) cause new industries based on the use of gas to locate elsewhere than in Alberta. (If they could not get the gas elsewhere, some reasoned, then such industries would have to locate in Alberta). The Dinning Commission, which held public hearings in Calgary, Medicine Hat and Edmonton, soon found that natural gas was a hot political issue.

Dinning hearings

In its report, the Dinning Commission estimated Alberta's gas supply, projected the province's future requirements for the next 50 years, and concluded that some export from the province might be justified. It recommended, however, that Albertans should have prior claim on use of the province's gas reserves.

Based on the Dinning Commission report, the Alberta legislature in 1949 passed the province's Gas Resources Preservation Act which required that gas could be removed from the province only by means of an export permit, and that only gas supplies considered surplus to the province's future, foreseeable requirements could be exported.

With the Gas Resources Preservation Act passed, the applicants lined up at the door of the Alberta Oil and Gas Conservation Board late in 1949 and early 1950 to seek the coveted export permits. Among the first to file was Westcoast Transmission.

Westcoast Transmission's two principal rivals to supply gas to the Pacific coast markets also filed applications with the board. A. Faison Dixon, a U.S. consulting pipeline engineer, headed Northwest Natural Gas, the entry backed by Morgan Stanley and Company. Houston entrepreneur Ray C. Fish's entry was Pacific Northwest Pipeline Corporation, which also proposed the $200 million, 1,500 mile gas line from Texas to Seattle. Alberta gas would be used to supplement the gas from Texas. So cocky was Fish in his bid that his application to the Alberta board stated: "Unless applicant can immediately be assured of obtaining its minimum requirements . . . from Canadian gas fields, then it must of necessity, purchase all of its gas requirements from the U.S. gas fields, thus excluding the province of Alberta from participating in this market."

Dixon and Fish

Westcoast concept jells

Public hearings on Westcoast's application, the first for a permit to remove gas from Alberta under the new Act, started late in 1949, and took two and a half years on an on-again, off-again basis before Westcoast won Alberta approval. Westcoast zigged and zagged several times during that period, as McMahon shifted to take advantage of changing political winds. The original concept, when Westcoast and Peace River Natural Gas were organized, was to develop Peace River area gas and move it some 1,000 miles south through British Columbia and into the United States. But when larger gas reserves developed first in southern Alberta, Westcoast proposed a route through the United States similar to its two competitors. Then it conceived a route from Edmonton, west to cross the Rocky Mountains through the Yellowhead Pass and down south through British Columbia, this offering the political advantage of a Canadian route as opposed to a U.S. route. Finally, by late 1950 following discovery of gas by Pacific and others on the Alberta side of the Peace River area, Westcoast's plans were back full cycle to McMahon's 1935 concept of a line running down almost the full length of British Columbia. When Pacific Petroleums late in 1951 discovered the first large gas field in British Columbia at Fort St. John, both Pacific and Westcoast were in a greatly strengthened position. Exploration activity in B.C. was accelerated, and industry holdings of petroleum permits in the northeast corner of the province jumped from 11 million to 35 million acres.

Year-long hearings

Hearings before the board by the competing applicants – which included also Western Pipe Lines with a proposal to move Alberta gas east to Winnipeg and then south into U.S. midwest markets – lasted throughout 1950. In Washington and Ottawa, others were getting a little anxious for an answer. The U.S. government was hopeful that Alberta gas might help meet an impending fuel deficiency in the U.S. northwest. Federal Trade and Commerce Minister C. D. Howe in Ottawa was eager to see gas export because of the trade and other economic benefits it would afford Canada.

Howe wrote Alberta Mines and Minerals Minister Tanner in September with a request that Alberta hurry up and make up its mind on gas export. "I have recently been advised by the Chief of the International Program of the United States Munitions Board that the Board is seriously concerned about the lack of fuel in the Pacific northwest section of the United States, where the war-time industrial development, together with diversions of normal oil supplies to the Far East, has seriously accentuated the scarcity," Howe wrote. The U.S. board had asked if Alberta gas might be available, and if not, had suggested that steps might be taken to obtain gas from Texas. Howe had replied that the answer was up to Alberta. "There would seem to be a great urgency for a decision, one way or the other," Howe advised Tanner. "I sincerely hope it will be forthcoming shortly, as pressure from the Munitions Board will certainly be a decisive factor in authorizing the granting of the franchise from Texas. I see little prospect of a line being built from Alberta to the Canadian northwest unless that line can be extended from Vancouver southward to service the U.S. Pacific coast cities."

But the Alberta board was not about to be stampeded into a hasty decision by Mr. Howe any more than it had been by the implied threat of market loss by Mr. Fish. In its own due time, the board handed its decision to the Alberta government early in 1951, and recommended that none of the export applications be granted, as it considered that there was not a sufficient volume of gas reserves surplus to the province's future requirements. But the board also suggested that the applicants could re-apply in September, when it would re-assess the reserves supply situation.

Alberta about-face

Following further hearings in the Fall of 1951, the board published its second report on the gas export applications in March, 1952, this time recommending the rejection of all the permits except Westcoast Transmission, which would be allowed to export a total of one trillion cubic feet of gas from the Alberta side of the Peace River country. This, combined with the gas which Pacific had discovered on the B.C. side, would be enough to meet Westcoast's requirements. The board's recommendation met stiff opposition from members of the Legislature, and Westcoast's approval was granted only after a heated, seven-hour debate.

Next step was to appear before the Board of Transport Commissioners in Ottawa, where Westcoast was again strongly opposed by its two rivals who had lost out in front of the Alberta board. The Board of Transport Commissioners, however, was quick to give its approval, and by mid-June, all that Westcoast required was the blessing of the U.S. Federal Power Commission.

While interest in the gas export front was centred before the Alberta Oil and Gas Conservation Board in Calgary, there was a seven-month side play in Ottawa which generated considerable steam and a lot of hot air. The debate which erupted in the House of Commons was interesting not so much because of its effect on plans to supply gas to the Pacific coast markets, as the fact that it sowed

Debate in Parliament

the seeds for The Great Pipeline Debate which rocked the House to its foundations seven years later.

Looking back, it is difficult to see what all the fuss was about, since all the participants in the debate vehemently espoused the same principle. That principle was that any gas line from Alberta to the west coast ought to be laid through Canadian rather than U.S. territory, in order to provide Canadian control over the flow of Canadian gas, assurance that Vancouver's gas supplies could not be cut off at the pass by coming up through the United States, and finally in order to supply gas to the maximum number of Canadian communities and industries.

Even A. L. Smith, the Conservative member from Calgary who had opposed his party by supporting the case for routing the Interprovincial oil line through the United States, took the opposite stand in the case of the gas lines. The circumstances of gas pipelines are not the same as those of oil lines, Smith pointed out. First, because gas lines passing through the United States had been much more subject to government control and regulation, than had oil lines. The gas lines were treated as public utilities. Second, because an oil line directly serves only a few refineries in a few large centres, with the refined products then distributed over a wide area, while a gas pipeline can supply only customers along its route. A U.S. route would have deprived a large number of British Columbia consumers of natural gas service.

"Canada First" fuss

Since everyone agreed with this principle, the Members of Parliament had to find another aspect to fight about. It boiled down to the manner of application of the "Canada First" principle. The government, led by Trade and Commerce Minister C. D. Howe, took the position that the approval of pipeline routes and such complex matters should be left in the capable and knowledgable hands of government regulatory bodies, rather than to ill-informed members of Parliament. The opposition MP's, and some Liberals too, did not seem to trust the regulatory bodies to make the right decisions, and certainly did not trust C. D. Howe. They came down for the supremacy of Parliament and the right to rule on pipeline routes themselves.

The particular issue involved the incorporation by special acts of Parliament of Westcoast's two rival firms. Westcoast had received its charter with little fuss in the Spring of 1949, but when private members' bills were introduced for the incorporation of these other two in October that year, they were not so fortunate. And without incorporation, neither Dixon nor Fish could get very far with their plans. Opposition members were not about to pass the private members' bills incorporating these firms until the backers of the companies provided assurance that they would build their lines through British Columbia rather than through the United States, and the backers were not about to provide that assurance. The result is that the two bills were filibustered for seven months before they were finally passed.

Seven-month filibuster

Support for the stand of the opposition and maverick-Liberal members was widespread. The B.C. Legislature passed a resolution to "urge upon the federal and provincial authorities concerned, the advisability in the interests not only of British Columbia but of Canada as a whole, that such pipelines be constructed through the interior of British Columbia to Vancouver." The Vancouver Sun in an editorial said it would normally be ashamed of a filibuster in the House but in this case was merely ashamed of the need for a filibuster. "The issue is whether surplus gas from Alberta shall be piped to Pacific coast markets through British Columbia or directly south into the United States. One company already incorporated (Westcoast Transmission) has undertaken to route its pipeline through the interior of British Columbia. The other applicants will give no such undertaking. There is every reason to suspect that they have no such intention." Davie Fulton, the Conservative Member for Kamloops, expressed the views of most opposition members when he declared that he was "opposed to the incorporation by this Parliament of any company for the purpose of transporting and supplying the ultimate consumer elsewhere a Canadian natural resource, when the company ... will not give the assurance that the route will be through Canada and will serve Canada first."

Howe outlined the government view when he declared that a bill for incorporation would not provide a licence to build a pipeline, but would allow both Alberta and the federal authorities to carefully consider the merits of the maximum number of proposals and select the best.

Government position

"This is not an application to build a pipeline," Howe carefully explained in the House, "it is simply an application to incorporate a company that would like to build a pipeline." Following incorporation the company would still have to (1) contract for the purchase of its gas supplies, (2) obtain Alberta's approval to remove the gas from that province, (3) obtain authority from the Board of Transport Commissioners to build any proposed line, and (4) in the case of exports to the United States would have to obtain an export permit from the Department of Trade and Commerce under the Electricity and Fluids Exportation Act. "The purpose of that Act," Howe told the House, " is to see that resources of Canada, such as power or fluids or gas, are used primarily for the benefit of Canada . . . the attitude of the government would be that the export of gas would be treated in exactly the same way we treat the export of electricity, namely that the needs of Canada would be served first and would be protected in perpetuity for all export purposes."

But hardly anyone, with the exception of Alberta's Premier Ernest Manning and the few Social Credit Members in the House, saw it the way Howe described it, and the debate at times grew impassioned.

Coal in baby carriages

One member seemed completely carried away with the emotion of it all when he declared in the House that "we are simply carrying out to completion a process of economic absorption into the United States by the alienation of our great natural resources." Describing a recent visit he had made to Vancouver when there was a shortage of sawdust for fuel, he told how he "saw a woman wheeling a 50-pound sack of coal in a baby carriage. Those are the conditions with respect to fuel that can exist today in the great cities of British Columbia; yet we are going to let our gas down to the United States and give it to the people of Seattle, letting mothers in British Columbia push coal instead of babies in the baby carriages."

Impassioned pleas like that were hardly the type of rational analysis and argument by which C. D. Howe, the great engineer and logical businessman, preferred to see issues resolved. It was little wonder that during the final years of his long career in the House he at times appeared somewhat disdainful of the ways of Parliamentary debate. But this was just a small taste of what was to come in the bitter pipeline debates.

Pipe dream comes true

With its project approved by both the Alberta and Canadian governments, the Westcoast Transmission project appeared all but wrapped up by April, 1952. All that remained was to obtain approval for the U.S. Federal Power Commission to import the gas, and with an urgent need for more fuel supplies in the Pacific northwest states already recognized by the U.S. government – as indicated, for example, by the letter from the U.S. Munitions Board to C. D. Howe – this seemed little more than a formality. A few months might be required to obtain certification from the FPC, but construction of the line could likely start late that year and sometime in 1954 gas could start flowing from the Peace River country to B.C. and U.S.

markets. The case before the FPC, however, took a record two years and two days, from June 16, 1952 to June 18, 1954, and involved 250 days of public hearings in Washington which were transcribed into more than 28,000 pages of testimony with more than 600 exhibits.

When the FPC handed down its decision approving Ray Fish's Pacific Northwest Pipeline Corporation project from Texas and rejecting the Westcoast Transmission project, the setback did indeed prove little more than a temporary obstacle for McMahon. Others viewed it as the end of Westcoast Transmission's plans, but McMahon and his associates were well aware of a vital factor in the equation: Fish had his pipeline certificate, but he lacked an adequate supply of natural gas. McMahon still had the Peace River gas reserves. Shortly after the FPC decision a friend advised McMahon that he would be wise to make a deal with Fish, offering him a half interest in Westcoast Transmission if Fish would buy gas from Westcoast at the U.S. border. That way, Westcoast might still manage to salvage something. "Why the hell should I? " McMahon is quoted as having replied. "I've got the gas."

Fish comes to McMahon

McMahon did not have to sell a half interest, or any interest, in Westcoast to Fish, but within six months of the FPC decision had negotiated to sell to Fish's Pacific Northwest Pipeline a total of 200 million cubic feet per day of Peace River gas to be delivered by Westcoast to Sumas on the International Boundary near Vancouver. The agreement permitted the construction of both lines to the Pacific northwest states. Fish's line from Texas and McMahon's line from the Peace River. The northern end of the Pacific Northwest Pipeline system, in effect, took over that portion of the system which Westcoast itself had originally intended to build in the United States to distribute the Canadian gas to the larger centres in Washington and Oregon.

This time it was Ray Fish who appeared before the Federal Power Commission with an application to import Canadian gas, which took a lot less time to process than McMahon's earlier request. FPC approval late in 1955 was, at long last, the final hurdle for Westcoast Transmission. Construction had, in fact, already started prior to the FPC certification, and was soon rolling in high gear. Initial public financing, consisting of $16 million raised from the sale of common shares and $31 million from senior debt financing, was completed early in 1956 with further public financing to follow before the $170 million line was in operation. In August the following year a welder made the final join to create the 650-mile, 30-inch pipe which was soon moving gas to markets throughout much of British Columbia and into the United States. McMahon's big pipe dream had come true. Canada's first major, long-distance gas transmission pipeline had been successfully built and placed in operation.

Before his Westcoast line was completed, McMahon felt ready to tackle another, much larger, job, one which finally proved to be more than he could handle. In 1956 Westcoast Transmission was all but an accomplished fact, while the much larger Trans-Canada Pipe Lines system from Alberta to Montreal was bogged down in a political mire. Trans-Canada had obtained its required governmental approvals long before Westcoast. Unfortunately, the economics of the project remained questionable in the eyes of the big insurance companies whose loans were required to build the line, and Trans-Canada's sponsors were unable to raise sufficient capital without government assistance. In Parliament, the request for government assistance had become the top political issue of the day. Into this impasse boldly stepped Frank McMahon with an offer to C. D. Howe to build the line without any government assistance if the project were turned over to him. But when the chips were on the table, McMahon abruptly withdrew his offer.

Borden Commission

McMahon later ran into a peck of trouble, too, from a Royal Commission on Canada's energy resources, headed by Henry Borden, Q.C., former head of the large Brazilian Light and Traction Company. Appointed by John Diefenbaker's government following the defeat of the Liberal government in the 1957 election, the Borden Commission probed deeply into the financing of Westcoast and the gas export sales price to the Pacific Northwest Pipeline Corporation.

The commission's preliminary report made some harsh comment. It pointed out that the price of 22 cents per thousand cubic feet of gas charged by Westcoast for sales to Pacific Northwest Pipeline at the International Boundary, was less than the price charged by Westcoast for sales to gas utility firms in British Columbia, and implied that Canadian gas consumers were subsidizing U.S. gas consumers in their purchase of Canadian gas. The commission's report, however, also acknowledged that without the export sales contract the Westcoast line could never have been built and Vancouver could not have been served with domestic natural gas.

This same question arose again a decade later when a new contract was signed increasing Westcoast's gas export price and covering much larger volumes. The U.S. Federal Power Commission would not permit Canadian gas to be imported under this higher price, ruling that it was too costly. When a lower price was negotiated, the National Energy Board would not allow the gas to be exported because it ruled the price was too low to satisfy the interests of Canada. A compromise price was eventually set.

The Borden Commission members also found fault with what they considered to be excessive profits earned by McMahon and his associates in the financing of Westcoast Transmission. It was not so much the block of 500,000 Westcoast treasury shares purchased in 1953 at a price of five cents per share which seemed to distress the commission, since there was an element of risk and uncertainty regarding Westcoast's future prospects at that time. But a second sale of 125,000 treasury shares at five cents each later in 1954, after Westcoast had signed sales contracts with Pacific Northwest Pipeline and B.C. utility firms, virtually ensuring an economically viable operation, was a bit much, in the commissioners' view. Westcoast shares two years later were offered to the public at a price of $5 each. The 625,000 shares purchased in 1953 and 1954 for a total of $31,248, by 1957 were worth well in excess of $12 million, at quoted stock market prices.

Board considered profits excessive

". . . the issuance of common shares for a nominal consideration, when subsequently the public is permitted to participate at a much greater price per share, results in the promoters obtaining a proportion of the equity and a return thereon completely out of scale with the return on the investment of shareholders who subsequently subscribe," the Borden report declared. The sale of the five-cent shares, it added, resulted in "potential capital profits beyond any amount which, in our opinion, could be considered as reasonable or adequate for the risks involved."

An oil promoter, to be successful, must find two things: first money, then oil. Frank McMahon had been spectacularly successful in finding money, and ultimately successful in finding oil and gas. Finding money, of course, means utilizing the money of other people in the hope of generating a profit both for them and for yourself. McMahon certainly did that. But in the process of using other people's money, McMahon's control over his companies had always been tenuous, and at times others controlled the companies which he managed. McMahon's last vestige of control over Pacific Petroleums, and through it control of Westcoast Transmission, disappeared in 1960 with the purchase by Pacific of the Canadian assets of Phillips

Finding money

Frank
McMahon —
husband,
father, and
racehorse owner.

Petroleum Company of Bartlesville, Oklahoma, and Sunray Oil Company, of Tulsa, Oklahoma. The assets acquired by Pacific had an appraised value of $315 million, and included interests in four million acres of exploratory oil and gas holdings, 25 million barrels of developed oil reserves, more than 600 billion cubic feet of natural gas reserves, and a half interest in a few retail gasoline outlets in British Columbia and a small refinery at Fort St. John which had been held 50-50 by Pacific and Phillips. The purchase price for these assets was some 6.5 million treasury shares issued by Pacific, the net effect of which was to transfer control of Pacific to Phillips and Sunray. Subsequently, Sunray sold its shares of Pacific, but Phillips invested heavily in further Pacific shares to maintain a 45 percent ownership, and thus effective control.

Enter
Phillips
Petroleum

Under the control of Phillips, Pacific invested heavily in further expansion through acquisitions and exploration. In 1960, Pacific's operations had resulted in a net loss of nearly $4 million, but by 1968 this had been converted to net earnings of more than $14 million, while the company ranked as the 9th largest oil producer

174

and the 3rd largest gas producer in Canada. Westcoast Transmission had grown to a $350 million corporation by 1968, and was working on long-range plans for a project which would multiply its size several fold — a 2,000-mile, billion dollar gas line from the Arctic coast to the U.S. border. Other interests of the Pacific group included a crude oil pipeline from northeastern British Columbia (Western Pacific Products and Crude Oil Pipeline Company) and another wildcatting firm (Westcoast Production Company).

Frank McMahon, too, continued to prosper, and although control of the Pacific companies was firmly held by Phillips, McMahon remained a director of all four firms and chairman of Westcoast Transmission, Western Pacific, and Westcoast Production. Market value of McMahon's share holdings in the Pacific group of companies in 1969 exceeded $20 million, while other major investments ranged from a distillery to a pipe manufacturing firm.

From dropout to jet-setter

With a French colonial mansion in Vancouver which he called home, a little Spanish-style cottage in Palm Beach, Florida, which could comfortably accommodate 100 dinner guests, and a permanent New York apartment, McMahon had become firmly established as a high flyer among the international jet set. His gambler's instincts had found additional profitable outlets on Broadway (where he had backed such big winners as The Pajama Game, Damn Yankees and Plain and Fancy) and in the king of sports (a stable owned jointly by McMahon, Bing Crosby, and Calgary newspaper publisher Max Bell, has included a winner of the Irish Derby and top events at Ascot, while a horse from McMahon's own stable has won both the Kentucky Derby and the Preakness).

For the dropout student from Gonzaga University who had set out as a diamond driller, it had been a long journey from the mines near his native Moyie, British Columbia.

C. D. Howe

Chapter Ten

The great pipeline debate
and Trans-Canada

Not since the founding of the Canadian Pacific Railway nearly a century before had Canada seen such a political maelstrom involving a private corporation as that which centred on the founding of Trans-Canada Pipe Lines Ltd in the 1950's.

It reached its climax in the most bitter, tumultuous political debate that has ever rocked the Parliament of Canada, and left in its wake shattered careers and broken lives. Shouts, jeers, angry insults, desk thumping and rowdy singing reverberated throughout the House of Commons. Parliament was likened to the Reichstag in the days of Hitler's Nazi Germany. Men who had been elected to lead the nation and settle national policy by reasoned debate, grew white with rage and shook clenched fists. So impassioned were the feelings that some men fainted, others were left fatigued and in broken health, and one Member of Parliament died of a heart attack. Never had Parliamentary democracy in Canada been so severely tested.

At issue was far more than the affairs of a corporation; more than the ambitions and careers of politicians. At stake was the development of one of Canada's vital natural resources, the burgeoning natural gas reserves of Western Canada, and how they were utilized held great potential impact for the entire country. Of even greater importance was the fact that the nation's traditions of Parliamentary democracy were on trial.

A Greek tragedy

There were charges that the government of the day sought to use public funds for the benefit of U.S. corporate interests; of a "sell-out" of Canadian interests to Texas oil "buccaneers;" that Canadians would lose control of their own resources; that the gas reserves would be exploited for American use and benefit. The government was accused of denying the rights of Parliament. The opposition parties were accused of thwarting the will of the majority and obstructing development vital to the national welfare in order to impose their own will and gain political advantage.

Air of unreality

There was an air of unreality about it all. Men of sincere convictions and possessing a common purpose and motivation to serve the interests of their country, instead of working to their common goals, found themselves seething with rage at each other. Facts became distorted. They were caught in a trap. They went farther than they wanted. Many wrecked their careers. They were in a labyrinth with no way out, and every step led deeper into the pit.

All objectives achieved

More than a decade later, it is almost difficult to discern what the Great Pipeline Debate was all about. All the participants wanted the same things. They wanted development of the shut-in natural gas resources in western Canada; they wanted Canadian control of the transportation of this gas; they wanted to ensure that the gas would be available first to serve Canadian requirements, with exports to U.S. markets limited to surplus supplies. If possible, they wanted Canadian ownership of Trans-Canada Pipe Lines.

And this is exactly what has been achieved. Development of the formerly idle gas reserves has resulted in one of Canada's fastest growing industries. The pipelines have been laid across the country in such a way as to reach the maximum number of Canadian consumers possible. Large volumes of gas export sales have been achieved, contributing to the nation's balance of payments and also helping to reduce the cost of gas to Canadian consumers.

Utilization of gas resources has been consistent with the policy of serving the maximum number of Canadian consumers. A highly-competent national regulatory body has been established to protect consumer interests and ensure the adequacy of supply for Canadian requirements. Trans-Canada Pipe Lines, the firm that started out under U.S. ownership, "the tool of American interests," in 1969 was more than 90 percent Canadian-owned.

Every stated objective of every political party that participated in the Great Pipeline Debate has been fully met. More than that, the processes of Parliamentary democracy in Canada have themselves been strengthened. The debate in Parliament was viewed by many voters as a national scandal. In its wake has come a re-examination of the traditions and processes of Parliamentary procedure. Some changes have been made, others are being considered, and more will be needed for as long as our society itself keeps changing. Perhaps more than anything before it, the Great Pipeline Debate demonstrated that Canada's great traditions of Parliamentary democracy can be protected and made to operate only if procedures established in the whip and buggy age are adapted to meet the requirements of an industrialized, jet-age nation.

That all this has been achieved at such needlessly high cost, in personal terms, is the Greek tragedy of the Great Pipeline Debate.

Texans from Athens

From the tiny Texas town of Athens came the prototypes of Texas oil wheeler-dealers, Clint W. Murchison and Sid Richardson.

Spreading their oil money into everything from newspapers to candy companies, the two friends amassed immense personal fortunes, which ran up to more than a billion dollars for Richardson, and more than $350 million for Murchison. Murchison spread his activities to Canada to launch what was later to become the longest natural gas pipeline in the free world.

A stocky, gregarious man, afire with energy and ideas, Murchison was described as "a natural-born horse trader" by his friends. "It's a challenge," Murchison is quoted as having said. "And if you trade in peanuts, you can trade in watermelons, too. We buy anything that adds up."

Peanuts and Watermelons

A lot of things added up for Murchison, and by the late 1950's he had important holdings in some 50 companies embracing oil and gas production, pipelines, an airline, banks, motels, drive-in theatres, a publishing house, a railway, insurance companies, a candy company, steamship company, several bus and taxi firms, a supermarket chain and several manufacturing firms. Many of these he controlled.

Although the two were not partners in every venture, they did participate with each other in a lot of deals, and were close friends. They made their headquarters and homes in Dallas. Richardson was a bachelor but Murchison was a family man whose two sons participated in running the family enterprises. Both had retreats where they entertained their cronies and business associates. Richardson had St. Joseph Island in the Gulf of Mexico where he had a cattle ranch and a hunting preserve and where he entertained such friends as Franklin

D. Roosevelt and Dwight Eisenhower. Murchison had a 75,000-acre ranch in the Sierra Madre of Mexico where guests included the Duke and Duchess of Windsor and, on one occasion, C. D. Howe – much to Howe's later political embarrassment. It was in the late 1940's, well before Murchison had any interests in Canada. Howe, at the time Minister of Transport, and several other Canadians, were on a holiday tour as guests of American Airlines, and had stopped off for a couple of days at the Murchison ranch, "where we shot turkeys," as Howe later recalled. It was this brief association which years later led to insinuations that Howe, in attempting to push the Trans-Canada Pipe Lines project through Parliament, was simply trying to help his Texas oil friend, Clint Murchison.

A visit from Howe

Richardson, five years the elder, had gone into the oil business in West Texas in 1911 when he was 20, trading leases and promoting wells until he had established substantial holdings. His friend Clint joined him eight years later, and before long both had established substantial production. Murchison did so well that he was able to sell out his holding in 1925 for a reported $5 million, and retire at a youthful age 30.

Murchison was soon bored with "retirement," and set out wild-catting. His first big strike found gas instead of oil. There was so little interest in natural gas in those days that most of the producers were flaring it off, as at Turner Valley, or dropping their gas leases to continue the search for oil.

Murchison had a habit of holding onto whatever he acquired, often waiting patiently for years until it assumed significance, and often rewarded handsomely for his patience and foresight. He reckoned there would someday be a substantial market for natural gas, and not only held onto his strike, but aggressively searched for more gas. His principal company, Delhi Oil, Ltd., eventually had gas producing and gas pipeline operations that overshadowed the oil interests.

Delhi moves into Canada

In the rush of American oil operators who moved north into Alberta following Imperial's Leduc discovery in 1947 came Murchison, forming Canadian Delhi Oil Ltd., initially as a wholly-owned subsidiary of the U.S. firm. Murchison saw in Alberta an opportunity to duplicate his U.S. gas success. Where most companies were intent on the search for oil, Canadian Delhi focused its activities on the search for natural gas on the plains of eastern Alberta. In less than three years, Canadian Delhi had drilled 12 wildcat prospects and made eight significant gas discoveries.

These discoveries provided the base for the most ambitious project Murchison had ever tackled, a $375 million natural gas pipeline from Alberta to Montreal.

If Murchison's plan was staggering in concept, it was also trimmed to the prevailing political winds. Canadian Delhi was not the first in the field for approval to pipe gas from Alberta when it filed an application before the Alberta Oil and Gas Conservation Board September 29, 1950, revealing plans for 1,800 miles of 30-inch pipe from Alberta to Toronto and a further 332 miles of 22-inch pipe from Toronto to Montreal. On the heels of Alberta's Gas Resources Preservation Act, which was passed late in 1949, there were already four other groups with applications before the Alberta board by the time Canadian Delhi announced its bid. There was Frank McMahon's Westcoast Transmission; Northwest Natural Gas Company, backed by Faison Dixon and the U.S. investment house of Stanley Morgan and Company; Ray Fish's Prairie Transmission Pipe Line Company and other Fish vehicles, and Western Pipe Lines Limited.

First gas line application

Of these other four, all but Western Pipe Lines proposed to move Alberta gas to markets along the U.S. west coast and in British Columbia. Western proposed a line eastward from Alberta as far as Winnipeg and then south to cross the U.S. border at Emerson, exporting gas to Northern Natural Gas Company for markets in Minnesota and North Dakota.

Political opposition to plans to move Alberta gas to U.S. markets without first fully serving Canadian markets had already been well established and loudly proclaimed in the House of Commons during debate on private members' bills for incorporation of various pipeline companies by special acts of Parliament. As already noted, both Conservative and CCF members as well as some Liberals, staged filibusters to prevent the incorporation of those firms which would not commit themselves to building on "all-Canadian" routes.

Political static

Western Pipe Lines had escaped this because it had been among the first five pipeline firms to be incorporated by Parliament April 30, 1949, just 25 days after Parliament had passed the Pipe Lines Act providing for incorporation of such firms by special acts. The "Canada first" pipeline principal was not then a political issue. Had Western, with its plan to move Alberta gas only as far east as Winnipeg and then south into the United States, come before the House

Western Pipe Lines

Western's gilt-edged backers

for incorporation the following year, it would almost certainly have had a rough ride. As it was, Western had obtained its federal incorporation with almost no questions asked, and in 1950 was outlining its application to the Alberta board.

Western was backed principally by Osler Hammond and Nanton Limited of Winnipeg, one of the oldest investment firms in western Canada, established in 1883. Osler Hammond and Nanton had participated in building several regional railways in the west, and as a result held control of nearly three million acres of mineral rights in the three prairie provinces, the legacy of government land grants made to assist railway construction. Osler Hammond and Nanton, primarily through two subsidiaries, the Calgary & Edmonton Corporation and Security Freehold Petroleums, had spent several million dollars in the search for oil and gas in western Canada, and held an overriding gross royalty interest in the big Pincher Creek gas field, discovered by Gulf Oil in the southern Alberta foothills. Also participating in Western were the Montreal investment house of Nesbitt Thompson and Company, and International Utilities of New York, which controls the two principal gas utilities in Alberta.

Lionel D. M. Baxter, president of Osler, Hammond and Nanton, appeared before the Alberta board as Western's chief policy witness. He told the board: "I was asked over a year ago to look into the question of taking gas to Ontario and I could not be convinced that it was economically feasible to take a line across a thousand miles of rock and muskeg and make it pay at the other end."

But that is exactly what Clint Murchison proposed to do.

Trans-Canada charter

His vehicle was to be Trans-Canada Pipe Lines Limited. First reading of the private member's bill to incorporate Trans-Canada, then a wholly-owned subsidiary of Canadian Delhi Oil, under the Pipe Lines Act, was introduced in the House of Commons on February 26, 1951. Frank A. Schultz, vice-president of Canadian Delhi, appeared before the standing house committee on railways, canals and telegraph lines to outline Trans-Canada's plan to move Alberta gas as far east as Montreal.

"We had to be able to supply gas to the consuming areas at a price which they could afford to pay for it," Schultz told the committee. "Now we feel that we can supply this gas at a price which is cheaper than the corresponding charge for coal or oil.

"The second consideration was that it should be an all-Canadian project, that it would be Canadian gas transported over an all-Canadian line, and that one hundred percent of the consumption would be in Canadian cities. It would be a project over which the Canadian government would have complete jurisdiction, both as to the projected line and, ultimately, as far as the prices which are realized are concerned.

"The third consideration was that the project had to be economically feasible . . . We are satisfied, at this stage, that the line is entirely feasible . . .

"We are committed to the principle of spending several million dollars a year looking primarily for gas to be dedicated to this eastern project . . ." In reply to a question, Schultz stated that "we want and need Canadian participation in this project, in all stages of the financing."

When members of the committee suggested an amendment to Trans-Canada's charter to provide "that the main pipeline or lines, either for transmission or transportation of gas or oil, shall be located entirely within Canada," the backers of the project readily agreed. With this, Trans-Canada was quickly incorporated by Special Act of Parliament March 21.

Main line to be in Canada

Murchison now had, on paper, a Canadian pipeline company. Where others had fought for as long as a year and a half to obtain incorporation, Trans-Canada had obtained it in less than one month. Murchison had gauged the political winds accurately. He had not, however, so accurately gauged the economics or financibility of his bold project. Trans-Canada was now a pipeline company, but it was seven years later before it had an operating pipeline. Even then it was accomplished only after considerable change in ownership, with massive government support, and following the most bitter debate in the history of the Canadian Parliament. As for the claim that one hundred percent of the pipeline's gas sales would be to Canadian cities, Trans-Canada ultimately became an economically viable project only by virtue of additional sales to U.S. markets.

It was Nathan Eldon Tanner, a former Mormon bishop, a leader in the Boy Scout movement, a school principal and cabinet minister in the Alberta government, who eventually saw the Trans-Canada Pipe Line project pushed through to completion. For his efforts, Tanner was well remunerated, but also earned a rebuke from a Royal Commission for having made excessive earnings from a project financed by government funds.

Born in Salt Lake City, Utah, Tanner was cast in the mold of those devout Mormons to whom hard work and self-reliance is both a way of life and a part of religion. Tanner's family moved when he was

Mormon teacher from Cardston

three months old to a farm near Cardston in southern Alberta, and a combination of school work and farm chores did, indeed, provide Tanner with a capacity for work.

After working through grade 11 in high school, Tanner took a year's training at a teacher's college in Calgary, obtained a teaching job in a small community near Cardston and, soon a family man, supplemented his income by purchasing a small general store, at which he clerked after school hours and on weekends. He also became postmaster and Scoutmaster at the tiny village of Hillspring. Later, as high school principal at Cardston in the midst of the depression of the Thirties, Tanner supplemented his slim teacher's salary by selling suits and insurance. By the mid 1930's he was simultaneously high school principal, a bishop of the Mormon church, a member of the town council, and a Scoutmaster.

Tanner in politics

Tanner was elected to the Alberta Legislature in 1935 in the wave which first swept William Aberhart's Social Credit party into power, was named Speaker of the House, and the following year was appointed Minister of Lands and Mines (later Mines and Minerals), a portfolio which he held for 18 years. As Mines Minister, Tanner launched a vigorous campaign to stimulate the flagging search for new oil and gas reserves in Alberta, seeking particularly to attract British capital, with little success. Visiting every oil producing state in the U.S., Tanner studied their conservation methods, adapted the best to Alberta, and came up with about the best set of petroleum conservation regulations that had been devised. As a result, the Alberta government was able to ensure that the oil boom which followed the Leduc discovery resulted in no wastage of the type which had earlier occurred in the development of Turner Valley. More than that, Tanner had helped set up the system whereby Alberta auctioned off carefully selected leases to oil companies, generating maximum revenue for the province. By 1952, the Alberta government had collected several hundred million dollars in cash from the oil companies, the province's economy had been transformed, and Alberta, deeply debt-ridden in 1935, had emerged as one of the most prosperous provinces in the country. Tanner skillfully managed Alberta's policy of tough bargaining with the petroleum industry, matched by meticulously equitable administration of the province's mineral rights, a winning combination which drew respect and trust from the oil companies.

Alberta petroleum conservation

Having helped make millions for the Alberta government, Tanner set out late in 1952 to accumulate his own fortune, leaving the Alberta government to head Merrill Petroleums, a new independent oil company backed by the world's largest investment firm, Merrill Lynch, Pierce, Fenner and Beane.

Trans-Canada Pipe Lines, meanwhile, had been in existence for three years before Tanner was called upon to put the project through. During those years, the form and substance of the company had been significantly changed.

The first hurdle in implementing the Trans-Canada project was to obtain a permit from the Alberta government to export the required volumes of gas from the province. This took four years and cost millions of dollars — for engineering studies, market surveys, contract negotiations, reserve estimates — and months of public hearings before the Alberta Oil and Gas Conservation Board. In the meantime, millions more were spent on exploration for gas reserves to be dedicated to the proposed pipeline. It was a straight gamble. If the bid succeeded, the investment could return generous profits; if it failed, the entire investment could be lost. Even when the first hurdle was cleared and Trans-Canada became the authorized vehicle to export Alberta gas to eastern markets, success was still anything but assured.

The efforts of Trans-Canada and others to obtain Alberta export permits were rejected time and again, as the provincial government grimly withheld its authorization until it was completely convinced that there was enough gas to provide for Alberta's own requirements for at least the next 30 years, and still leave an exportable surplus.

Call from Trans-Canada

The chronology of principal events affecting Trans-Canada's bid was as follows:

September 29, 1950: Canadian Delhi Oil files formal application with the Conservation Board for a gas export permit to serve its proposed 2,300-mile, pipeline to Montreal.

January 8, 1951: Opening of public hearings on Canadian Delhi's application postponed until May 7 at request of applicant, which was not yet ready to proceed.

January 20, 1951: Alberta Conservation Board report to provincial government recommends that all gas export applications heard the previous year be rejected, finding that there was no gas surplus to Alberta's own needs. It suggested, however, that the applications might be reconsidered that Fall.

March 26, 1951: Trans-Canada Pipe Lines incorporated by special act of Parliament, takes over application filed by parent Canadian Delhi before Alberta board.

Events affecting Trans-Canada bid

May 7, 1951: Public hearings on Trans-Canada application open before Alberta board, and last for three days before being deferred until September to be considered in consolidated hearing of all applicants.

September 10 to December 14: Consolidated hearings on all gas export applications.

March 29, 1952: Conservation Board report to government recommends approval of gas export to British Columbia and U.S. west coast markets by Westcoast Transmission, and deferral of all other applications. This left only two principal contenders in the running; Western Pipe Lines, with its proposal for a line east to Winnipeg then south to the United States, and Trans-Canada, with its "all-Canadian" scheme.

May 11 to September 21, 1953: More public hearings before Alberta board or renewed applications by Western and Trans-Canada. Western had amended its application to add "phase two," an extension of its proposed line to eastern Canada, which it said would be built within three years after the line to Winnipeg and the U.S. markets had been completed.

November 24, 1953: Another report from the board again recommended rejection of both applications. This time the board found that there was enough surplus gas to meet the requirements of either of the two applicants. The board, however, was not satisfied with the economic feasibility of either project. It intimated that the price at which Western proposed to export gas to Northern Natural Gas Company for sale in Minnesota and North Dakota was too low, while the Trans-Canada project did not appear to be economically viable unless it had some export sales to add to its revenues and reduce the cost to the potential consumers in Ontario and Quebec.

Alberta pushes joint approach

At this point, the Alberta government stepped behind the scenes in an effort to have the two proposals merged into one. Premier Ernest Manning called on C. D. Howe to seek his support in persuading the companies to join forces. On January 12, Howe announced in the House of Commons that, following several days of discussions in which he had acted "as an honest broker," the two firms had agreed to a merger. The continuing vehicle would be Trans-Canada Pipe Lines, but ownership, pending public financing, would be split 50-50 between the original sponsors of the two firms. It was just the first reduction in Murchison's interest in the project.

Conservative opposition leader George Drew greeted the plan with approval, expressing hope that "we might proceed as rapidly as possible to do anything that might be necessary to expedite this important venture. I would point out that we have already indicated our support of the general plan that is involved." That was just about the last word of support for the project that was to come from the opposition benches in the House.

Having effected the merger, the next step was to find a president for Trans-Canada Pipe Lines who would be acceptable to both groups of original backers, between whom no love had been lost during four years of intense competition before the Alberta board. Tanner was picked for the job, attracted from his position as president of Merrill Petroleums by a salary of $37,000 per year, plus an option to purchase a sizeable block of Trans-Canada shares. The option could be highly valuable if the project succeeded; worthless if it failed. Tanner accepted the challenge and was appointed president of Trans-Canada Pipe Lines in March.

Tanner heads merged company

The hearing which followed a few weeks later was little more than a formality. On May 14, the Alberta government authorized Trans-Canada to remove a total of 4.2 trillion cubic feet of natural gas from the province over a 25-year period. Approval by the federal Board of Transport Commissioners two months later, on July 26, to construct the proposed line, was also little more than a formality.

Trans-Canada now had all its required Canadian authorization from both the Alberta and federal governments. It still required financing of nearly $300 million, a new sales contract to export gas south of Winnipeg to Northern Natural Gas Company, and approval by the U.S. Federal Power Commission for Northern Natural to import the Canadian gas. Anyone who thought that Trans-Canada was at last off and running was soon rudely disappointed. Trans-Canada's real troubles had not even started.

Clarence Decatur Howe has been called the architect of the industrialization which transformed the nation's economy as it emerged from the second world war. He has also been called the Czar of Canada, a dictator, the man who ran roughshod over Parliament, the most controversial living Canadian of his time.

Engineer from Massachusetts

Few individuals, if any, contributed more to the nation's industrial and economic growth during the 1940's and 1950's than the fiery,

Donald Fleming,
after ejection
from Commons
during pipeline
debate.

blunt-spoken engineer from Whatham, Massachusetts, who became "the minister of just about everything." He was, said Progressive Conservative leader George Drew, the great "Pooh-Bah of the government." But it was precisely those qualities which enabled C. D. Howe to direct with skill and force the building of so much of Canada's industrial fibre, that also led inevitably to an impatience with the partisan political fighting in the House of Commons which continually sought to impede his great engine of progress.

A sense of urgency, of excitement, of satisfaction in serving his *A sense* adopted country with great projects, was the steam power which drove C. D. Howe. In a rare moment of public self-analysis, Howe, in *of urgency* the heat of the pipeline debate, paused to ask in the House, "Why are we pressing this?" His curious reply to his own question: "Well, I do not know; perhaps I get over-enthusiastic about a project. I have been working on sizeable projects all my life, and somehow I reach a point in the development when I think a project is important; and if it is a serious enough project, I begin to think it is the most important thing in the world, and it does seem to me it is important that we do not lose a year in the undertaking of this pipeline."

Few of Howe's political opponents could ever bring themselves to recognize or admit his contributions. Often after Howe had correctly and succinctly analysed a complex situation or development with the incisive logic of an engineer and corporate executive, his opponents were still lost in a fog of bombast. Too often they fought him with a rage of personal vindictiveness. Repeated, long-winded speeches bored him greatly. "I have never found a subject yet that could profitably have anything more said about it after the first 10 speeches," he once observed in the House.

After more than 20 years of political infighting and harassment, of obstructionism of undertakings which he considered to be of monumental importance, Howe's attitude at times seemed to indicate he felt he had been suffering fools long enough — an attitude not wholly unjustified in view of the calibre of debate in the House at times.

Executive in Parliament

Howe's fuse grew short. A Vancouver reporter once approached him to ask about something which Howe did not care to discuss, was curtly told to "go to hell." In political campaigning, Howe gave as good as he got, and whether or not he instigated much of the personal bitterness which grew in the House, he did little to ameliorate it.

He was no Parliamentarian, with passionate love for great traditions, for intricate, complex and time-consuming procedures and rules, for discursive debates and compromises. "I was never very strong on rules," he once admitted in the House. He was the civil engineer, the great builder, the corporate executive whose passion was to get things done. In matters of Parliamentary procedure, he relied completely on the advice of others, as a corporate executive would rely on lawyers in legal matters.

Perhaps the best political assessment of C. D. Howe came from one of his opponents during the pipeline debate. At a time when tempers were getting out of hand and personal feelings were running high, CCF member Colin Cameron was one of the few who could still take a reasoned view, and presented one of the rare tributes accorded Howe from the opposition benches. "I would be the first, not to admit but to proclaim that the right honourable Minister of Trade and Commerce has made splendid gifts of service to the Canadian people," Cameron said. ". . . he is a man with most extraordinary capacities and abilities . . . Unfortunately he has been served by people who have advised him in a field in which, shall I say, by his own admission, he is not very well versed in the methods by which measures can be brought safely through the House of Commons."

It was Howe's growing impatience, his unflinching determination to see one final, great, vital project carried through to completion, and poor advice in how to carry his measure through the House, that brought the end to a political era in Canada, with the defeat of the Liberal government. Ten years later, the Toronto Daily Star was to note that "the government as a whole had to accept responsibility for this heavy-handed, arbitrary course but it has never been established who or what group master-minded it. It certainly wasn't Howe. He told Sharp (Mitchell Sharp, then Howe's Deputy Minister): 'I don't know anything about parliamentary procedure. I do what I'm told'."

Mackenzie King, St. Laurent and Howe had led the country through a period of dramatic change, accomplishment and progress, but when the Liberal party became too filled with its own importance the voters shot it down.

Howe's climb

Howe headed for Canada in 1908, a 22-year old civil engineering graduate from the Massachusetts Institute of Technology. It was the same year that Peary had left to discover the North Pole, and Howe expected to be home before Peary. Howe had accepted a position as engineering professor at Dalhousie University, Nova Scotia, a job which he had intended to hold only for a couple of years. Five years later he was still at Dalhousie when he was offered a job as chief engineer with the federal Board of Grain Commissioners to supervise construction of grain elevators. "I've never seen one of those things in my life, but I'll take the job," Howe is reported to have replied. The following year he took out his Canadian citizenship.

Howe set up his own engineering and construction firm in 1916, based at Port Arthur, to build grain elevators. His first one was only half finished when it was destroyed by a hurricane. Howe borrowed bank money to complete the job on schedule, but in the process would have lost everything he owned had not the Saskatchewan Co-Operative Elevator Co. Ltd. surprisingly, and without being asked, voted extra money to cover his loss.

Howe left business for politics in 1935 as a candidate for the Port Arthur riding in the national elections, assured by Mackenzie King that he would receive a cabinet post. Howe was 39 and a millionaire. His firm had built $100 million worth of grain elevators, bridges, docks and factories. It had designed the great wheat terminals which line the waterfront at Buenos Aires, Howe's last major engineering assignment.

If Howe's accomplishments in·industry were spectacular, his accomplishments in the government sphere during the ensuing 23 years were stunning. Howe had not been in office for six months as Minister of Railways and Canals before he had sparked the first of many stormy political battles with a plan to replace the country's patronage-ridden system of local labour boards with a national board. By the time Howe had been an MP and cabinet minister for two years he had created the National Harbours Board; re-organized the financial structure of the Canadian National Railways, cancelling some $600 million worth of government advances which could never be collected, and putting the railway on a solid footing; sponsored the bill which eventually led to the establishment of the Canadian Broadcasting Corporation; established Trans-Canada Air Lines (now Air Canada), the nation's first national airline and the first of many Crown corporations organized by Howe.

New directions for government

In 1934, the budget for the Department of National Defence was $13 million. "That was the year they just bought postage stamps," Howe later commented. With war clouds gathering in Europe, this had risen to $36 million 1938, and $63 million in 1939. When Canada entered the second world war in September, 1939, Howe headed the newly-created Department of Munitions and Supply. Under his direction, the nation's industries geared for the production of war material. "What Howe started in 1940 was an industrial revolution so widespread that most Canadians were unaware of its extent or penetration into the country's economy," Howe's biographer, Leslie Roberts, has written. By 1943, production of war material hit a peak of $3.5 billion, Canada was fourth among the Allied nations in industrial war output, exceeded only by Great Britain in per capita production. To its allies such as Britain and Russia, Canada gave away more material per capita than any other nation at war with the Axis, including the United States. Assessing Howe's contribution, Lord Beaverbrook described him as "one of a handful of men of whom it can be said, 'But for him the war would have been lost'." Howe himself, in 1943, prophesied that "Never again will there be any doubt that Canada can manufacture anything that can be manufactured elsewhere."

Builder for war

Before the end of the war, 28 Crown corporations were reporting to Howe, who was in the business of mining and refining, making synthetic rubber, producing aircraft, and a host of other activities. One of the largest war-time Crown companies he created was Polymer Corporation, still government-owned and a major petrochemical firm. Under Howe's direction, the government purchased Eldorado Mining and Refining Limited to develop uranium production in northern Saskatchewan, and to expand supplies, implemented one of the largest prospecting expeditions in Canada's history. As a result of this start, Canada became the world's largest uranium producer. Howe vigorously pushed post-war development of atomic energy and Canada's heavy-water nuclear power plants, licensed for use throughout the world.

Postwar activities

As the war drew near a close, Howe became simultaneously Minister of Munitions and Supply and Minister of Reconstruction. "With one hand he would liquidate the industrial war program; with the other he would restore Canada to a peacetime economy," Leslie Roberts wrote. Howe set up the War Assets Corporation to dispose of surplus military equipment ranging from boots to battleships, and by 1948 WAC had brought in nearly half a billion dollars to the federal treasury. When the United States found that its own surplus program quickly bogged down after the war, it copied the Canadian method, even to use of the same corporate name.

With the war over, the swords beaten into plowshares, Howe, in 1948, took over the task of promoting Canada's peacetime industrial and economic growth as Minister of Trade and Commerce, his major portfolio for the next decade, culminating in the pipeline debate and his last great project.

The gathering storm

The authorization to construct its pipeline system which Trans-Canada Pipe Lines had obtained from the federal government on July 26, 1954, and the earlier approval of the Alberta government, both required that Trans-Canada secure the necessary financing for its system no later than the end of 1954. Construction was to start early in 1955, with the line to be completed to Montreal in 1956. It took two years longer than anticipated. The financing deadline was first extended from December 31, 1954 to April 30, 1955; then to October 30, 1955; then to May 1, 1956; to November 1, 1956, and finally to March 31, 1957. In the end, financing of the $375 million cost of the initial system was secured only with the aid of $180 million – nearly half the total – in funds from the federal government. Construction did not start until the summer of 1956, with completion in the fall of 1958.

Not since the founding of the Canadian Pacific Railway had the financing of a private venture raised so much political controversy in Canada.

A first step in Trans-Canada's plan called for construction of a 76-mile pipeline from Niagara Falls, New York, to Toronto, to import U.S. gas on a short term basis from Tennessee Gas Transmission Company. The purpose was to build up demand for natural gas in Ontario so that there would be a larger market available when construction of the main transmission line from Alberta was completed. The U.S. imports would cease when the Trans-Canada main line was completed, and the flow through the Niagara-Toronto line would be reversed, exporting Canadian gas to the United States. The Niagara-Toronto line was completed on schedule to bring U.S. gas to Toronto in the Fall of 1954, but it was four years before the gas from Alberta arrived.

Trans-Canada faced three major problems. It had to secure financing, most of which would be obtained from banks and insurance companies in the form of first mortgage bonds. It had to negotiate sales contracts, which in the case of export sales to the United States, also required approval from the U.S. Federal Power Commission to import the gas from Canada. And it had to sign contracts for the long-term purchase of the gas from the oil companies in western Canada. The three problems made an interesting triangle. The banks, insurance companies and institutional investors did not want to guarantee the money until Trans-Canada had secured the gas purchase and sales contracts to ensure the financial stability of the project. The gas utilities were reluctant to sign long term contracts until Trans-Canada was able to offer assured delivery at firm prices. And the oil companies were reluctant to sell the gas at the prices which Trans-Canada could offer. The producers favored a more economical project which would permit them to receive higher prices. Export sales to the U.S. midwest, with a shorter, less costly line, such as had originally been proposed by Western Pipe Lines, would have been much more acceptable to the oil companies, and even to the government of Alberta. If a line had to be built all the way to Ontario and Quebec, they would have favored a shorter line through the United States, similar to the route followed by the Interprovincial Pipe Line. But this would have left northern Ontario without a natural gas supply, and neither the federal government nor the Ontario government was prepared to tolerate that.

Trans-Canada's three problems

Since government policy, for reasons of national interest, dictated that Alberta gas should be moved to eastern Canada by the longer, more expensive and less economic route, it was natural to speculate whether the government would assist Trans-Canada in overcoming its financial difficulties. As early as June, 1954, the Conservative member for Vancouver-Quadra had asked in the House if the government intended to assist in financing construction. "I cannot speak for what may happen at a future date," replied Transport Minister Lionel Chevrier, "but certainly at the moment there is no intention of granting any subsidy."

Tanner exudes confidence

Eldon Tanner, meanwhile, exuded an air of supreme confidence. "A number of conditions remain to be fulfilled before the 31st of December of this year and in the main they relate to the satisfying of the various dominion and provincial governmental agencies as to the adequacy of financing arrangements," Tanner told the Victoria, B.C. Chamber of Commerce in August. "The magnificent co-operation we have received from all these agencies and the very capable testimony of outstanding financial and pipeline experts both in the United States and in Canada leaves me free to assure you that we have every confidence in our ability to satisfy the various requirements before that date." In September, he reiterated before the Independent Natural Gas Association in the United States his belief that "we have every confidence in our ability to satisfy the requirements before that date."

Contract signed

Early in October, Trans-Canada announced that it had signed a contract to deliver gas at Emerson, on the Manitoba-North Dakota border south of Winnipeg, to Northern Natural Gas Company. This replaced the contract which Western Pipe Lines had previously held to deliver gas to Northern Natural. It was subject to Northern obtaining approval from the Federal Power Commission to import the gas, and to Trans-Canada satisfactorily meeting its governmental requirements on time.

The contract with Northern was an important step, but Trans-Canada still had a long way to go. It had not yet been able to sign a sales contract with any of its prospective gas utility customers in Canada, and had been able to secure contracts for the purchase of less than a quarter of its gas requirements.

On October 22, the Ottawa Citizen quoted Tanner as again expressing confidence that the financing would be secured by the end of the year deadline. But a week later the Toronto Star observed that "unless the federal government is prepared to provide substantial tax and other subsidies the $300 million Trans-Canada gas pipeline may never advance much farther than the drawing boards. From the point of view of the gas and oil industry, one of the major stumbling blocks continues to be the wellhead price for the gas."

By November, even Tanner was starting to admit that there just might be a few small problems. Gas producers, pipeliners and municipal distributors are "going to have to take a little less" in the initial years of operation in order to get the project off the ground, he told the Canadian Club in Toronto. "No one would expect me to say we are having all clear sailing . . . This is one of the largest engineering, construction and financial programs ever embarked upon in Canada and it is not one we can do alone." In December, Tanner admitted in a statement in Winnipeg that "it is true that problems have arisen which have retarded our program to some extent. However, we are confident that we will commence construction next year and will carry out our program as previously planned."

Tanner admits problems

Tanner was, in fact, by this time banking on government assistance in order to arrange financing and permit construction to start in the Spring of 1955 as scheduled. Extensive and lengthy negotiations on possible assistance were held with the government. Everyone seemed well aware that the negotiations were being held; there was constant speculation in the press, and repeated questioning in the House of Commons. Neither party, however, was about to admit publicly that such discussions were being held, much less provide information. Calgary South Conservative member Carl Nickle's question in the House January 20 was typical of the questions being asked: he wanted to know if the government intended "to facilitate the financing of the all-Canadian gas pipeline by a government guarantee of principal and interest of bonds issued by the pipeline company." And Howe's response was typical of the terse replies such questions received: "The government has taken no action along that line. If and when action is taken, I will be glad to make an announcement."

Banking on government help

Trans-Canada had, indeed, asked the government for exactly such assistance – for a deficiency guarantee under which the government would undertake to make any payments of interest and principal on the first mortgage bonds which could not be met from the revenue generated by the company's proposed pipeline system. According to Trans-Canada, it was "very unlikely that the government would ever be called on under the deficiency agreement." The proposal produced a major split in the cabinet, with Howe urging approval and

Company seeks deficiency guarantee

Finance Minister Walter Harris adamantly opposed. Howe lost out, and the government rejected the proposal. A second proposal, that the government's Industrial Development Bank pick up any of the first mortgage bonds which the company was unable to sell elsewhere, was also turned down. The Industrial Development Bank made a counter proposal under which it would have participated in the financing but which would also have given the government a controlling position in the company. This proposal was unacceptable to several U.S. oil companies which were not willing to sign a sales contract for their gas reserves with a government-controlled company. Major stumbling block in this regard was Gulf Oil Corporation of Pittsburgh whose large reserves in the Pincher Creek field were essential to Trans-Canada's gas supply.

Financing plans collapse

On March 17, Trans-Canada issued a statement reporting the breakdown in negotiations. "To date, the representatives of the company have been unable to negotiate a type of financial assistance which does not result in an agency of the government of Canada being in a position to control the company, and such an arrangement makes it impossible for the company to purchase its gas requirements," the statement declared. "Under the circumstances, the directors of Trans-Canada have most reluctantly reached the conclusion that there are no further steps within their power which could now be taken to arrange the financing to meet this year's construction program."

A start on construction of the pipeline system had been delayed for at least a year.

Another look at U.S. route

Although bitterly disappointed at this latest in the long series of delays in providing a market outlet for their rapidly growing gas reserves, the producers saw at least one possible benefit. Company statements called for a second look at the possibility of laying the line to eastern Canada south of the Great Lakes at a saving of some $40 million compared with the proposed route through northern Ontario. A. G. Bailey, a former chairman of the Alberta Oil and Gas Conservation Board and then president of Bailey Selburn Oil and Gas, commented that failure to finance Trans-Canada would, in the long run, prove beneficial. A more southerly line through the United States, he said, would result in a more economic project, higher prices to gas producers and easier sales contracts and financing. But from Ottawa, Tanner was quoted as saying that Trans-Canada would retain its plans for its "all-Canadian" route.

With the collapse of its financing plans, at least for 1955, Trans-Canada's only sales contract, its export agreement with Northern Natural Gas Company, lapsed by default. Trans-Canada was now in the position where it had no financing, no government assistance, no customers signed up, and still less than a quarter of its gas supplies under contract. The company backers had spent $8 million on the project (excluding the $5 million Niagara to Toronto pipeline and exploration expenditures in Alberta) but seemed little farther ahead than when they had started five years earlier.

Export contract lapses

The possibility of government assistance, however, was still alive, as indicated in an address by Tanner in Calgary in May. The Calgary Herald quoted Tanner: "C. D. Howe had told him to go ahead as rapidly as possible, as the government wanted the line built in 1955. 'What help you need will be forthcoming,' he quoted Howe as saying." This proved to be most indiscrete on Tanner's part, since the government had continued to refuse information to Parliament on discussions with the company on the grounds that it might embarrass Trans-Canada in private negotiations. Tanner's statement raised demands in both the press and in the House for information on just what help the government had in mind for Trans-Canada.

Negotiations, meanwhile, were resumed for a new sales contract to supply markets in the U.S. midwest, but this time the discussions were not limited to Northern Natural. Tennessee Gas Transmission Company, whose pipeline system moved gas from the southwest United States to markets in the northeast and Great Lakes regions, saw an opportunity to enter the U.S. midwest market if a deal could be negotiated to buy gas from Trans-Canada. The contemplated arrangement also provided for additional short term U.S. gas supplies for the Ontario market, pending completion of the Trans-Canada line.

Discussion on new contracts

The major gas firms in the U.S. midwest regions were not particularly pleased at the prospect of further competition in the general region they served. Three of these firms — Northern Natural of Omaha, Nebraska; People's Gas, Light and Coke Company of Chicago, and American Natural Gas Company of Detroit — combined to offer a proposal to Trans-Canada. The proposal was outlined in a letter July 21 from Northern Natural president John Merriman to Tanner, a copy of which was sent to Howe. ". . . our three companies are the only ones who can either build a major pipeline all the way

Three-company combine

from the Winnipeg border to eastern Canada for maximum volumes, or build piecemeal in small steps to handle maximum volumes," Merriman wrote. "No one else can do this. We are prepared to extend to you and the Canadian authorities the full co-operation of our companies in working out the program of handling the gas supply question in the best possible manner for the public interest of our two countries."

The three-company combine must have been most encouraged by the response to this letter which Merriman received from the Canadian Minister of Trade and Commerce. Wrote Howe: "I had a talk with Mr. Tanner and some of his associates this morning and understand that he will have a discussion with you shortly. I am hopeful that a program can be worked out with you and your group that will make it unnecessary to deal with others proposing to serve your territory. I will let you know if there would be any purpose in your group coming to Ottawa for further discussions."

Contract with TGT

This "group," however, must have been pressing Trans-Canada for a favorable decision. On August 8, Tanner sent the following telegram to Merriman: "Am unable to advise more definitely at this time. Use your best judgement regarding proposed study. Eldon."

Three days later, on August 11, Trans-Canada signed a gas sales contract with Tennessee Gas Transmission, calling for the delivery of 200 million cubic feet a day to TGT at Emerson, with an option to double this rate if and when additional gas became available. A subsidiary of TGT, Midwestern Gas Transmission, would build a thousand-mile pipeline system from Emerson to take delivery of the gas. At the same time, the contract provided for TGT to deliver 90 million cubic feet of gas per day to Trans-Canada for use in Ontario until the Trans-Canada main line was completed.

On August 15, Tanner wired Merriman: "Further to my wire to you on August 8, Trans-Canada has executed a contract which meets its requirements." This telegram was not signed "Eldon", but "N. E. Tanner."

Another contract, with Gulf.

Although they had lost out in their negotiations with Trans-Canada, this was not the last to be heard of this group. Later they were to offer their plan to Frank McMahon, much to the embarrassment of Trans-Canada and C. D. Howe. And later yet, the group was to be indicted by a U.S. court under anti-trust legislation.

Trans-Canada's next break came in October when, at long last, it was able to conclude a contract with Gulf for the purchase of gas from the Pincher Creek field at rates up to 170 million cubic feet per day. Combined with the contracts it had secured in 1954, Trans-

Canada now had a gas supply of 315 million cubic feet daily, two-thirds of its initial requirements. "This has broken the back of the supply problem," noted Oilweek magazine.

The back of the financing problem was still to be broken. It was the "all Canadian pipeline" policy – endorsed not only by the government but also by the opposition parties and the province of Ontario – which obviously presented the stumbling block. By requiring the longer, more costly route through northern Ontario, this policy so impaired the economics of the project that it could not be financed. A study for the Ontario government by chartered accountants Clarkson, Gordon & Co., confirmed that there was little chance that Trans-Canada would ever be able to finance this all-Canadian line without substantial assistance. Yet Ontario was unwilling to consider any alternate route. "A pipeline running through northern Ontario would make a very desirable form of fuel and source of power available which would be of the utmost assistance in development of our natural resources and our industry," a provincial government press statement noted. "For all of Ontario it would supplement power resources and for the whole nation would contribute to our economic self-sufficiency. From the Canadian standpoint, therefore, the reasons for an all-Canadian pipeline are unassailable. It is a prime national necessity." The statement also recognized that "the span across northern Ontario presents an added difficulty, which means that the line could become self-sustaining only after a number of years."

Financing still a problem

What if "the span across northern Ontario" were to be built by government? This would eliminate the handicap which appeared to be preventing financing (a handicap, however, which Trans-Canada had at the start imposed upon itself in order to win authorization). Howe and Ontario Premier Leslie Frost discussed how the two governments might join forces to build this section of the line. The results were announced in a government statement November 21.

Northern Ontario span

Howe announced that he would ask Parliament to approve the incorporation of a Crown company, Northern Ontario Pipe Line Corporation. The Crown firm would build the 675-mile section of the line from the Manitoba-Ontario border to Kapuskasing, at an estimated cost of $118 million. The Ontario government would contribute up to $35 million of this, and the federal government would contribute the balance (in the end, the federal government provided the entire financing). The line would be leased to Trans-Canada under a

Crown participation

199

rental formula which would cover the cost to the governments and provide some return on its investment. Trans-Canada would undertake to purchase the section of the line from the Crown company (at cost, plus interest) as soon as it could. Trans-Canada would have until May 1, 1956, to secure the financing for the construction of the balance of its system.

"A bridge in time"

"What the Canadian government is here providing is essentially a bridge in time," Howe commented. The Ontario government cautiously observed that Trans-Canada still had problems. "The participation of the federal-provincial partnership, however, is predicated upon the solution of these difficulties," the Ontario statement said. "If these difficulties are not resolved, a new approach will be necessary to make this project a reality, as we believe it must be."

Change of ownership

Trans-Canada gained further support for its project with the sale of 51 percent interest in the company to Tennessee Gas Transmission, Gulf, and Hudson's Bay Oil and Gas, leaving Canadian Delhi and the original sponsors of Western Pipe Lines with the remaining 49 percent. (Ownership was to change further with the completion of public financing, which would offer half of the equity interest to Canadian investors, thereby diluting the position of the sponsoring firms).

U.S. import hearings

In Washington, hearings before the U.S. Federal Power Commission on the application by Tennessee Gas to import the gas from Trans-Canada were proceeding on schedule (which meant not very fast), despite the determined opposition of Northern Natural and others.

Howe introduces Ontario line resolution

In Calgary, Oilweek asked Howe if he thought the bill providing the financing of the line would be passed by Parliament. Howe's reply: "If they don't ratify it there will be new governments in Ottawa and Ontario."

March 15, 1956, Howe rose in the House to introduce his first resolution to create the Northern Ontario Pipe Line Corporation. In a masterful presentation, Howe outlined this great undertaking in glowing terms that would swell the heart of every Canadian with national pride. It was a gigantic undertaking, involving $375 million for construction of the pipeline; $250 million for drilling more gas wells, for processing plants and gathering lines in Alberta; additional large sums for customer distribution lines in urban centres from Sask-

200

atchewan to Quebec, and the manufacture and installation of gas appliances. Altogether, more than a billion dollars would be pumped into the Canadian economy.

There were problems, too. "Once again, as in the days of railway building, the difficult and sparsely populated pre-Cambrian shield appeared to present an almost unsuperable barrier to economic transportation between western and central Canada," Howe told the House. "Once again, this special problem of Canadian geography has called forth a unique solution." The Canadian government had exhaustively examined the alternatives and concluded that this was the best solution. The Ontario government too, said Howe, had studied the problem, examined the same alternatives, and reached the same conclusion, the legislature of Ontario having passed its bill to participate in this project "not merely by a majority, but unanimously."

Yet Howe had his worries. The agreement with Trans-Canada had been signed on November 21, four months previously. It called upon Trans-Canada to complete its financing arrangements by May 1. There were only six weeks left, and little indication that Trans-Canada had been able to make any progress.

"It has now become clearly improbable that Trans-Canada will be able to complete its financing arrangements by May 1," Howe admitted. "Officers of the company expect, however, to arrange and carry out a substantial amount of construction this year under interim financing."

Howe forgot to mention that the "interim financing" with which Trans-Canada would carry out its 1956 construction would also come from the government. Parliament was to be asked not only to provide $118 million for the northern Ontario line, but also to lend Trans-Canada up to $80 million to help finance the balance of the system.

Howe had just completed the staging for The Great Pipeline Debate.

John Diefenbaker, the firebrand Conservative from Prince Albert, Saskatchewan, who later became Prime Minister, warned that the battle was coming. In a radio address he recalled the 11-day filibuster which the opposition parties had mounted the year before against extending Howe's sweeping powers under the Defence Production Act, and which caused the government to back-track. "The fight we put on then will appear but a skirmish beside the battle we will wage" when the Trans-Canada bill comes before the House, Diefen-

The debate begins

baker declared. And the CCF's Hazen Argue, in an interview, warned that this party would filibuster the bill to the finish.

Delays could wreck project

The Liberals knew at the outset that they had a fight on their hands, and they were in a hurry to get the bill through. Delay would have at least postponed construction of the gas line for a full year. After so many delays, one more might wreck the entire project. Howe knew that there was no time to be lost if construction were to start in 1956; if the entire Trans-Canada project were not to be scrapped; if the hopes for a national gas line system were not to be dependent on the prospects of an entirely new venture, starting out all over again from the position Trans-Canada had started from six years before. In their urgent rush, and faced with a determined opposition, the Liberals rammed their bill through. It was exactly this — the manner in which the bill was rushed through Parliament — that became the central factor in the Pipeline Debate.

Proposal should be laughed out

Howe had no sooner introduced the resolution on March 15, than the position of the Conservative and CCF parties was made clear. ". . . we are being asked to set up a crown corporation which will use public funds to assist financial interests in establishing effective control over one of our major resources," George Drew declared. "A proposal of this kind should be laughed out of the house." CCF leader M. J. Coldwell described it as "a proposition which will send the bulk of the gas to the United States via Emerson and transport the rest through a spur line to eastern Canada; via a spur linee, let it be said, which Canada and Ontario are going to build with public funds for a company under foreign control."

McMahon's offer

Business proceeds through Parliament by fits and starts. Legislation is brought before the House and set over for weeks or even months before advancing to the next stage, while Parliament turns its attention to other matters. Thus it was nearly two months from the time that Howe introduced his first resolution on the Northern Ontario Pipe Line Corporation, until it came before the House again. Meanwhile, there were other developments in the affairs of Trans-Canada, both behind the scenes and before the House.

There was the offer of Frank McMahon to build an all-Canadian gas line from Alberta to Montreal without any government assistance, save for the remission of import duty and sales tax on materials to be used in construction of the line. It was a "secret" offer, which everyone knew about; an offer which Howe denied had ever been made to the government; an offer which was abruptly withdrawn on the day on which it eventually was disclosed in the House; an offer which later involved McMahon in anti-trust suit in the United States.

March 27 marked the start of the case which could be called "the offer that never was." That was the day on which McMahon met with the Minister of Trade and Commerce to express serious misgivings about the ability of Trans-Canada Pipe Lines to complete its project, and to suggest an alternate proposal which, McMahon said, he could effect without any government assistance. McMahon left with Howe an outline of his proposal marked "private and confidential," and followed this up with further "private and confidential" letters and memoranda to Howe dated April 4, 13, 16 and 24.

In his memorandum to Howe dated April 4, McMahon wrote: "I will finance and construct an economically feasible pipeline in Alberta to Montreal and complete the same by 1958 without federal or provincial ownership or debt guarantee ... I will place sufficient equity money and arrange for interim loans to permit the construction of the 34-inch pipeline from the closest gas fields in Alberta to Winnipeg to supply gas to Saskatchewan and Manitoba by late 1956 or early 1957." McMahon said that his proposed pipeline would be at least 70 percent Canadian-owned and that it would be financed without government ownership or debt guarantee. He claimed that Trans-Canada was "dominated by Tennessee Gas Transmission," and "proposed an uneconomic plan to favour Tennessee Gas to the detriment of Canada and at the same time requests the governments of Canada and Ontario to subsidize the $122 million pipeline 'bridge' across northern Ontario in order to make it possible to put the proposal into effect."

70-percent Canadian ownership

Finally, McMahon disclosed that his proposed line would export gas at Emerson at a rate of 400 million cubic feet per day to Northern Natural Gas Company, American Natural Gas Company, and People's Gas, Light and Coke Company. "These companies are in a position to pay the best price for surplus Canadian Gas to supplement their supplies," McMahon said, since their existing facilities obviated the need to build new, unnecessary lines in the U.S. region. "The best market for Canadian gas in the United States as well as the most logical one is the existing pipeline companies and distributing utilities in the great plains-midwest area."

Would export to the three-company group

Somehow, the McMahon offer didn't stay "private and confidential" very long. Almost complete details of the proposal were outlined in The Financial Post on April 4, just eight days after McMahon's visit to Howe.

The Opposition moves in

There were, of course, some questions in the House. On April 13, Diefenbaker asked Howe if he would table offers made by Gairdner and Company, a Toronto investment firm, and by Frank McMahon, for alternatives to the Trans-Canada project. Howe said he would table the Gairdner documents but that he had received no documents from McMahon. (The Gairdner documents were tabled, and that was the last that was ever heard of them). Diefenbaker made a second attempt on April 16 and again Howe replied that there were no McMahon documents; and a third attempt on April 25, asking for copies of "any memoranda taken or made since March 25th . . . of any discussion or discussions with Mr. Frank McMahon . . . relative to any offer . . . to construct a gas pipeline between the Alberta-Saskatchewan border and eastern Canada." Howe retorted that "when it comes to tabling memoranda of talks with persons or telephone conversations, I must take exception." Diefenbaker again pressed the question on May 2, asking both Prime Minister St. Laurent and then Howe if they had received a proposal from McMahon. Howe weakened this time, replying that he had "received no letter that I am free to table in this House." On being pressured, he added that "if I have received a letter it is marked personal and confidential and that being the case I am not prepared to do anything about it."

The following day, Howe announced in the House that he had been in touch with McMahon by telephone and that McMahon had "agreed to allow me to remove the 'private and confidential' from his letters". This being the case, Howe said he was tabling all the McMahon correspondence. By this time, however, the offer was academic. Within an hour of the telephone conversation, McMahon had wired Howe withdrawing his offer to build the pipeline.

The Opposition parties, led by Diefenbaker, moved in to nail Howe, charging him with having misled the House. Howe's defence was that he had no documents or offers to the government from McMahon since he considered that letters to him marked "private and confidential" were neither offers to the government, nor documents. Howe's argument may have been somewhat strained, but he stuck to it, severely criticized, both in the House and in the press.

Mrs. Ann Shipley, the Liberal member for Temiskaming, was one of the few to rise to Howe's support over the McMahon correspondence. "There is something rather peculiar about that proposal," said Mrs. Shipley. "Here is correspondence, marked personal and confidential, in the hands of our minister concerned. But what happens in the meantime? Members of the opposition obviously have complete copies of that document. The newspapers in Canada obviously have full copies of that information. There is something peculiar about that. When it became evident that the confidential information had been given freely to everyone else, our minister said it must be released. What happened? Within five minutes the offer was withdrawn . . . it seems extremely peculiar to me."

Whether Howe's argument that it would have been a breach of trust to acknowledge the proposal, was his real motivation in declaring that there were no McMahon "documents" to table, or whether he simply wanted to keep the proposal hidden, may always be a matter of conjecture. There were compelling reasons why Howe may not have given McMahon's offer serious consideration. Only Trans-Canada had the necessary government authorizations from both Alberta and Canada, purchase contracts from the producers, sales contracts with the utility customers, a U.S. export customer with a pending application well advanced before the U.S. Federal Power Commission, a supply of pipe under contract at a time when there was a severe shortage of this material for pipeline construction, and detailed engineering work completed. McMahon had none of these. To obtain them would have taken at least a year, and possibly two years, if he could obtain them at all. The government of Ontario had concluded that there were no alternatives to the Trans-Canada project which could be put into effect without great delay.

Before McMahon's proposal had run its course, Howe was confronted with the next problem in the saga of Trans-Canada Pipe Lines. Once again there was speculation in the newspapers, this time to the effect that the government was planning to lend $70 million or more to Trans-Canada. On May 1, Diefenbaker asked the Prime Minister if there was any truth in these reports, "and on what constitutional basis such an arrangement could be made without legislative authority of Parliament." Prime Minister St. Laurent replied that no such arrangements could be made without Parliamentary authority, and that when there was anything of substance to communicate, Parliament would hear of it from the government. Hon. Earl Rowe demanded: "Is the report in the paper true, or not? " The Prime Minister replied: "I am not going to say anything one way or the other to encourage such speculation in the newspapers."

Speculation or not, the newspapers had the correct story. Despite the fact that the government had undertaken to build the $118 million "bridge" across northern Ontario, Trans-Canada had still not been able to raise the interim financing with which to pay for that

Loan speculated

year's construction from Alberta at least as far east as Winnipeg. The problem was the slow progress which Tennessee Gas was encountering in its application before the U.S. authorities to import gas from Trans-Canada at Emerson. Without this sales outlet, the money markets were reluctant to advance the funds.

Howe's solution was to have the proposed Northern Ontario Pipe Line Crown Corporation advance a loan to Trans-Canada of up to $80 million or 90 percent of the construction cost. The loan was to be repayable in less than a year. The Crown corporation would not complete construction of its segment of the line in Ontario until 1957, and by that time Trans-Canada would have paid back the $80 million. In this manner, assuming all went well, the Crown corporation would not require more funds than had originally been anticipated, but Parliament's approval to make the loan would still be required. If Trans-Canada failed to complete the line as far as Winnipeg by the end of 1956, or to repay the loan by March 31, 1957, the government would take over the entire project, lock, stock and compressor stations. Trans-Canada's backers, in that event, would be completely out of the picture, and out of pocket to the extent of perhaps $20 million.

Filibuster starts

Howe disclosed his plan in a statement immediately after the opening of Parliament on May 8. He then tabled a resolution concerning the incorporation of the Crown company. It was couched in "somewhat broader terms" than that of March 15, to provide the authority for the Crown corporation to advance the money to Trans-Canada under the terms just outlined. In its haste, the government had made a minor slip, upon which the opposition was quick to pounce. The CCF and Conservatives argued that the amended resolution was in fact a new resolution which duplicated the earlier one introduced by Howe on March 16, and that the earlier resolution must be acted upon first. The result was a fight over procedures which lasted a week, a delaying action which everyone had recognized as such. The filibuster had started.

A prolonged filibuster could thwart the planned 1956 construction program on the Trans-Canada line. Howe and the government of Canada felt it urgent that construction get under way that year, and the Alberta, Manitoba and Ontario governments felt the same way. Alberta Premier Ernest Manning had written to the Prime Minister to express concern "over the serious threat to the whole national gas development and gas utilization program occasioned by the repeated frustrations and delays that have attended the proposed Trans-Canada pipeline project . . . any further delay in commencing at least the western portion of the line may well prove disastrous to the entire project." Manitoba Premier Douglas Campbell, in a letter to the Prime Minister, had declared that "it is imperative that construction of the pipeline between Alberta and Winnipeg be completed this year." Ontario Provincial Treasurer Dana Porter, writing to Howe, claimed that "further delays in the construction of this project would have very adverse consequences. Time has become of the essence. Every day's delay invites the most serious consequences to the development of Ontario, and to the national economy. In these circumstances, it would appear essential that the western section of the line be completed during the year 1956."

Premiers urge action

To complete the line to Winnipeg in 1956, Trans-Canada had said that it would need to start construction not later than July 1. In order to get construction actually started by that date, it would need to have the proposals which Howe had before Parliament completed and approved by June 7. It was mid-May. That left three weeks in which to have the Act incorporating the Northern Ontario Pipe Line Corporation cleared through the House. Social Credit, with its Alberta members, was the only party which supported the government's proposal. The Conservatives and CCF were determined to do all in their power to delay passage of the Act. These were the circumstances under which the Liberal government used the most extraordinary measures ever employed in the House of Commons to ram its legislation through in the shortest possible time and with the least possible debate.

It was three p.m. on May 15 and the clerk of the House had just completed reading a resolution providing for the creation of the Northern Ontario Pipe Line Corporation with power to lend up to $80 million to Trans-Canada Pipe Lines.

Howe moves closure

C. D. Howe rose to move "that at this sitting of the committee of the whole on the resolution respecting the constitution of a corporation to be known as Northern Ontario Pipe Line Corporation, the further consideration of the said resolution shall be the first business of the committee and that the consideration of the same shall not be further postponed."

In the history of Canada's Parliament, closure – a device for limiting the time which may be spent on debate of a measure – had previously been invoked to secure the passage of only seven measures. Never before had closure been invoked before debate had even started. In the three weeks of the pipeline debate, the bill was carried under closure through all four stages – resolution, second reading, committee, and third reading. Never before had this occurred. In the committee stage, closure was applied to each separate clause of the bill – another unheard-of practice. In addition to use of closure on an unprecedented scale, there were repeated incidents of what one observer has charitably called "strained interpretation of the rules," which seriously imputed the position of the Speaker of the House whose primary responsibility is the correct and impartial application of the Parliamentary rules.

"As a result of the use of closure at every stage, the virtual circumvention of the committee stage, and the strained interpretation of the rules by the Chair," noted H. G. Thorburn in The Canadian Journal of Economics and Political Science, "the bill was passed by the government's declared deadline of June 7; and it was passed in exactly the form in which the government had brought it down." Debate on the bill occupied 16 days, much of which time was spent in debate upon procedural matters rather than upon the measure itself.

Howe's motion meant that each member would be allowed no more than 20 minutes debate time during the resolution stage, that the debate would have to terminate at 1 a.m. and that the vote on the resolution would have to be taken at that time.

Conservatives and CCF against

Conservative and CCF members greeted Howe's motion with cries of "shame," "the club," and "the guillotine." Stanley Knowles declared that by the government action "this free and independent Parliament of a sovereign nation is bound by a commitment that the government of this country had made to a private company." Another CCF member, Alistair Stewart of Winnipeg North, called the scheme "a Colombo plan for Texas Tycoons." Donald Fleming, the Conservative member for Toronto-Eglinton, claimed that "the House of Commons has been gagged and fettered in this debate by a despotic government. This is indeed a black day in Canadian Parliamentary history."

Social Credit for

Only the Social Credit party stood in solid support of the government. ". . . both the Conservatives and the CCF served warning before this measure ever came on the floor of the House that they were going to filibuster and completely destroy it if they possibly could," said Solon Low. "Now . . . let nobody say the Conservatives and CCF did not bring what has happened upon themselves." So staunch was the Social Credit support that the Reverend E. G. Hansell was moved to assert that anyone who voted against the bill was following the "communist line."

Most important development of the day was a speech by Calgary Conservative member Carl Nickle in which he announced that he was going to break with his party and vote for the government measure; "not because I believe it to be the best solution but because the only other politically possible alternatives to it would involve more long delays, higher cost, a further denial of industrial and population growth, particularly in western Canada, and a far heavier burden upon the whole Canadian economy than the present plan." Nickle had long held the view, supported by most of the oil industry in Alberta, that the province's gas reserves should be sold in the closest, most economic market – the United States midwest – where it would return a higher price. If Alberta gas were to be moved to Ontario, then, in Nickle's view, it should follow the shorter, more economic route through the United States.

Calgary Conservative decides to break ranks

As early as 1953 he had taken public issue with the "all-Canadian" route policy, endorsed not only by the Conservatives but also the Liberals and CCF. Now, however, the all-Canadian line was at least preferable to further delay.

The closure motion may have reduced the time available for debate, but did not preclude the Conservative and CCF members from rising with as many points of order as they could find. Each point of order was defeated by Liberal and Social Credit members, but the process took time. The House sat throughout the night of May 16 and into the dawn of the next day. By the time first reading on Howe's bill had passed, it was 4:42 a.m.

Points of order slow proceedings

Second reading of the bill was moved by Howe May 17, but following limited debate and further procedural delays, it was not passed until 3:17 a.m., May 22, after Liberal House Leader Walter Harris had moved the closure motion again.

The following afternoon the House went into committee, the stage at which a bill, having been approved in principal although not in detail, is normally debated and voted on clause by clause, with each member free to suggest specific amendments. Davie Fulton, Conservative member for Kamloops, moved an amendment to stipulate that the Crown corporation could not lend money to Trans-Canada "unless the majority of its issued shares were owned by Canadians." Speaker Rene Beaudoin, citing precedents and procedure rules, ruled Fulton's amendment out of order. Stanley Knowles then moved another amendment, framed to conform with the procedures which the Speaker had just outlined as proper. "How long am I going to act as if the Minister of Trade and Commerce should not have his motion put forward from the chair? " the Speaker plaintively asked.

Speaker challenged

Raising his voice to be heard over the government benches which tried to shout him down, CCF leader M. J. Coldwell demanded a ruling on Knowles' motion. "I am wondering whether we are in the old German Reichstag or the Canadian Parliament," cried an angry Coldwell.

The Speaker ruled against the motion, and his ruling was upheld by the Liberals and Social Crediters.

Mr. Speaker by this time was clearly seen in the eyes of the opposition parties to be acting in support of the government measure, rather than administering rules with impartiality as required under Parliamentary tradition. (Dr. Eugene Forsey, an eminent Parliamentary authority, later wrote: "What would anyone think of a hockey referee who asked, 'How long am I to allow the visiting team to score goals? How many goals must I allow them to try before I let the home team have a chance? ' ") "I think the Speaker of the House is being placed in a most invidious position (by the government)," stated Alistair Stewart. Before the debate was over, the Speaker's position was to become far more strained.

On May 24, as soon as he was given the floor, Howe moved that further consideration of the first clause of the bill be postponed, an unprecedented closure-within-closure motion, which caught a breathless opposition by surprise and resulted in quick approval of the first clause. Attempts by Knowles, Diefenbaker and Drew to block the same technique a second time failed, and the second clause was passed. "What is taking place now is the rape of our liberties," cried Davie Fulton.

Passage of the third clause took a little longer, as opposition members led by Knowles, the United Church minister and former printer who displayed a superb mastery of Parliamentary procedure, stepped up the questioning of the Speaker's rulings. Rulings, points of order, questions of privilege and appeals from rulings, piled one upon the other to turn the scene into one of confusion and delay passage of the third clause for four days.

Fleming expelled

Tension and bitterness increased on May 25 when Donald Fleming defied the chairman and was expelled from the House for the balance of the day. The fight had been headlined across the country and there was standing room only in the public galleries on that Friday afternoon when Fleming, Howe and others were on their feet, demanding that committee chairman William Robinson gave them the floor. As he had previously, Robinson recognized only Howe, and allowed him to proceed with another closure motion.

Fleming remained on his feet, demanding the right to raise a question of privilege. "If you do not hear me now, Mr. Chairman, you are ... making a farce out of these proceedings and destroying the usefulness of this House," Fleming warned. Repeatedly, Robinson directed Fleming to resume his seat. Fleming kept demanding that he be heard. "This is not any way to run a peanut stand, let alone Parliament," Fleming remarked with disgust.

Robinson summoned Mr. Speaker to report the incident. A white-faced, tight-lipped Walter Harris, as House Leader, had the duty of moving Fleming's suspension. It was exactly the dramatic incident that the Conservatives wanted. "I knew I was ending my own career," Harris is quoted later as having said.

Fleming walked slowly to the door. "Farewell, John Hampden," shouted Diefenbaker, referring to the British statesman who had fought Parliament's battle against Charles 1. Ellen Fairclough, Conservative member for Hamilton, draped the Union Jack over Fleming's desk. Fleming flew home to Toronto for the weekend, greeted at the airport by hundreds of his constituents who cheered him as a champion of freedom.

Flag draped on Fleming's desk

The fight continued in the House that night. Drew moved a motion of censure against Robinson. Diefenbaker called it the "sorriest day in Canada's history." Howard Green fainted in the Parliamentary dining room, the first of five MP's whose health was impaired by the strain and emotion of the debate and the long hours of sitting.

It was much the same through the following week. On Monday, Prime Minister St. Laurent announced that once the third clause had been passed, the government was prepared to allow debate on clauses four through seven during the remainder of the week. It was a sincere attempt to reach a compromise with the opposition and revert to normal Parliamentary procedure. The offer was angrily rejected. "Freedom which is granted only by way of sufferance is not really freedom," said Knowles, quoting to the Prime Minister the words of an earlier Liberal leader from Quebec, Lapointe, spoken in 1913.

Prime Minister stays aloof

Throughout most of the proceedings the Prime Minister had remained aloof, spending much of his time with a book. Distraught at the shambles which had been made of Parliamentary procedure, he had no liking for this particular battle, and he was accused by the Conservatives and CCF as having abdicated his leadership responsibilities. "Through all this hubbub, the most arresting figure on the government side of the House was Prime Minister St. Laurent," wrote Grant Dexter in the Winnipeg Free Press. "He sat, impassive, expressionless, chin on hand, an open book on his desk, silent. His aloofness is almost unbelievable. Especially at a time of high controversy, Prime Ministers, regardless of who the House Leader may be, always dominate proceedings and lead their own party. Mr. St. Laurent does neither."

The afternoon of May 31 was one of the rare occasions when the Prime Minister did break from his aloofness to participate. If he failed to display leadership, he at least indicated his support for Howe and the pipeline bill. Final reading of the bill had not gone beyond clause three when the Prime Minister rose in the House that afternoon to move that "the further consideration of clauses 1, 2, 3, 4, 5, 6, 7, the title of the said bill, and any amendments thereto, shall be the first business of this committee and shall not be further postponed." Closure had once again been moved, with a vengeance.

Progress on the bill was delayed that evening when Colin Cameron, the CCF member for Nanaimo, B.C., rose on a question of privilege, and set the stage for the dramatic climax of the debate which was to occur the following day. Cameron had read into the record two letters which had that day appeared in the Ottawa Journal. The first, from Eugene Forsey, complained of the partisan behavior of the Speaker and declared that if the rules "are to be interpreted to allow only such procedure, or so many motions, as the government sees fit to put up with, then we shall indeed have said farewell, a long farewell, to parliamentary government." The second letter, from a Marjorie Le Lacheur, declared that the "debate in the house has long been a farce, with the cat-calls and jeers of the Liberals, and the systematic garrotting of the opposition by Mr. Speaker, making a mockery of this democracy."

Cameron maintained that the letters represented an attack not only on the Speaker but on the dignity of Parliament (as though there was still much dignity left in Parliament) and demanded a debate on this question of privilege. Beaudoin, increasingly feeling the attacks on his position as Speaker, was also eager for a debate in order to have these charges resolved, once and for all. He not only ruled that he would allow the debate, but went so far as to guide Cameron as to how to properly bring the matter before the House.

The Liberals were aghast. A debate on this could last for weeks, completely destroying any hope of having the pipeline bill passed in time to meet Trans-Canada's construction schedule. Harris stated that the debate on this question of privilege should not be proceeded with until after the House had completed dealing with the pipeline

*Toward
the
climax*

Crowd waiting
to enter Commons
gallery during
pipeline debate.

bill. For once the Speaker ignored the government's position and declared that "if members care to debate this matter . . . I am not going to object."

When the sitting ended that evening, the Conservatives and CCF were overjoyed. They had set out to kill the pipeline bill by delay and filibuster. Now, against all odds, it seemed that victory was within their grasp. In the ranks of the Liberals, there was confusion and panic.

Black Friday

The following day, June 1, had been recorded in the press as "Black Friday," in the history of Canada's Parliament. As the House met, the Conservatives and CCFers were jubilant — until the Speaker smashed their mood in one of the strangest developments ever seen in Parliament.

Drew rose first to speak. He uttered two words: "Mr. Speaker." The Speaker rose and interrupted him. "I have read carefully the articles complained of," the Speaker announced, "and I have come to the conclusion that because of the unprecedented circumstances surrounding this pipeline debate, and because of the remarks that were made in House by the Members themselves, it was and is impossible, if we are to consider freedom of the press as we should, to take these two articles as breaches of our privileges . . . Therefore I rule the motion made by the Honourable Member for Nanaimo out of order."

*Pande-
monium*

The Speaker summarily rejected demands to hear further discussion on the matter, and a vote was called on appeals to his ruling. Pandemonium broke out on both sides of the House. While the bells rang to summon the members for the vote, the back benches of the Liberal party exploded in noise. They banged desks, shouted, and sang several choruses of Onward Christian Soldiers; Hail, Hail the Gang's All Here, and I've Been Working On The Pipeline.

Opposition members stormed into the centre aisles. Coldwell and Knowles advanced into the forbidden territory at the foot of the Speaker's dais, where Drew and others joined them. Coldwell shook a finger at the Speaker, others shook their fists.

"Why don't you throw away the Mace," roared a Conservative MP, referring to the Speaker's symbol of office. "What took place in the dark? " demanded Earl Rowe, later Lieutenant Governor of Ontario. "We shall never know what sordid means were used to lure you from your path of duty," exclaimed George Pearkes to Beaudoin.

"I am prepared to take the responsibility before this House and the country for what I do," declared the Speaker. He then proceeded to advance a proposition which he admitted was "absolutely unprecedented." He stated: "I consider – and I have thought very seriously about this – that yesterday around 5:15, when I was called back to the chair for the purpose of receiving the chairman's report, I made a very serious mistake in allowing the point of order and other dilatory motions; and I feel the House should not suffer any prejudice or detriment on my account . . . I intend at the moment to submit to the House that, in my view, the House should revert to the position where it was yesterday . . . at 5:15."

The time that never was

The effect of the Speaker's proposition was to wipe out all that had taken place in the House of Commons on the previous evening. It was still all recorded in Hansard, but it was as though it had never happened. It was described by Arthur Blakeley in the Montreal Gazette as "the time that never was." The House adopted the Speaker's motion by a vote 142 to 0; the Conservatives and CCF declined to vote because they held that there was no question properly before the House. "There is no House," exclaimed Knowles. "I protest against this," cried Coldwell. "Parliament has ceased to function."

Cold fury was maintained throughout the balance of the pipeline debate, but it was anti-climatic and efforts to delay the bill proved futile. The first motion of censure ever made against a Speaker in a Commonwealth Parliament was moved by Drew, but the Speaker was upheld by the Liberal majority. The pipeline bill passed Parliament on June 5 and received Senate approval two days later, just in time to meet the deadline by which the funds for the 1956 construction were to be advanced to Trans-Canada Pipe Lines.

The pipeline debate marked the end of an era in Canadian political history, and the election the following year which turned out the Liberals after a 22-year unbroken period in office, merely confirmed it. The Liberals lost 66 seats in that election. One post-election survey showed that of the persons who abandoned the Liberals, 38.2 percent did so because of the pipeline debate, the major single factor cited.

Postscript to the pipeline debate

It also marked the end of the political careers of Beaudoin, St. Laurent, Harris, Howe and several other Liberal cabinet ministers. Drew, exhausted by the strain, resigned the leadership of the Conservative Party three months after the pipeline debate.

In the aftermath of the debate, the position of the Speaker of the House has been removed from partisan politics so that there can no longer be any suspicion that Mr. Speaker is an arbiter whose decisions and interpretations of the rules may be designed to favor the team in power.

The House of Commons also began to move slowly toward Parliamentary reform designed to preclude undue delays in the passage of legislation, while at the same time ensuring adequate time and opportunity for thorough debate.

Tanner's options questioned

A Royal Commission, appointed by the Conservative government following the election in 1957, strongly criticized the profits which Trans-Canada chairman N. E. Tanner and president C. E. Coates had made from company stock options.

In a preliminary report the commission, headed by Toronto industrialist Robert Borden, appeared satisfied that the stock options exercisable at $8 per share, which Trans-Canada had granted to Tanner and Coates (60,000 shares for Tanner), were reasonable and fair. Shares of the company were later offered to the public at $10 per share.

The commission suggested, however, that they should not have been given the opportunity to make large profits on these options once the government had stepped in to help Trans-Canada with an $80 million loan.

"The commission feels that when temporary financing by the government was assured and thereby he (Tanner), personally, stood to reap very large financial benefits . . . either the government of Canada should have insisted, as a condition of financial assistance, that steps be taken or Mr. Tanner should have voluntarily taken such steps as would have precluded him from reaping very large capital profits from the option for the purchase of shares in a company by which he was employed and which was being financed, in an essential part and at a crucial time, with public funds."

The commission's report was even more critical of a further option on 10,000 Trans-Canada shares at a price of $1 per share which Tanner had been granted by Trans-Canada's two founding firms, Canadian Delhi Oil and Western Pipe Lines.

"The commission regards this option of 10,000 shares as an unusual transaction. Undoubtedly it was given to Mr. Tanner as an additional inducement to him to accept his new employment. The Commission feels, that regardless of the fact that Trans-Canada later received financial and other assistance from the government, Mr. Tanner would have shown better judgement had he declined to accept this potential financial benefit. Such acceptance immediately placed him in a dual position. He was being reasonably remunerated by Trans-Canada for his services ($37,000 a year in addition to the

Signing of the
Trans-Canada
agreement.
Left to right:
W. J. Mulock,
David Golden,
Nathan Tanner,
A. D. Nesbitt.

other option) and as the chief executive officer of that company his first and only loyalty undoubtedly was to it."

Trans-Canada shares traded in a range of $20 to $38 in 1958, which placed Tanner in a profit position well in excess of $1 million on his options on 70,000 shares. A few years later Tanner left Trans-Canada and retired to Salt Lake City, Utah, where he became a spiritual leader of the Mormon Church.

However questionable may have been the methods and tactics which the Liberals used to ram their pipeline bill through Parliament, subsequent events have clearly vindicated Howe's decision to back the Trans-Canada Pipe Lines project.

Trans-Canada successfully secured its public financing early in 1957, and repaid ahead of schedule the loan from the Crown Corporation. Final weld on the line was made on October 10, 1958, and the first gas from Alberta arrived at Toronto on October 27. In 1963, Trans-Canada purchased the northern Ontario section of the line from the Crown corporation, which was then woundup. The line met the requirement of all the political parties for an "all-Canadian" system which would provide gas to the maximum number of Canadian consumers, including northern Ontario which would have otherwise remained without gas service. The desire to minimize the cost of

Loan repaid

moving Alberta gas to Ontario and Quebec markets has also been achieved by a second line which now moves additional gas by a shorter route via the northern United States from Emerson, Manitoba to re-enter Canada near Sarnia. The repeated charges that the pipeline bill was merely a scheme to benefit the "Texas tycoons" who were said to own control of Trans-Canada has proved completely unfounded: by 1970, Trans-Canada was more than 90 percent Canadian-owned and controlled.

Investment doubled

The original investment of $375 million in the Trans-Canada system had been nearly doubled by 1969 to $730 million in pipeline facilities, and was continuing to grow at a rapid pace. Sales in 1970 were expected to exceed a quarter of a billion dollars with net earnings of more than $20 million.

Tennessee Gas Transmission Company obtained approval from the U.S. Federal Power Commission to import gas from Trans-Canada at Emerson in 1959, four years after its application had been filed with the FPC. Trans-Canada has since obtained additional export contracts, and by 1971 was expected to be selling gas to U.S. markets at a rate approaching $100 million per year.

A final footnote on Frank McMahon's last-minute offer to build the gas pipeline without government assistance, predicated on the sale of gas at Emerson to three U.S. firms, was disclosed on April 30, 1958 when U.S. Attorney-General Rogers announced the return of a criminal indictment by a federal grand jury for violations of the Sherman Anti-Trust Act. Charged with having conspired to prevent the importation of Canadian gas by Tennessee Gas Transmission were Northern Natural Gas Company, American Natural Gas Company and People's Gas Light and Coke Company. Also named as co-conspirator, although not a defendant in the case, was Frank McMahon. Fines of $100,000 were imposed under the charges against each of the three firms.

Northern Natural Gas Company, which had first contracted in 1949 to buy Canadian gas from Western Pipe Lines, predecessor of Trans-Canada Pipe Lines, was still looking for its first Canadian gas supplies 20 years later. But it had not given up. It applied in 1969 to the Alberta and Canadian government authorities for approval to move Alberta gas to its U.S. midwest markets. It was also working on long-range plans to move gas from the Yukon and Northwest Territories – eventually, perhaps, from as far as the North Slope of Alaska, across Canada – to its market area. Working with Northern Natural on these long range plans for what could become the world's biggest natural gas pipeline system was Trans-Canada Pipe Lines.

Chapter Eleven

A short portfolio
of oil fortunes

> *"And wouldn't it be nice to be loaded with riches, not gained by freezing out some other fellow, by looting a bank, by wedding an unloved bride, by grinding the poor, by manipulating stocks, by cornering grain, or by practices that make the angels weep, but by bringing oil honestly from the bowels of the earth?"*
>
> *Sketches in Crude Oil, John J. McLaurin, Harrisburg, Pennsylvania, 1896.*

When John J. McLaurin described how nice it is to make a fortune by producing oil from the bowels of the earth, North America's oil producing industry was just 37 years old – still in its infancy – but already it had produced a number of significant fortunes. During the next half century or so, it would produce more of the great personal fortunes of the world's richest nation than any other single endeavor; more, in fact, than all the other endeavors combined.

Prototype of the American millionaire, of course, was John D. Rockefeller, son of a traveling patent medicine salesman, who founded the Standard Oil Trust in 1870, and who by 1913 had donated half a billion dollars in philanthropic gifts and still retained a fortune estimated at $900 million. When Andrew Mellon of Pittsburgh, who founded Gulf Oil, died in 1937 "he left only $37 million," according to an article in Fortune Magazine. By way of explanation, Fortune added that he had already passed the greater part of his wealth on to members of the family. In 1967, the Mellon family fortune was estimated at $3 billion (of which $1.9 billion represented the family interest in Gulf Oil), while philanthropic donations by Mellon foundations and personal family contributions were estimated at $700 million in the 20 years following the second world war. The Pew family of Philadelphia, which controls Sun Oil Company, had poured $170 million into their foundations by 1959. The list seems almost endless.

The billionaires

Among the more recent oil fortunes, those of Haroldson Lafayette Hunt of Dallas, Texas, and J. Paul Getty, who built his oil fortune in the United States then moved to London, are the largest. They were each estimated in 1967 in the order of $2 billion. Unlike the Mellons, the Rockefellers and countless others, neither Getty nor Hunt established outstanding reputations as philanthropists or public benefactors. Getty once reportedly installed a pay phone in his London residence because his house guests were making too many long distance phone calls at his expense. Hunt, whose fortune stemmed from the discovery of the largest U.S. oil field at East Texas in 1931, in 1967 still took his lunch to work in a brown paper bag, according to one magazine article, and kept a tight rubber band around his bundle. Once in response to a request from his sister to help raise money to restore the church at which their parents had worshipped, Hunt managed to scrape up a donation of five dollars.

Measured by U.S. standards, the oil industry in Canada has produced no great personal oil fortunes. A very few have created some modest wealth, but compared with their U.S. counterparts, they are mere paupers.

No really big money in Canada

There are a number of reasons why no really great fortunes have yet been spawned in Canadian oil.

The first is that the oil industry in Canada is much younger. While North America's first oil production was found in Ontario in 1859, it was not until 1947 that Canadian oil production became a really significant factor. By contrast, the U.S. oil producing industry took off in 1859, and has never looked back. It has had a much longer time to generate fortunes.

Another factor is that most of the great U.S. oil fortunes were born in an earlier era when income taxes were neither non-existent, or very modest. Most were established by the efforts of individual operators, at a time when exploring for oil involved little more than post-hole digging. Today, when finding oil has become a much more costly enterprise and wildcats are drilled as deep as five miles, exploration programs are almost the private preserve of substantial firms which can afford to risk millions of dollars. Yet another factor is the extent of U.S. risk investment in Canadian oil development. With foreign investment controlling more than 70 percent of the Canadian petroleum industry, the opportunity of establishing great Canadian oil fortunes has been somewhat restricted.

It may well be that the day has long since gone when it was possible to amass tremendous personal oil fortunes on the scale of a Rockefeller, a Hunt or a Getty. Or, perhaps, the really big Canadian oil fortunes are yet to be made.

A very few modest fortunes have, however, already been generated by Canadian oil, and some of them are recorded briefly in the following portfolio.

Eric Lafferty Harvie, Q.C., LL.B., corporate lawyer turned oil man, former honorary lieutenant-colonel of the Calgary Highlanders, patron of the Calgary Council of Boy Scouts of Canada, philanthropist and collector extra-ordinary, fits no one's conception of an oil tycoon. Born in Orillia, Ontario, in 1892, Harvie lived for decades in the same modest Calgary bungalow at the edge of the city's fashionable Mount Royal district, favors nondescript automobiles (he used to drive a Studebaker until they stopped making them), has a reputation as a penny pincher, and an intense passion for anonymity that has made him Canada's least known public benefactor.

The richest Canadian?

Yet if he is not exactly an oil tycoon, Harvie has at least amassed a greater personal fortune from petroleum than any other Canadian, and may well be in the running for the title of the richest man in Canada. Time magazine in 1952 estimated the Harvie fortune at $90 million, and by 1955 had escalated the figure to $120 million. Both figures could have been no more than wild guesses, and probably over-stated the amount, but outside of the Harvie family, no one really knows. Harvie's public benefactions probably exceed $20 million. But again no one knows, because most of his benefactions have been made anonymously.

What is known is that in 1955 Harvie sold his interest in one of the two oil companies on which his fortune was based for $20 million, and that just one of his many public benefactions involved about $10 million of Harvie money.

The latter was the Glenbow Foundation, established by Harvie in 1955 to collect Canadiana. By 1966, it had grown to a collection of nearly 200,000 items, ranging from art and archeological items to zoological specimens, which bulged the seams of half a dozen Calgary buildings and warehouses. The Harvie family's centennial project was to donate to Albertans the entire Glenbow Foundation together with a cheque for $5 million, through the Glenbow-Alberta Institute.

The Harvie legend

There's a story that Calgarians like to tell (it was first reported in 1952 in Time Magazine) about how Harvie acquired his instant oil fortune. The story goes that Harvie, as a leading Calgary corporation lawyer, acted for an English land settlement firm which had held the mineral rights on vast tracts of land in Alberta. The land company, according to the story, was financially hard pressed during the second world war, and in lieu of payment of $30,000 in legal fees Harvie accepted title to mineral rights covering some 250,000 acres. Within a few years, the big Leduc and Redwater fields were discovered, embracing portions of the land on which Harvie had acquired the minerals. He became a millionaire.

It makes a good story, but unfortunately it is only half fact. Harvie has never bothered to set the public record straight, probably not because he enjoyed the legend, but more likely because to set it straight would involve even more publicity, and Harvie has never been known to grant a newspaper interview in his life.

Harvie did acquire a spread of mineral rights from an English land settlement firm covering not 250,000 acres but closer to half a million acres. But it was not acquired in lieu of payment of legal fees; Harvie had never acted on behalf of the firm. It was acquired following an offer, the terms of which have never been disclosed. According to the legend – which was believed even by top operating personnel in the oil companies he later formed – Harvie simply lucked into his fortune. In fact, the acquisition by Harvie of what were then generally considered worthless titles, represented a heavy financial commitment. He undertook a bold and calculated gamble, and his "luck" was that the gamble paid off.

A bold plunger

"Eric Harvie was certainly never a penny-pincher," says Jack MacKenzie, one-time land manager of Harvie's oil enterprises, and now an independent Calgary oil man. "He was a bold plunger who never hesitated to pay the full price as long as he thought he was getting full value for his money." A lawyer who once headed the legal de-

Eric Harvie,
1930.

partment of Harvie's oil operations says that "Harvie preferred to gamble for the big play. When the oil business, to his mind, seemed to develop into a more routine operation where risk factors and profit potentials are carefully calculated by computers and where you put in 80 cents to take out a dollar, the attraction waned. He wanted something bigger, bolder and more imaginative than that."

But still he had a habit of frugality that became legendary among Calgary oil men.

"He used to examine every invoice," recalls one of his former accountants. "Once he questioned me about a three-dollar charge for a car wash. He was accustomed to paying only $2.50 to have his car washed once a week. I had to explain that since whitewall tires had been installed on his car, the garage made an extra charge for cleaning these."

Stories like this abound. There was the elderly couple who had served for years as caretakers on Harvie's ranch west of Calgary.

Reputation for frugality

223

When they left his employment, they packed up about five dollars worth of groceries from the kitchen, which Harvie deducted from their final pay.

When Harvie was first getting into the oil business in the late Forties, he hired a California oil man, Charles Barlow, to supervise operations that involved a multi-million dollar drilling program. "Dad couldn't stand to work for Harvie too long because of the lack of authority he was granted," recalls his son, Charles Barlow, Jr., a petroleum engineer with his own Calgary-based oil operations. "Dad quit several times, but each time Harvie just continued his paycheck, until finally a different business arrangement was agreed upon."

Eventually Barlow worked for several years for Harvie on a re- tainer basis, rather than as an employee, before retiring to California. At one stage, when Barlow was in charge of Harvie's development operations in the Redwater field, he was granted authority to author- ize payments of up to a few hundred dollars. He had already been authorizing payments up to many thousands of dollars. When in- formed of his "authority," Barlow's response was "hell, my cigar bill amounts to more than that."

Never a free-wheeler

Harvie never really fitted in with the free wheeling oil men of Calgary who were accustomed to verbal agreements and the formal signing of deals "after the fact." Harvie first wanted to examine every legal ramification in painstaking detail, and often had his staff renegotiate with third parties when they had seemed to have already just about completed a deal. Leases for oil and gas rights are normal- ly on a 10 or 20-year basis; Harvie bewildered the whole industry when he leased out on iron-clad terms a large block of mineral rights to Imperial Oil for 979 years, probably the longest term oil leases that have ever been signed.

Generosity to staff

The other side of Eric Harvie disclosed a paternalistic generosity towards his staff and business associates, several of whom have become wealthy in their own right as a result of stock bonuses and other merit awards granted by Harvie for faithful service. When one of the department managers of Harvie's oil operations returned to work after an extended illness (Harvie had paid all the medical ex- penses) he was told to take off another month for an expense-paid vacation for himself and his wife "anywhere in the world."

If as an oil man, Harvie was indeed a penny pincher it may well have been a habit acquired from an early stage of his oil career when, financially over-extended, he had to pinch pennies in order to gamble big. In the end, it became clear that Harvie never did operate his oil business in the manner of an oil man; he operated it in the manner of the lawyer that he was. It has been said of John Diefenbaker that, as Prime Minister, he tried to run Canada like he ran his small-town, prairie law practice. Harvie ran his oil companies in the same fashion. It may have cost him the opportunity to build the largest Canadian-owned oil enterprise. Or perhaps it was just that Harvie saw even bigger things to do with his fortune.

Some day the full story of how the Harvie fortune was made may be told, but even now it is possible to piece together – from records at the Alberta Land Titles Office, the Alberta Registrar of Companies and from a former official of the British Dominions Land Settlement Corporation – a somewhat more complete story than the prevalent legend.

How to make a fortune

Eric Harvie's career started in Calgary, in 1915, when, at age 23, he joined the law firm headed by his uncle, Dr. J. D. Lafferty, a former Calgary mayor (1890). His fledgling career was interrupted by the first world war in which he saw active service with the Alberta Light Horse Regiment, was wounded on the Somme front in France, invalided home, and later served with the Royal Flying Corps until demobilized with the rank of captain. (In the second war, he was successively troop leader, assistant commandant and commandant of the Calgary Mounted Constabulary.)

Along with thousands of other Calgarians, Harvie dabbled in oils during the Turner Valley plays in the Twenties and Thirties, but took his big plunge in 1944 with the purchase of nearly half a million acres of freehold mineral rights in Alberta. Within five years it made him a multi-millionaire.

Big move in 1944

Throughout most of western Canada the mineral rights underlying the surface lands have been reserved to the Crown, and – since 1931 – have been owned by the provincial governments. In Alberta, more than 90 percent of the mineral rights are owned by the government.

Small lots of "freehold" mineral rights are held on lands homesteaded prior to 1888, and on large land spreads granted to the Hudson's Bay Company, the Canadian Pacific Railway, and other railways. Between 1893 and 1930, the CPR sold some 23 million acres of farm lands in western Canada for $178 million, and – following the government example – on most of this retained the ownership to all minerals below the surface.

One of the larger CPR sales was a block of some half million acres in Alberta (including mineral rights) sold in 1906 to the Western

225

Canada Land Company Limited, which in 1925 became the British Dominions Land Settlement Corporation. Backed by English capital, this was a land colonization venture which sold farm parcels to settlers, and again retained the mineral rights.

When all its lands had been sold, British Dominions Land Settlement Company was left with a half million acres of mineral rights, but no minerals. In 1931, it organized Anglo-Western Oils Limited to which it leased the mineral rights, and set out to look for oil. It was a vain search. A few exploratory wells were drilled by others, all of which were dry holes, and by 1941, Anglo-Western Oils had been placed in receivership by action of the Supreme Court of Alberta.

Then the Alberta government hit the financially strained British Dominions firm with another blow, the province's 1942 Mineral Taxation Act which imposed an annual levy of five cents per acre on freehold mineral rights. For British Dominions, that meant a tax bill of nearly $25,000 per year.

Resident agent in Canada looking after the depleted properties of British Dominions at that time was Harry M. E. Evans, a former Edmonton mayor (1918) and financier. I met Evans in 1967, when he was 90, but still active in business. "Harvie phoned me in 1943 to inquire if the mineral rights were available," Evans related. "They were. British Dominions had no money, a big tax bill, and the mineral rights didn't seem to be worth much. No one else was interested in them." But Harvie was, and made an offer which was accepted. Terms of the offer were not disclosed.

Acquires mineral rights

Records of the Land Titles Office in Edmonton show that the mineral rights on 487,342 acres were transferred on January 17, 1944 from British Dominions to Harvie "in consideration of the sum of one dollar and other valuable consideration," the latter including the payment by Harvie of the back taxes, which probably amounted to at least $50,000. Harvie was suddenly in the oil exploration business, with a spread of nearly half a million acres in scattered blocks stretching from the Saskatchewan border to 60 miles west of Edmonton.

Two companies formed

To operate the contemplated exploration program, Harvie set up two companies: Western Minerals Ltd. was formed to hold title to the mineral rights, and granted an option to lease these, subject to royalty payments, to Western Leaseholds Ltd. The latter was designed as the vehicle which would raise the required finances, make farmout deals, and conduct the exploration and (hopefully) development work. Western Minerals would simply sit back and reap income from royalty charges on any production found, and from annual rental fees.

If the idea was simple, the execution wasn't. Raising the millions of dollars necessary to actively explore the acreage himself was out of the question, and Harvie had little luck in interesting the oil companies to undertake it. Just hanging on to the acreage and meeting the annual $25,000 tax bill strained his resources to the limit. In 1946, he managed to get $30,000 from Shell Oil for an option to purchase 300,000 acres. Shell never exercised the option and thereby missed a tremendous opportunity. In November of that year he leased 480 acres to Imperial Oil southwest of Edmonton near a wildcat Imperial was then drilling, its Leduc No. 1. On February 4, 1947, an option was granted to Imperial Oil Limited to lease 193,000 acres for an unheard of period of 979 years. Just nine days later the Leduc well was completed as western Canada's first oil discovery in 11 years, the strike that triggered the western Canada oil boom. The following year, Imperial discovered the even larger Redwater field, northeast of Edmonton.

Option to Imperial

The "Harvie luck" was in timing. The British Dominion Lands Company and its predecessor, Western Canada Land Company, had held this spread of mineral rights for 38 years, with no indication that it would ever be of any value. Harvie held it for only three years before the Leduc discovery placed an immediate multi-million dollar value on his holdings. In the three years following the Leduc strike his companies received $3.3 million in cash, plus annual rentals and royalty payments, on some 340,000 acres of his spread, leased out to Imperial and other oil companies. The remaining 145,000 acres, retained by Western Minerals and Western Leaseholds, included substantial producing acreage in the Redwater and Leduc fields. By 1951, the two companies held varying interests in 84 oil wells, had expanded their land holdings to more than two million acres, including both freehold and crown rights, and Western Leaseholds was generating net earnings of more than $1.5 million per year. In 1951, Western Leaseholds was converted from a private to a public company, and, with an operating staff of 100, appeared well on its way to becoming a major factor in the Canadian oil producing industry.

Harvie's early successes, however, were not sustained. A string of dry holes in Western Leaseholds' exploration program cut the company's net earnings from $1.6 million in 1949 to little more than half a

Luck in timing

million dollars in 1955. To top it off, Harvie lost an appeal to the Supreme Court of Canada against the income tax department which held that the $3.3 million received by the Mineral and Leaseholds companies for the sale of leases represented taxable earnings rather than a tax-free capital gain, as Harvie contended. Leaseholds had to pay taxes of $1.1 million on these sales, while Minerals had to pay taxes on some $200,000 of income.

Sells control to Petrofina

If ever Harvie had held any hope of building a major Canadian oil company the idea was clearly abandoned in 1955 when control of Western Leaseholds was sold to Canadian Petrofina Limited, a subsidiary of the giant Belgium oil firm, Petrofina, S.A. By this time Harvie's interest in Western Leaseholds had been diluted to less than 50 percent, but his share of the sale still netted $20 million – this time, undoubtedly, a tax free capital gain. Harvie, together with a few close associates, retained Western Minerals, which in 1970 still gathered a royalty of 10 percent of all the production revenue from more than 200 oil and gas wells. Western Minerals in 1970 was still drilling the occasional wildcat, and held an interest in more than four million acres of federal government permits in the Eagle Plains area of the Yukon where, in 1959, it drilled an oil discovery which 10 years later was still waiting for a market outlet. But for the most part, Harvie was no longer an active oil man and Western Minerals no longer an active oil company; they just counted the rent and royalty cheques that came rolling in each month.

The unknown benefactor

If 1955 marked the end of Harvie's short career as an active oil man, it also marked the start of a longer career as possibly the most generous, and certainly the most anonymous philanthropist in western Canada. And if his career as an oil man was unorthodox, no less so has been his career as a public benefactor.

When a four-ton bronze statue of King Robert the Bruce suddenly appeared one day in 1967 in front of the Southern Alberta Jubilee Auditorium that stands on a hill overlooking Calgary, students of the University of Calgary vehemently protested against this "monstrosity" which supposedly created an artistic blight on the landscape. But aesthetically pleasing or not, Robert The Bruce still stands resolutely on guard on top of auditorium hill. So does an identical casting 30 miles northwest of Edinburgh at the site of the Battle of Bannockburn where Robert's small band of highlanders defeated the English nearly seven centuries ago, the latter statue unveiled by Queen Elizabeth in 1964. Both statues, cast by Scottish sculptor Charles Pilkington-Jackson, were paid for by Eric Harvie, whose commission contained two restrictions: Jackson was to keep the price confidential (he has said it was "very expensive"), and no other castings were to be made.

The statues of Robert The Bruce somehow typify the multi-million dollar public benefactions of Eric Harvie and reflect something of the man himself. He couldn't care less about aesthetic values or art for art's sake; the 14,000 items he acquired for the Glenbow Foundation's art department are all illustrative records, and include not a single non-representational piece of art. The emphasis is on history, tradition and the natural sciences.

Robert the Bruce

The full range of Harvie's philanthropic endeavors is not known, but among institutions to which he has contributed in generous amounts are the Fathers of Confederation theatre at Charlottetown (he was chairman of Fathers of Confederation Memorial Citizens Foundation); Heritage Park, a Calgary pioneer village stuffed with artifacts from Harvie's Glenbow Foundation; the Calgary Zoo (one of Canada's finest); the Banff School of Fine Arts; the Calgary Allied Arts Centre, and Harvie's crowning achievement, the Glenbow Foundation.

PEI theatre

Glenbow Foundation

Harvie established the Glenbow in 1955, the same year he sold Western Leaseholds to Petrofina, "for the primary object," he has stated, "of researching, assembling, preserving and displaying the history of our Canadian west." It started out with a one-man staff which had grown, by the time the Glenbow was deeded to Alberta in 1966, to 60 people, and embraced not only western Canada, but every continent on the globe.

This fantastic collection included an archaeology department with some 57,000 items: an archives with 500,000 pages of documentary material, 73,000 photos, negatives and transparencies, 40,000 feet of microfilm, 10,000 feet of movie film and 250,000 feet of tape recordings; an art department with 14,000 items (including 1,500 research files); an earth sciences department with 5,000 mineralogy, petrology and paleontology specimens; an ethnographic department with 20,000 artifacts from North America, South America, West Africa, Indonesia and Australia; a library with 20,000 volumes and pamphlets; a military department with 4,000 pieces; a natural history department with 24,000 specimens, and a pioneer section with some 10,000 specimens of furnishings, clothing, tools, vehicles, and household, agricultural, industrial and commercial articles.

Glenbow is considered to have Canada's finest natural history and archaeological collection outside of the National Museum in Ottawa, while the library and archives constitute the most extensive source of reference material on western Canadian history available anywhere.

Glenbow's exotic collection embraces seemingly everything from African face masks, medieval armor suits from Europe and Japan, and a wardrobe that once belonged to Queen Victoria; to ancient automobiles, a 1900 steam-operated locomotive, farm machinery and a home-made aircraft. The library contains such valuable first editions as the 1663 printing of "The Strange and Dangerous Voyage of Captaine Thomas James in his intended Discovery of the Northwest Passage into the South Sea." In the military department are weapons ranging from ancient "cutting edges" (spears, arrows, swords, daggers and stone-age axes) to a cannon ball from the siege of Paris in 1871, a sled from the British Antarctic expedition of 1910, and a pair of pistols once owned by the Archduke Nicholas of Russia.

At the time it was deeded to the province, the collection was housed in an Indian museum at Banff; Calgary's former Court House building and its former public library; the former estate of one of Calgary's first millionaires, Roper Hull; a former church manse, and three large warehouse buildings, with an overflow of several hundred items at Heritage Park.

The Glenbow Staff

Almost as amazing as the collection itself are the people Harvie gathered to run it. There was Harold Hussey, hired as Glenbow's chief restorer after a magazine article described how he designed and built his own aircraft that flew cross-country from his native Bathurst, Nova Scotia. Anyone who could design and build an aircraft ought to be able to fix up such things as antique water clocks, player pianos and a 1912 La France fire engine. There is Mrs. Erika Valters, a native Estonian who studied the art of fine bookbinding in Paris in the 1930's but found no outlet for her talent after emigrating to Canada until she joined the Glenbow and created what is possibly Canada's finest book-bindery department. Rare editions, some 300 years old, some so fragile and tattered as to be unreadable, are restored and preserved, bound in fine leather with intricate, hand-stamped designs of golf leaf, and inlaid with such exotic materials as the skin of water snakes.

Donald King was a former store clerk, carpenter and electrician with an amateur interest in archaeology when he joined Glenbow in 1957, later heading the department which has performed more archaeological work on the western Canada Indians than any other organization. "Only time I ever went to university was to lecture in archaeology," says King. Mrs. Evelyn Hodge, a widowed grand-mother who went to work at Glenbow "to do a little sewing and mending ," stayed on to become one of the few real experts in Canada in textile restoration and preservation.

Captain J. R. Schmitz, who was hired to head Glenbow's military department when he retired from the Queen's Own Rifles in 1965, landed his job as a result of a casual conversation with a complete stranger. Schmitz, while still with the QOR, assisted the Glenbow Foundation in arranging a display of historical military items at the Calgary Stampede. Showing the display to a visitor one day, Schmitz remarked that when he retired he intended joining the Glenbow Foundation to head up its military section as a separate division. It was then a part of the "agricultural and pioneer" section. "That's nice," the visitor told Schmitz. "I'm Eric Harvie. Let me know when you're ready to come to work for me."

When the Harvie family donated the Glenbow Foundation to the province, through the Glenbow Alberta Institute which was incorporated by a special act of the legislature, cost of the collection was listed at nearly $3 million. The real value has been estimated as high as $10 million, in part reflecting the vast number of items that were donated by Albertans. Almost anything they cared to donate, from democrat buggies to faded photographs, was welcomed by the Glenbow.

A $10 million gift

The total contribution by the Harvie family was also probably close to $10 million. There was the $3 million invested by Harvie in the collection and the buildings to house them; the cost of operating the foundation for a period of 11 years, and the cheque for $5 million which was donated along with the foundation's entire assets. The Alberta government made an additional $5 million grant to the new Alberta Glenbow Institute, and also undertook to provide $100,000 a year toward the annual operating expenses. The ultimate objective is believed to be two major new museums in Calgary and Edmonton, and a host of satellite museums throughout the province. That way it might be possible some day to display the collection. Up until the time the Glenbow Foundation was deeded to the province, less than 10 percent of its collection had been publicly displayed.

In the little niche in history that Eric Harvie has carved for himself, there is small danger that he will ever be recorded as an oil tycoon. Long after his last well has pumped its last barrel of oil, the collection that his Glenbow Foundation started will probably still be growing. Some such title as "patron of Canadian heritage" would probably be far more to Harvie's liking, and more accurate too.

Wildcatter R. A. Brown, Jr.

Robert Arthur Brown, Jr. knows how to use leverage as effectively as anyone in Canada. Leverage is the technique by which financiers and entrepreneurs are able to control money and assets far in excess of their own net worth. Brown has been able to use the leverage technique with consummate skill to build one of the largest Canadian-controlled oil producing companies. By use of leverage, Brown has been able to utilize an indirect interest of some eight percent to achieve firm control of Home Oil Company Limited, with book-value assets of $213 million at the end of 1968.

"I have an effective arrangement with the senior employees who manage the operations of Home Oil," Brown has said. "I find the money, and they find the oil."

In his father's footsteps

Following in his father's footsteps, Brown has been looking for money for more than 30 years, in increasingly large amounts. In the 1930's Brown Sr. and his associates were looking for money in units of tens of thousands of dollars to finance the drilling of a single wildcat well on the flank of the Turner Valley field southwest of Calgary. By 1969, Brown was looking for money in units of tens of millions of dollars, to finance wildcat operations which ranged from the North Sea off the coast of England to the Arctic coastal plain on the northern fringe of Alaska, as well as across western Canada.

Brown was 21 in 1936 when he left the University of Alberta in Edmonton, where he had been a commerce student, to work with his father. R. A. Brown Sr. and his two partners, George M. Bell and J. W. Moyer, were drilling on a 60-acre lease at the edge of the Turner Valley field which was producing large volumes of natural gas and condensate stripped from the gas. Brown, Jr.'s first job was driving supplies out to the well from Calgary. Within a few months after he had joined his father, they brought in Turner Valley Royalties No. 1 which discovered the large oil leg in the Turner Valley field and ushered in the largest oil field in Canada until the Leduc discovery, 11 years later.

Finding money was difficult, in the middle of that depression era, and to get the capital they required the Brown group devised a royalty system of financing. Under this system, a new company was formed for each well drilled, and royalty interests were sold until funds to cover the cost of drilling the well had been raised. Within a year of the discovery, the Browns controlled a string of one-well companies – Four State Petroleum, Royal Crest Petroleum, Three Point Petroleum, B. & B. Royalties, and several others – producing oil from the Turner Valley field at a combined rate of several thousand barrels per day. Brown, Jr. was president of B. & B. Royalties, and a director of the other companies.

"What this meant mostly," Brown has recalled, "was going out and raising money from anyone you could talk into investing a thousand dollars, or even less." It was his first lesson in finding money, and he proved pretty good at it. Eventually, the Brown group ran up a string of a dozen producers in Turner Valley.

Turner Valley

During the second world war, Brown served in Ottawa as a naval oil procurement officer, returning to Calgary after the war to find the oil business dormant. Production at Turner Valley had passed its peak and was declining, and wildcatting in western Canada had not produced another sniff of oil in the decade following the Turner Valley Royalties discovery. The Brown family's interests at Turner Valley were producing modest revenues, but were far from enough to sustain an exploratory program which would have a reasonable chance of finding a new field. Brown and some of his wartime Navy associates decided to launch an import agency, obtaining franchises to import electrical appliances from the United States. The venture turned out to be a financial flop after the federal government slapped an embargo on certain imports, including electrical appliances, because of a serious deficit in the nation's balance of trade.

Imperial Oil's Leduc discovery in 1947 re-kindled the exploration fever in western Canada, and Brown was soon back into oil up to his boot-tops. On the death of his father in May, 1948, he assumed command of the Brown Family's oil interests, most of which by that time had been consolidated into Federated Petroleums and United Oils, the latter largely a holding company which was the key to control of Federated.

A new ball game

This was a different ball game from Turner Valley. To get a piece of the action required finding money not by the thousands, but by the millions of dollars. Brown set out to do just that. He suspected that Imperial Oil, faced with a need for large sums to finance development at Leduc, might be willing to sell its producing properties at Turner Valley. Brown obtained an agreement to buy a portion of Imperial's Turner Valley interests, involving 38 wells. He then persuaded the Canadian Bank of Commerce to loan him the total amount of the purchase price, $8 million, the largest oil loan that had ever been made by a Canadian bank to that time. With the increased flow of revenue from the new Turner Valley wells, Brown was able to launch Federated on an aggressive drilling program, participating in development of production at Leduc and Redwater.

Brown next took an envious look at Home Oil Company, which had its offices on the same floor as Brown and his staff of half a dozen in Calgary's old Lougheed Building.

Home Oil

Home was one of the pioneer operators in the Turner Valley field. Organized in 1924 by Major James Lowery, an Edmonton lawyer, with 800 acres of leases, and with $275,000 working capital provided by a group of Vancouver backers, it had developed gas and condensate production in the field prior to the discovery of the oil leg by the Brown group. Flushed with their initial success at Turner Valley, the Home Oil directors envisioned the possibility of an integrated operation, and in 1928 set up Home Oil Distributors, a retail gasoline marketing operation in the Vancouver area. By 1929, the original $275,000 subscription in Home had a market value of $25 million, and Home shares traded at up to $24. Later that year, following the stock market crash, Home shares nose-dived to $3.

Burdened with debt in the midst of the depression, Lowery bailed out Home in 1934 with the sale of its producing Turner Valley acreage to Imperial Oil, but retained the non-producing exploratory acreage. The following year Home sold its west coast marketing operations to Imperial Oil for $66,000, and 35 years later, Home Oil Distributors was still operated as a wholly-owned Imperial subsidiary. During the next couple of years Home participated in a few British Columbia mining ventures, but was relatively inactive.

Home returned to the Turner Valley field following the oil discovery by Brown Sr. and his associates, extending the oil producing area several miles to the north. Home completed three times as many oil wells at Turner Valley as the Brown interests, and for a few years until the Leduc discovery it was the largest oil producer in Canada.

1950
takeover

Home Oil, in 1950, was a modest but prosperous company with a steady flow of revenue, and under conservative management it was not about to risk its assets in a lot of wildcatting. Brown reckoned that if he could find the money to obtain control of Home Oil he could make more aggressive use of the company's revenue flow. Back to the bank for further loans; then Brown started buying shares of Home stock on the open market. By late 1952 he had acquired effective control of Home. Three years later he merged his Federated Petroleum into Home Oil and further consolidated his position.

Under Brown's bold leadership, Home became one of the most successful wildcatters in Canada with a string of discoveries, including Canada's second largest oil field at Swan Hills in 1957.

234

An early photo
of R. A. Brown, Jr.
and R. A. Brown, Sr.

With Home in the fold, Brown had still not satiated his hunger to buy, and next set his sights on the free world's longest natural gas pipeline, the $500 million system of Trans-Canada Pipe Lines. Brown talked to his bankers once more, and in 1957 Home started buying Trans-Canada shares. Three years and $38 million later, Home was the largest single shareholder in Trans-Canada, with a 14 percent interest. Later, however, Canadian Pacific Investments started buying Trans-Canada shares and by 1967 had wound up with a larger interest than Home.

Brown's control of Home Oil is held through the Cygnus Corporation Limited, a holding company whose principal asset consists of shares of Home Oil. Brown, at mid-1969, held 42 percent of the equity ownership in Cygnus, an investment worth some $16 million at stock market prices at that time. Capital stock of Cygnus is divided between voting and non-voting common shares, with the effect that while Brown owned only 42 percent of Cygnus, he held more

*Control
mechanism*

235

than half the voting shares. Cygnus in turn held 19 percent equity in Home Oil, but again because of voting and non-voting shares, it held more than 40 percent of the voting power. The shares of Cygnus held by Brown in 1969 represented an indirect ownership of about eight percent of Home Oil, leverage enough to provide Brown with firm control.

Last of the classic wildcatters

Bobby Brown is one of the last of the big-time, independent, classic wildcatters in North America. A short and stocky man with a powerful, barrel-chest build, and dark, kinky-curly hair, he wears conservative, blue-striped suits and speaks with a soft, gravel-grated voice. A hard-working, hard plunging, hard living man, he runs his empire from the opulence of his executive suite at the top of the Home Oil Building in Calgary, and hops the company's executive jet aircraft at a moment's notice for a business trip to Alaska, New York, Toronto, Tulsa or London. His bold plunges have often seemed too desperate, too risky, for fainter-hearted Home Oil investors who have at times been apprehensive that one of his bigger gambles might some day blow the whole game. In 1960, for example, when conditions in the oil business were none too buoyant, Home was $52 million in debt, operated at a loss, and its $38 million investment in Trans-Canada, based on stock market prices, was worth less than $30 million.

Alaskan gamble

Brown's biggest gamble was still being played in 1970. It stemmed from the discovery by Standard Oil of New Jersey and Atlantic Richfield Company, in 1968, of the largest oil field ever found in North America, on the narrow coastal plain which separates the Brooks Mountain range of Alaska from the Arctic Ocean. The Prudhoe Bay discovery, in the North Slope of Alaska basin, dramatically revealed the possibilities of Arctic oil reserves so immense that they might someday constitute a larger supply of oil reserves than the Persian Gulf area, which in 1968 accounted for 60 percent of the remaining, discovered oil reserves of the world.

The prospect of such immense Arctic oil reserves posed a serious competitive threat to both Canadian and American oil companies which were not represented in the Arctic. Home was one of those which were not in the Arctic play. With lightning speed, Brown put Home in the middle of the play, committing to a risk investment of at least $70 million.

Home's first step was to acquire, at a cost of several million dollars, half a million acres of leases on the Alaska North Slope within a

100-mile radius of the Prudhoe Bay discovery. Then Home invested $50 million in the purchase of shares of Atlantic Richfield Company, which had shared in the Prudhoe Bay discovery. Finally, Home entered into an agreement to spend a minimum of $11 million on exploration in order to earn an interest in an additional spread of half a million acres held by Atlantic Richfield.

Brown, by borrowing in Germany and wherever he could, had once again found the money. Now it was up to his people at Home to find the oil.

Turner Valley was no more than a modest-sized oil field, a fraction the size of many giant fields found later in western Canada. But seed money planted decades ago in Turner Valley by the risk plungers has nurtured and grown well, providing the roots for some of today's largest commercial organizations in western Canada. From Turner Valley came Frank McMahon, with Pacific Petroleum and the first major natural gas transmission pipeline in Canada; R. A. Brown, Jr., with his globe-spanning wildcat ventures; and Max Bell, with the largest newspaper chain in Canada.

Elusive and publicity-shy, Max Bell likes to work quietly behind the scenes. Least known of this trio from Turner Valley, he may well be the wealthiest.

Race horses, religion, gambling and newspapers have filled the life of George Maxwell Bell, a non-smoking, teetotalling health addict who could still run a measured mile in six minutes in his mid-fifties. A husky five-foot-10-inches, Bell has short, thick iron-grey hair that looks like a steel brush; a boyish face, with a ready grin; the trim figure of an athlete, and favors casual dress. Despite such accoutrements of wealth as a luxurious yacht, palatial ranch, horse racing, and hob-nobbing with movie stars and other assorted celebrities, Bell is a quiet, almost prim-living man whose idea of real debauchery, newspaper columnist Jim Coleman is quoted as saying, "is to have three flavors of ice cream in the same dish." Proud of the resourcefulness of his pioneer western ancestry, Bell likes to espouse the virtues of hard work, individual resourcefulness, free enterprise and the capitalist system. A staunch Presbyterian who donates generously of both his time and money to his church, Bell is an avid student of the Bible and horse racing forms, which sit side by side in his office.

Bell's two boyhood ambitions were to amass a fortune, and to become a sports star. Jim Coleman, who grew up with Bell in Regina, says his young chums called him "millionaire Bell." He never made it

Max Bell: newspapers racehorses and oil

as a sports star, although after University he played hockey with the Kimberley Dynamiters ("I was the guy who held the bench down when the other fellows went out to skate," he has said.) Years later he coached kids in neighborhood hockey teams, in his mid-fifties was still proud of his sustained prowess in tennis and golf, and was known as a fiercely competitive player who took his games seriously, determined to win. His prowess in accumulating wealth, however, is beyond dispute. Bell has said that his life has been one of striving for achievement, and money, in his view, is a means of measuring achievement. Measured by his own yardstick, his achievements have been outstanding.

A careful analyst

Bell's success is due not so much to his skill as a builder or manager of business as it is to his acumen as a gambler, or as an investor. In Bell's case, the two may not be so very greatly different. Bell's career as a horse race gambler was launched on a train trip from Regina to McGill University, where he was a student. By the time the train had reached Montreal, fellow student Jim Coleman had initiated Bell into the fine art of handicapping, and Bell was an addict for the rest of his life. Bell reduced handicapping from a sport or intuitive art to a science. A reputed mathematical wizard, Bell has spent a life time devising and perfecting his handicapping methods with all the thorough study of breeding, lines, performance and track conditions involved in the art, and is reputed to be one of the best handicappers in North America. Bell's approach to business appears to have been much the same as his approach to handicapping – thorough, analytical study resulting in an enviable record in picking the winners.

Max Bell's grandfather, George Alexander Bell, was one of the first blacksmiths in western Canada in the early 1880's, and became minister of telephones in the second Saskatchewan Legislature, a Liberal government. The anvil and blacksmith's hammer used by his grandfather still sit in Max Bell's Calgary office, a reminder of the pioneering spirit of enterprise which Max values so highly.

Max Bell's father, George Melrose Bell, started out as a postal clerk in Regina, later established modest wealth in the insurance business, then blew it all as a newspaper publisher.

Max, born in Regina on Oct. 13, 1912, grew up in the newspaper business. His first job was delivering copies of his father's newspaper, the Regina Leader Post. The senior Bell had acquired the Leader Post in 1920, and four years later was publishing four daily newspapers in Saskatchewan. After selling his Saskatchewan papers, Bell moved to Calgary where he purchased the morning Albertan in 1927, and in 1930 added the Vancouver Star. Max spent four summers working in the business department of the Albertan while attending McGill University, graduating with a bachelor's degree in commerce in 1932.

When Max graduated, in the depression years, there was no job opening for him at the money-losing Albertan. He moved to Kimberley, B.C., where for three years he worked in lumber camps and prospected for gold in the mountains around the Kootenay Valley, managing to garner a total of six ounces of gold, which was stolen from him. While at Kimberley, the enterprising Bell obtained a contract to provide 100,000 railway ties for the CPR at a price of 52 cents for No. 1 ties and 42 cents for No. 2 ties. Bell sub-let the contract, and re-invested his earnings in a one percent gross royalty interest in a wildcat test at Turner Valley.

Max returned to Calgary in 1935 to work at the Albertan as business manager at a salary of $35 per week. In March of the following year his father died and the Bell family was left with a bankrupt estate. The Vancouver Star had gone under, sinking a considerable portion of the Bell fortune with it; the Albertan was losing money, and wildcat ventures in search of an oil bonanza had taken more. His father's estate had left debts of reportedly more than half a million dollars, mostly due to the Royal Bank of Canada, which took over ownership of the Albertan. Subsequently the Albertan was purchased by supporters of Alberta's new Social Credit Party, and for a brief period became the official organ of Social Credit in Canada.

Troubled newspapers

At the time of his death, the senior Bell had been president of Turner Valley Royalties, which for two years had been struggling to finance and drill a well in search of the elusive oil column on the flank of the Turner Valley field. Bell and Brown each held a 47.5 percent interest in Turner Valley Royalties. The remaining five percent was held by J. W. Moyer. Financing had been accomplished primarily by the sale of royalty interests covering 70 percent of any production found, each unit of one percent gross royalty selling for $1,500. Max had purchased one of the royalty units from his profits on the contract to supply railway ties to the CPR. Three months after Bell, Sr. died, the well came in.

The historic oil strike at Turner Valley marked the turning point of the Bell fortunes. Slowly Max was able to accumulate some savings and by 1943, with the help of loans from friends, he had raised $35,000 for a down payment to buy back the Albertan. Within a few years he had paid off the full purchase price, repaid the loans, and had sole ownership of the newspaper. In the ensuing quarter century,

Turner Valley discovery

Bell's career was devoted to oil and ultimately other large resource investments, newspaper buying, and horse racing.

When Imperial brought in its Leduc discovery in 1947 followed by the even larger Redwater field in 1948, Max Bell with partners Ronald Graham, a Vancouver millionaire, and Wilder Ripley, was quick to jump into the action. By moving fast, the partners managed to purchase some choice leases in the Redwater field. Based primarily on the Redwater leases, Bell and his associates organized Calvan Consolidated Oil and Gas in 1951, which sold public shares and carried out an aggressive land acquisition and exploration program in western Canada for four years. In 1955, Calvan Consolidated was acquired by the large Petrofina organization of Belgium for securities worth some $35 million. After that, Bell gradually disposed of his oil interests to fish for even larger catches. Just how much Bell's profits in the oil business amounted to is his secret, but in an article in the Star Weekly in 1966 he is quoted as saying: "I've spent more as an individual and maybe got more out of it (oil) than any other Canadian I know of."

Largest single shareholder of CPR

Bell had borrowed heavily to plunge into oil, but that did not stop him from borrowing even more, in order to buy newspapers and go running after control of a pair of venerable English institutions: the 300-year-old Hudson's Bay Company and the giant Canadian Pacific Railway. Bell abandoned his campaign to buy up HBC, selling his shares at a handsome profit, but has wound up as a director and the largest single shareholder of the CPR.

In 1948, the same year he was buying leases at Redwater, Bell borrowed more to purchase his second newspaper, the ailing Edmonton Bulletin. Two years later, faced with major expenditures to replace the Bulletin's obsolete plant and figuring it wasn't worth the investment required, Bell sold the Bulletin to the Southam chain which operates Edmonton's leading newspaper, the Journal. Packing his money off to Victoria that year, Bell bought into first the Victoria Times, then the Victoria Colonist, and soon controlled both. Next came the Lethbridge Herald.

FP chain

In 1955, Bell and Winnipeg Free Press publisher Victor Sifton, both publishers of staunch Liberal papers, pooled their resources to form FP Publications Ltd. and purchased the Conservative Ottawa Journal. Victor Sifton was chairman of FP Publications and Bell was president until Sifton's death in 1961 when Bell stepped up to chairman and John Sifton became president. In 1963, FP stepped into Vancouver to purchase the Vancouver Sun from Donald Cromie. Bell had been attempting off and on to buy the Sun since 1948. For Bell it must have been satisfying to have a newspaper in Vancouver where 30 years before the Vancouver Star had bankrupted his father. The Sun also put Bell and the FP chain into a partnership with the rival Southam newspaper chain. Both the Sun and the Province in Vancouver are owned by Pacific Press, which in turn is jointly owned 50-50 by FP and Southam, the Province being published for Pacific Press by Southam and the Sun by FP. Both papers have their editorial offices in the same building, and both are printed on the same presses. It is a unique newspaper arrangement, and highly satisfactory in generating profits.

FP's biggest coup was in 1965 when it issued a block of shares to Montreal millionaire Howard Webster to purchase the Toronto Globe and Mail, Canada's most prestigious newspaper, and the largest morning paper. Webster had purchased the Globe and Mail just 10 years earlier for $10.8 million, and putting it into the FP fold resulted in a three-way partnership in the chain: Max Bell, the Sifton family and Howard Webster. The chain's eight newspapers (Victoria Times, Victoria Colonist, Calgary Albertan, Lethbridge Herald, Winnipeg Free Press, Ottawa Journal and Toronto Globe and Mail) had a circulation by 1970 approaching one million, out-distancing the second place Southam chain by an appreciable margin. Value of the chain's assets probably exceeded $70 million in 1969, although details on assets and earnings are not known since FP is a private company. Each FP member paper has its own, independent editorial policy. Some are Liberal supporters; others support the Conservative party. Bell confines his interest to the business side, except with the Albertan where he does provide some editorial direction. The day of locally-owned newspapers, Bell has said, "is a thing of the past. It just isn't possible any more. Newspaper chains help minimize costs, strengthen editorial resources, and provide a better product."

Toronto Globe into the FP fold

While Bell disposed of his oil interests following the sale of Calvan Consolidated to Petrofina in 1955, he has not exactly abandoned resource-oriented investments. In 1950, he stirred a storm in Britain when, backed by a group of associates, he set out to acquire control of the Hudson's Bay Company, which he calculated could be had for $6 million. HBC was grossly under-priced (just the money it had in the bank was greater than the market value of its outstanding shares),

HBC bid

but under conservative management it appeared to be just sitting on its resources. Bell was probably intrigued mostly by HBC's spread of four million acres of freehold mineral rights in western Canada, including valuable potential oil acreage. Control was within easy reach when he called the bid off, deciding that he did not have available the executive talent required to run the organization. But Bell did manage to prod HBC's British management into more aggressive development of its Canadian resources, and when Bell and his associates sold their HBC shares it was at a handsome profit.

Two years later, this time with $60 million in financing arranged, Bell set out to purchase a large block of Canadian Pacific Railway shares held by Britain's Westminster Bank, only to find that the shares were held in trust for a large number of European investors, and were not for sale. Bell kept an eye on CPR stock, however, and started buying in the early 1960's at between $20 and $25 per share. Within three years, the value of CPR shares had tripled. In 1969, Bell's holdings in Canadian Pacific were worth in the neighborhood of $15 million, making him probably the largest individual shareholder. As with HBC, it was probably the large natural resources interests which attracted Bell to the CPR.

Defender of capitalism

Bell is noted for his ardent defence of the capitalist system, which he views in the simple terms of the Adam Smith school of economics. In one of his infrequent public addresses, Bell has said: "I hew to this system as the most ethical device that has as its purpose assembling capital through the pursuit of profit, and is the only system that pays genuine homage to the individual in democratic terms."

Yet Bell is one of the few supporters of capitalism who has publicly endorsed the principal of a capital gains tax which, until 1970 at least, had never been applied in Canada. Most of Bell's fortune has stemmed from capital gains, and few would have paid as much had such a tax been in effect.

Bell has also been equally forthright in his defense of foreign investment in Canada, maintaining that it has been essential to the national economy and that most apprehension of foreign investment control is unwarranted. "Canada would be a mighty backward country without U.S. investment," Bell has said. Yet he has also recognized that there are certain sensitive areas, such as newspapers, which should remain Canadian controlled. It is characteristic of Bell that he argues that newspaper publishers themselves should ensure continued

Max Bell
with jockey
John Longden
and horses, 1948.

Canadian ownership, rather than ensuring this by government legislation. In 1965, FP Publications Ltd. did just that by petitioning the Secretary of State of Canada for approval of changes in the company's bylaws which would limit all ownership in the company to Canadians. In announcing this step, FP Publications said that this self-imposed control is preferable to government legislation "which in any way might subsequently be interpreted as a form of government licensing or state control."

Bell has been as spectacularly successful with his horses as he has with his business investments. Bell and Frank McMahon are joint owners of Alberta Ranches Ltd., which runs some 70 thoroughbreds, while on his 500-acre Golden West ranch at Okotoks south of Calgary, Bell breeds additional stock on his own. Horse racing is something like wildcatting; you can't win them all, but you hope to get enough winners to more than cover the losers. Max Bell has.

His biggest winner was Meadow Court, an Irish-bred horse which Bell found while looking through a catalog one day in 1963. Intrigued by Meadow Court's ancestry, Bell contacted an Irish trainer, asked him to take a look at the horse, and if he was impressed, to bid for him. Bell got Meadow Court, then a yearling, for $9,000.

Bell had earlier promised his friend Bing Crosby that if he came up with a really promising horse, he would let Bing in on it. The same offer was open to Frank McMahon. When Meadow Court was still a two-year-old in training, Bell advised his friends that this was the horse. Meadow Court the next year came in first at the Epsom Derby for a $23,000 purse. On June 1, 1965, on the eve of the classic Irish Derby, Crosby and McMahon met Bell at Dublin and exercised their option to buy a one-third interest each in Meadow Court. The next day, Meadow Court took first place in the Irish Derby, and a $165,000 purse. Two weeks later, Meadow Court won the King George VI and Queen Elizabeth stakes at Ascot, and a further purse of $93,000. In just three races, the horse which Bell had bought for $9,000 had won purses totalling $281,000. At the end of the 1965 racing season, Meadow Court was retired to a stud farm in Dorset, England and the three owners sold 40 shares in the colt – each share entitling the buyer to have one mare serviced by Meadow Court each year – at $31,500 per share, or a total of $1,260,000.

Backing winners – horses like Meadow Court, wildcats like Turner Valley Royalties, stock like CPR – is what has made the Bell fortune.

Neil McQueen: from Petrolia to Rainbow

The classic, go for broke, small-time wildcatter who risks his entire stake on the outcome of a single hole, or even a handful of holes, is almost a thing of the past – a character from the early pages of the oil industry's history. The chances are almost certain that instead of hitting an instant fortune his money will be poured down dry holes and he will wind up broke. Most of the go-for-broke wildcatters of yesterday died broke. Those few who hit, laid the foundations for the organizations which now carry out multi-million dollar exploration programs involving dozens or hundreds of wildcats every year, thus spreading the risk. No one bets the whole bankroll on just a couple of turns of the wheel – not any more.

Central-Del Rio Oils Limited was one of the go-for-broke ventures that didn't go broke. It started out in 1947 raising gambling funds at

28 cents per share. Ten years later the market price of the shares had increased by 50 times to $14. Today it is part of the Canadian Pacific Group of oil interests, one of the classic wildcat successes.

An evening rumor, bouncing around between the martinis and sirloin steak at the Calgary Petroleum Club, was the catalyst which set in motion the action leading to the Central-Del Rio venture. It was early 1947, and Imperial Oil was drilling a wildcat southeast of Edmonton at Leduc. The tests which confirmed the well as a commercial oil discovery had not yet been run, but rumors were spreading that Leduc had hit oil. When Neil McQueen heard the rumor he knew that it was time to act — and fast.

McQueen perhaps became the only living man whose connection with the petroleum industry ultimately spanned from the pioneer Ontario fields of Oil Springs and Petrolia to the discoveries at Rainbow Lake in northwestern Alberta in 1965. At the time of the Leduc discovery, McQueen had already spent close to 30 years exploring, drilling, wildcatting and prospecting throughout the length and width of western Canada, involved not only in oil but, at one time, in gold as well.

Second generation oil man

McQueen was born in Petrolia in 1900, and grew up in the cradle of the petroleum industry where his father, Alex McQueen was in charge of producing operations for one of Ontario's largest oil producers, J. H. Fairbanks. The senior McQueen joined Imperial Oil in 1915 to head Imperial's new exploration and production department, which had just been organized the year before, later becoming a vice-president. He set up an exploration department in western Canada with offices in Edmonton, launched subsidiary International Petroleum Company on its extensive exploration and producing operations in South America, and acquired control of Royalite Oil Company for Imperial.

Neil McQueen was just 16 when he first accompanied his father to western Canada and joined a six-man exploratory party which trekked into the Athabasca tar sands of northeastern Alberta. Three years later he was back again, and in Edmonton met a young Imperial geologist, Ted Link, who so impressed him that McQueen decided then and there he would become a petroleum geologist. McQueen enrolled for a course in petroleum engineering at the University of Pittsburgh, the only university in North America which offered such a course at that time. In 1920 he joined Ted Link and a field geological party, canoeing along the MacKenzie River and its tributaries near Fort Norman on geological reconnaissance. Later that year Link's drilling crew brought in the discovery well for the Norman Wells field.

For four years McQueen spent his winters at the University of Pittsburgh and his summers with Imperial field parties in western Canada, but he never did earn a degree from the university. "I spent six months every year on field parties with the result that I always missed the start of classes and the final exams," he later explained.

Geologist on Royalite No. 4

Even without the degree, McQueen got a job as a geologist with Imperial in 1923, and the following year was the wellsite geologist on Royalite No. 4, the well which discovered the wet gas in the Mississippian formation at Turner Valley. The well had been drilling intermittently for two years. At about 3,500 feet it was 250 feet into the Mississippian formation and on the point of being abandoned when it blew in with the largest gas flow in Canada to that time, a rate estimated up to 30 million cubic feet per day together with more than 500 barrels per day of condensate.

"We put a gate valve on the well to shut off the flow of gas, and then watched while the pressure on the gauge kept building higher and higher," McQueen later recalled. "Finally we figured we better get the heck out of there."

From a safe distance the crew watched the well to see what would happen next. The force of the gas was so great that it pushed the drill pipe out of the hole. "The pipe just started walking out of the hole until there was 60 feet of six and eight-inch pipe standing straight up in the air," according to McQueen. This allowed more gas to escape and relieve the pressure. Then the pipe just settled back into the hole. Later a spark ignited the escaping gas, and at night the roaring ball of flame from hell's half acre, as it became known, was visible 25 miles away at Calgary for several weeks before the fire was extinguished and the well finally tamed.

Into Mining

In 1927 McQueen left Imperial Oil and headed for Vancouver where he became involved with several mining ventures. Five years later he participated with a Vancouver group in the formation of Bralorne Mines Limited which, with McQueen as a director, brought into production one of Canada's most profitable gold mines. The property, near Bridge River, B.C., had been staked in 1897 and was held by bankrupt Lorne Gold Mines Ltd. Bralorne Mines acquired the property for 400,000 shares, paid off $90,000 in debts, and

Royalite No. 4
well flaring off
natural gas.
This well found
the "wet" gas in
the Mississippian
formation at
Turner Valley
in 1924.

spent another $200,000 to bring the mine into production. Price of
Bralorne Mines' shares jumped from a low of 50 cents in 1932 to a
high of $17 in 1934, and the mine which had been brought into
production for less than $300,000, ultimately yielded more than $90
million worth of gold.

"Gold was the only thing that was any good during the depression," according to McQueen.

McQueen returned to Calgary in 1939 to manage a contracting
firm which provided servicing work for wells in the Turner Valley
field, and for a brief period also acted as a consultant in charge of
field operations for Pacific Petroleums. McQueen was still operating
the contracting firm, Oil Ventures Ltd., on the day early in 1947
when he heard the rumors about the Leduc discovery. Next morning,
McQueen was first in line when the Canadian Pacific Railway's Natural Resources Department opened its doors. McQueen filed on
16,000 acres of CPR leases at Armena, 20 miles southeast of Edmonton, for a fee of 10 cents per acre. A friend of McQueen's, D. C.
MacDonald, also sought some CPR leases that day, but was too late
to pick up anything near Leduc. McQueen sold MacDonald, at cost, a
half interest in the 16,000 acres of Armena leases. McQueen and

*Well
servicing
contractor*

others later formed Central Leduc Oils Limited; MacDonald and his partners formed Del Rio Producers Ltd. Ultimately the firms merged into Central-Del Rio.

With the CPR leases tucked away, McQueen headed for Edmonton, to try to pick up more acreage. At Edmonton he joined forces with Art Newburn, a former driller with Imperial Oil who was also seeking leases, and with Lethbridge rancher George Ross.

The Leduc area is rich farming country, one of the early areas settled in Alberta. Many of the farms had been homesteaded before the government had started reserving mineral rights from acreage acquired by settlers. Thus while the government holds the mineral rights covering some 90 percent of Alberta, there were a fair number of freehold leases in the Leduc area.

"Imperial Oil people in Calgary had not yet received authorization from the head office in Toronto to pay any more than one dollar per acre for freehold leases," McQueen recalled. "By moving fast we were able to pick up quite a number of leases."

Launch of Central Leduc

The lease which got Central Leduc launched consisted of 160 acres obtained from farmer Andrew Pyrcz, which Imperial had previously acquired under a lease that McQueen and Newburn discovered was technically invalid. After first checking with Imperial to ensure that there would later be no litigation, McQueen offered Prycz an undisclosed cash payment plus the normal one-eighth gross royalty, and concluded the deal on the strength of a handshake.

McQueen and his partners then farmed out the lease for drilling to British American Oil, which drilled a dry hole, finding the Devonian reef water-laden. British American handed the lease back to McQueen and his associates.

"We figured that the reef dipped quite steeply and that a well a little higher on the reef would find the oil. We thought we were just at the edge of it," McQueen has said. Saskatchewan Federated Co-Operative Refineries, which wanted some production of its own for its Regina refinery, agreed with McQueen's theory, and took a farm-out covering 40 acres of the 160-acre lease, on the same wellsite as the abandoned hole by British American. The Co-Op agreed to pay McQueen and his associates a 70 percent royalty on any production. The Co-Op drilled 400 feet from the abandoned hole, and brought in a modest oil producer.

With a modest spread of leases and a 70 percent royalty from one oil well, McQueen and his associates decided to form an oil company.

"The thing that sold stock at that time was the name Leduc," McQueen has said. "There was already a West Leduc oil company and an East Leduc oil company, so we decided that we would call our company 'Central Leduc'."

Central Leduc Oils Limited was incorporated on July 11, 1947. It issued a total of 600,000 escrowed shares to McQueen, Newburn and Ross for the leases, and sold 400,000 shares to the public at a price of 28 cents to provide a total of $112,000 working capital. That was just enough money to drill one well, and it went into the Prycz lease to drill Central Leduc Prycz No. 2, which ultimately produced more than one million barrels of oil.

Central-Del Rio

McQueen's friend, D. C. MacDonald, later that same year formed Del Rio Producers Ltd. and Central Leduc Oils and Del Rio Producers operated as equal partners in joint venture operations from then on, with management services for Del Rio provided by Central Leduc for a contract fee. The two firms filed on large holdings of oil and gas rights, participated in several plays, and slowly built up production and revenue, but for years remained in the league of the penny oil stocks.

What ultimately proved to be its most spectacular play was launched in 1950 when McQueen filed on nearly 400,000 acres of permits in southeastern Saskatchewn where he thought there were prospects for oil production from the Mississippian formation. Central Leduc and Del Rio farmed out this block to Socony Vacuum Oil (later Mobil Oil Canada Ltd.) which agreed to drill a wildcat test, for which it received half of the 400,000-acre permit spread. The well, Socony CDR Ratcliffe, 80 miles south of Regina, discovered a small oil pool. It was not much of a discovery, and the initial followup wells were dry and abandoned. But it was possibly the most important wildcat well drilled in the province. It was the first to find any Mississippian oil in Saskatchewan, and as such pointed the way to the discovery of more than a billion barrels of oil in the southeast corner of the province.

Weyburn discovery

Two years later, in 1954, Central Leduc and Del Rio drilled their Ralph wildcat, 35 miles northeast of Ratcliffe, discovering what became the Weyburn field, the largest oil field in Saskatchewan. The discovery well itself was a modest oil producer, and with cautious stepout drilling the field grew slowly. Several years later, by the time the full extent of the field was known, recoverable oil reserves at Weyburn were estimated at 340 million barrels. Central-Del Rio's

Neil McQueen

share of this – about one fifth – constituted its principal asset for more than a decade, and lifted it from the ranks of the penny oil stocks.

Central Leduc Oils and Del Rio Producers were merged into Central-Del Rio Oils in March, 1957. Later that same year Art Newburn died. McQueen continued as president until 1965 when he became chairman of the board and John Hardy was named president. Hardy, who had worked for U.S. wildcatters Mike Benedum and Joe Trees, and had looked after their sporadic exploration ventures into Canada since 1938, had joined Central Leduc as general manager in 1954, just 10 months before the Weyburn discovery.

Following completion of development of the big Weyburn field by the late 1950's, Central-Del Rio set out on a land acquisition and exploration program throughout western Canada, developing additional production in new pools. In 1961 it drilled a pair of promising gas discoveries on a block of 360,000 acres near Rainbow Lake in the northwest corner of Alberta. Four years later, Banff Oil discovered the big Rainbow field less than two miles from the Central-Del Rio acreage, and CDR subsequently shared in a pair of the pinnacle Devonian reefs which dot the Rainbow-Zama region. But in 1969,

Weyburn continued to supply the bulk of the company's production of 10,000 barrels of oil per day.

Late in 1964, Canadian Pacific Investments, a Canadian Pacific subsidiary, was the then un-named buyer behind an offer to Central-Del Rio shareholders to purchase a minimum half million shares at a price of $8.70 per share. The offer was resisted by CDR management, and McQueen advised shareholders by letter that the price was "entirely inadequate." Canadian Pacific, however, succeeded in its bid, and by 1968 had increased its ownership in CDR to 52 percent. In 1969 the two firms merged, and Central-Del Rio, the continuing firm, became 85 percent-owned by Canadian Pacific Investments.

Enter CPI

Central-Del Rio had started, in 1947, with assets of $280,000. By 1969 its assets totalled $47 million, it had no debts, revenues were more than $9 million per year, and earnings more than $3.5 million per year. It was one of the wildcat gambles that did pay off.

Glenn Nielson came off a sheep ranch in southern Alberta to build the only integrated Canadian oil company which in 1969 was not controlled by one of the giant international oil companies. With headquarters in Calgary, Nielson's Husky Oil Company operates production, pipelines, refineries and marketing outlets in Canada and the United States, owned by shareholders in both countries and in Europe.

Glenn Nielson: Sheep rancher turned oil man

Born on the ranch of his Mormon father near Cardston in southern Alberta, Nielson was 25 when he took over the operation of the family ranch on his father's death. For several years he divided his time between running the sheep ranch at Cardston and seeking a sheepskin scroll from the University of Alberta in Edmonton, where he graduated in 1933 with a bachelor of science degree in agriculture and economics.

It did not require a degree in economics, however, to realize that sheep ranching in Alberta during the depression years of the Thirties was an unprofitable business. The price for lamb had sunk as low as 2 1/2 cents per pound with wool at four cents per pound, and in 1934 Nielson moved with his wife and family to Montana and a job selling oil products with the tiny Cut Bank Refining Company at Cut Bank, Montana.

Demand for petroleum products did not exactly constitute a seller's market either, but by working 12 hours a day or more, Nielson was at least able to sell enough to keep bread on the table for the family. No skill, experience, or training is more important to an entrepreneur in the petroleum business than the ability to sell, and in the depression-ridden Thirties, Nielson was learning that skill the hard way.

First refinery

Nielson soon decided it might be a somewhat more profitable business if he were selling his own petroleum products. With the help of several partners, he managed to scrape up enough money to make a down payment on the run-down assets of the Park Refining Company: four wells in the Oregon Basin field of Wyoming which were producing less than 400 barrels a day of heavy oil, and a 900 barrels-per-day refinery at Cody, Wyoming, which was shut down because the refined products could not be sold fast enough to keep it operating.

Concentration on heavy oil

Husky refining was thus born on January 1, 1938, with a total of 19 employees. Earnings for the first year were $50,000. Thirty years later, they had increased to more than $10 million.

Husky's success rested on two factors: Nielson's selling ability, which kept the products moving in a glutted market; and the decision to concentrate on a side of the petroleum business which others ignored. Heavy, asphaltic, crude oil, black and as thick as molasses, has historically been the least profitable type of oil production in North America. Refining of this type of oil yields relatively little gasoline, the industry's premium and highest-price product, but large quantities of asphalt, fuel oil and diesel oil. Heavy crude oil sells for about a dollar a barrel less than lighter crudes which provide higher yields of gasoline. Black oil, the stuff which few others in the industry wanted, provided the foundation for Husky's rapid growth. By developing specialized production and pipelining technology, and by learning how to keep costs at a minimum, Husky has been able to squeeze profits from the heavy oil.

"By getting up early in the oil business and staying up late, we made the refinery pay," Nielson has said. Markets were aggressively developed for the refinery's output of diesel fuel and paving asphalt, while the nominal production of gasoline was sold primarily through farmers co-operatives.

Navy contract

Nielson purchased his partners' interests in the organization in 1941. During the war he won a contract to supply bunker fuel for the U.S. navy. To fill the contract, he built a second refinery at Riverton, Wyoming, which was soon shipping a train load of bunker fuel to the west coast every day. Production from Riverton and Wyoming refineries reached 14,000 barrels per day before the end of the war. At the end of the war, a terse telegram from Washington terminated the navy contract, and shut down the Riverton refinery.

Glenn Nielson, seated, and J. M. Taylor, then general manager of CP Oil & Gas, sign an agreement covering mineral rights in Saskatchewan.

In 1946, Nielson took a hard look at another heavy oil area, the Lloydminster region which straddles the Alberta-Saskatchewan border. Several pools of heavy oil had been developed by a number of companies here, but no one had been able to develop commercial production on a sustained basis. Nielson figured that if he built a refinery here he might be able to sell bunker fuel for the steam locomotives of the Canadian Pacific and Canadian National railways. His decision was to build a plant "someplace where the two railroads come together." Backed by loans from the Chase Manhattan Bank ("which thought it was a mistake," according to Nielson), the Industrial Development Bank of Canada and the Royal Bank, Husky moved the pieces from the shut-down Riverton refinery, and opened a new refinery at Lloydminster. "My most satisfying experience since entering the oil business was to return to Canada," he has said.

On to Lloydminster

253

Within four years, capacity of the Lloydminster plant had to be more than doubled to meet a contract to supply 5,500 barrels per day of bunker fuel to the railways. In both Canada and the United States, Husky avoided wildcatting for new fields, instead sustaining its growth by continued development of heavy oil and a steady string of acquisitions, which included producing, refining and marketing operations. First public financing was in 1952 with the sale of 200,000 shares. By the mid-1950's, Husky had become one of the largest suppliers of asphalt products between the Rocky Mountains and the Great Lakes, in both Canada and the United States.

Corporate
organization

When Nielson launched his venture at Lloydminster he established a separate Husky company in Canada as a wholly-owned subsidiary of Husky Oil of Cody, Wyoming. In 1953, the Canadian firm was spun off with some of the shares distributed to the shareholders of the U.S. firm, so that Husky in Canada became a 60 percent-owned subsidiary of Husky in the United States.

The two firms continued separate operations for several years. The heavy oil operations, Nielson has said, provided "the springboard from which Husky was successfully launched into other departments of the petroleum industry." Canadian Husky extended its exploration and production operations beyond the heavy oil fields at Lloydminster to embrace an active wildcatting program, which led to appreciable production of light gravity crude oil and natural gas. The Lloydminster refinery supplied asphalt for road building throughout western Canada, and slowly a chain of service stations was built up in western Canada to handle retail gasoline marketing. The Canadian organization set the growth pace, and soon outranked U.S. Husky in oil and gas reserves and production, although not in refining and marketing.

Tough time
in 1958

Changed conditions in the petroleum industry brought a brief but abrupt halt to the growth of the Husky organizations in 1958. The economic recession of that year hit North American oil companies with greatly increased competition from foreign oil imports, soft markets, reduced product prices and declining earnings. Many of the smaller independents were being absorbed by larger firms. Conversion of the railways in Canada from steam to diesel power had resulted in a loss of markets for bunker fuel produced by Husky at Lloydminster. Combined oil production of the two Husky organizations dropped by 1,000 barrels a day that year. Refinery runs were down more than 2,000 barrels a day, and the combined loss on operations was more than $2 million.

254

"Husky's directors and management had no desire to allow our companies to become casualties caused by surpluses, and after much consideration it was determined that it would be advantageous to join the U.S. and Canadian Huskies into one operating organization," Nielson stated.

Result was that the Canadian firm acquired the U.S. firm on a share exchange basis. Husky Oil Ltd. became the parent organization with head office in Calgary, and Husky Oil Company became the U.S. operating subsidiary, with headquarters in Cody.

Combining the two companies created a more efficient, streamlined operation, and Husky had soon resumed its growth, based on a steadily increasing output of oil and gas production and a string of acquisitions of other companies, acquired in exchange for Husky shares. In the eight-year period following the merger, Husky's gross revenues jumped from $38 million to $153 million; assets increased to more than a quarter of a bilion dollars, and the 1960 loss of $2.2 million had been converted to net earnings of more than $10 million in 1968. The company's five refineries in Canada and the United States turned out 46,000 barrels per day of products, marketed in 1,600 outlets in 18 U.S. states and five provinces, from Ontario to British Columbia. Close to $20 million per year was being spent in a search for new oil and gas reserves which extends from Colorado to the Arctic coast of Alaska, from the continental shelf offshore from Nova Scotia to British Columbia.

Husky has developed a close working relationship with the giant Canadian Pacific organization, a working relationship which seems likely to grow. In 1967, Husky signed a long-term development agreement covering a million acres of petroleum leases in the general Lloydminster area owned by Canadian Pacific Oil and Gas. In 1968, Husky and Canadian Pacific Investments completed construction of the jointly owned 626-foot Husky Tower which dominates Calgary's skyline; the tallest structure of its type in North America with a revolving restaurant, cocktail lounge and observation deck at the top. The Husky Tower is the focal point of a $35 million development by Canadian Pacific which includes transportation centre, stores, theatres, office buildings, hotel, high-rise apartment and the city's largest parking structure.

Working with Canadian Pacific

Canadian Pacific Investments, meanwhile, had been purchasing shares of Husky on the open market, by 1970 had invested $6 million for 5 1/2 percent ownership. But effective control still rested with Glenn Nielson and his family with 25 percent ownership of Husky worth, at 1969 market prices, some $40 million.

255

Chapter Twelve

The big four in Canadian oil

Imperial, Gulf, Shell and Texaco are the big four in Canadian oil. In 1969 they accounted for 35 percent of all the oil produced and 70 percent of all the refined petroleum products manufactured and sold in Canada. They are all subsidiaries of international, major oil companies – three U.S. firms, and one Dutch-English firm. The remaining 30 percent of Canada's petroleum refining capacity is also foreign-controlled.

Large firms with global operations dominate the world of oil. They include American, English, Dutch, Belgian, French and Italian companies. But no Canadian firms. Perhaps one reason there are no Canadian-owned oil companies with fully integrated operations in Canada is that there are no Canadian-owned oil companies with global operations.

The big four in Canada talk of themselves as "family members" of giant, multi-national organizations. For each of them, however, the origin of operations in Canada can be traced to the efforts of Canadian entrepreneurs, well back in Canada's industrial history. They first started life here as Canadian enterprises, which were later absorbed. Their histories here are an important segment of Canada's history, none the less so because they are now foreign controlled.

The Great Canadian Oil Patch

Formed
to fight
U.S.
competition

The Imperial Oil Company, Limited — now more simply, Imperial Oil Limited — was organized in London, Ontario by a group of independent Canadian petroleum refiners to meet the threat of U.S. competition. It was a desperate attempt by the Ontario operators to avoid being flattened by John D. Rockefeller's big steamroller, Standard Oil, which already had monopoly control of the U.S. oil industry, and was aggressively extending its reach throughout the world. Within 18 years, Imperial Oil became a subsidiary of Standard.

In with
ESSO

It may have lost the battle, but in defeat it prospered in a manner it could never have accomplished as an independent. Under Standard's control it emerged as the dominant factor in Canadian oil, and 90 years after its founding was still the leading oil company in Canada. It was, in fact, the largest of all firms in Canada in terms of total sales (almost $1.5 billion in 1968), fifth largest in assets ($1.4 billion) and fourth largest in earnings ($100 million). It accounted for 15 percent of Canada's oil production, and more than a quarter of the total sales of refined petroleum products. In a larger setting, it ranked about 20th among world oil companies.

Supplied
20 percent
of energy
needs

Imperial's sales of petroleum products and natural gas provided approximately one-fifth of Canada's energy requirements in 1969, more than the output of all hydro-electric plants. It is the largest retail marketer, with more than 7,000 outlets from the largest metropolitan centres to the smallest Arctic outposts. Its $40 million a year search for new oil and gas reserves extends over the Grand Banks off Newfoundland, throughout western Canada to the shores of the Arctic Ocean, and beyond that beneath the Beaufort Sea. Its diversified operations embrace the manufacture and retail sale of products from plastic bottles, bailer twine and building products; to fertilizers, a large complex of petrochemical plants, an iron ore reduction plant, and exploration for hard-rock minerals. In income taxes, property taxes, excise taxes, sales taxes collected from the sale of its products, and payments stemming from its leasing of government-owned mineral rights, it contributes close to $400 million a year in government revenues, almost equal to the combined provincial government revenues of the four Atlantic provinces.

Throughout much of its four decades, until the beginning of the 20th century, the petroleum industry comprised essentially one product, kerosene for lamp fuel; one principal supply source, the United States; and one dominant operator, Standard Oil.

John D. Rockefeller, who founded Standard, was the son of a patent medicine salesman from Cleveland, Ohio, who billed himself as "Dr. William Rockefeller, the celebrated cancer specialist." Young John D. went to work at age 16 as a clerk with a produce firm. Pronounced Scottish-Calvinistic traits, inherited from his mother, made him America's all-time most successful businessman. He showed unrivalled business acumen, penny-pinching thrift in business, and charitable, Christian generosity in private life. His initial salary was $3.50 a week, and from his first four month's earnings his donations to church and charity, recorded in a ledger which he kept all his life, amounted to $7.50. Rockefeller had not waited until he was wealthy to start his policy of donating a portion of whatever income he had. By 1913, he had amassed a personal fortune of $900 million, and his public benefactions had totalled more than half a billion dollars. Yet he never lost the ability to pinch pennies, whether by reducing the amount of solder used to seal cans of kerosene, or by shortening the overlap on the iron straps which circled the wooden barrels in which Standard's products were shipped.

The Standard background

In 1860, at the age of 20, Rockefeller, with a partner, set out in business as a commission merchant, backed by a loan from his father of $1,000 at 10 percent interest. Soon he was involved in another business partnership which purchased a run-down refinery at Cleveland, and in 1870 he incorporated Standard Oil Company of Ohio, with three refineries.

Rockefeller set out deliberately to create an oil monopoly, because he saw this as the only means of stability in a chaotic industry plagued with ruinous competition, excess production and oil prices which fluctuated wildly, from a low of 10 cents per barrel in 1862 to a high of $12 per barrel in 1864. Buying every potentially profitable oil firm he could, Rockefeller soon had a string of Standard Oil companies, eventually controlled through Standard Oil Company (New Jersey), and known as The Standard Oil Trust. At one point in the 1880's, Rockefeller controlled 80 percent of U.S. petroleum refining capacity, 90 percent of the pipelines, and more than 90 percent of the marketing. He was, said the New York World, "the father of the trusts, the king of monopolists, the czar of the oil industry."

Creation of a monopoly

"It is fair to say that the Standard of the eighties was the largest and richest of American industrial organizations – the largest and richest in the world," wrote Allan Nevins in John D. Rockefeller. "The fact that there was not a drop of water (over-capitalization) in the stock was much to Rockefeller's credit in an era of atrocious stock-watering." It was also possibly the most competent, efficient and competitively ruthless industrial organization ever developed.

Trust busting

The explosive petroleum industry, however, was growing too rapidly for Rockefeller to maintain his monopoly. At the turn of the century, Standard Oil was still prospering and growing, but new firms were springing up faster than Rockefeller could either buy them or put them out of business, and Standard's percentage of the market was slipping. The end of Standard's control resulted from enraged public outcries against the trusts, monopolies and the business barons who dominated U.S. industry in the late 19th century. Standard Oil and Rockefeller were the focal point of the attack. The U.S. Government passed its Sherman Anti-Trust Act in 1890 and six years later President Theodore Roosevelt, the "trust buster," brought suit against Standard. In 1911, the U.S. Supreme Court upheld a lower court decision which levied a $29 million fine against Standard Oil Company (New Jersey) and gave it six months to dissolve its holdings in 34 separate subsidiaries (accomplished by giving each Jersey stockholder his equivalent number of shares in each of the subsidiaries). Operations of each of the companies were to be separate from then on.

Up to four billion barrels per day

With most of its holdings gone, Standard Oil Company (New Jersey) emerged from the 1911 dissolution a fraction of its former size. Yet by 1968, it had grown to nearly 12 times its size prior to dissolution, with revenues of $15 billion a year and earnings well in excess of one billion a year. Its world-wide production of some four million barrels a day was six times as great as total 1911 U.S. production. But no longer is it a monopoly. Where once it was almost the entire world oil industry, in 1968 it controlled less than 15 percent of world oil production and marketing. Prior to the 1911 dissolution it was owned by 6,067 shareholders; now it is owned by more than 700,000. In 1911, majority interest in Standard Oil was held by 10 men, and Rockefeller alone had 25 percent. No shareholder now owns as much as three percent, and the largest shareholders are not individuals but insurance companies, banks, pension funds and other institutions. The company's 15 directors combined own less than one-tenth of one percent of the company.

One of the assets which Jersey did not lose on dissolution was its interest in Imperial Oil, which now amounts to 70 percent.

The history of Imperial Oil is almost the history of the oil industry in Canada. Its origins date back to the founding of oil production in

North America, and there have since been few major developments in Canadian petroleum in which Imperial has not participated.

Canada's petroleum industry, spawned from the development of North America's first commercial oil field at Oil Springs and the nearby Petrolia field in south-western Ontario, by the mid 1870's was in danger of being wiped out by the burgeoning American oil industry. There were more than 100 refineries in Canada, most of them in Ontario and half of them in London, simple cast-iron stills producing mostly kerosene and lubricating oils. The "sour" crude of Ontario was laced with sulphur, and at its best its product was a stinking lamp fuel which, if it did not blow up in the lamp, produced a smoky flame. Some improvements in the refining processes helped reduce the sulphur content, but still by the mid-1870's Canadian kerosene had to sell at five cents a gallon less than the better quality American kerosene. American oil seemed to hold all the advantages. The sweet crude from Pennsylvania produced a cleaner fuel; new discoveries provided an ample supply; and the refineries of Standard Oil were larger, more efficient and far more economical than the maze of small pots in Canada. It was little wonder that independent jobbers in Canada were turning to U.S. sources, especially Standard, for their supplies.

Sulphur problem

It was mostly for survival under these conditions that 16 Canadian refiners — all but one of them from London — pooled their resources in 1880 to form Imperial Oil. The founding fathers contributed to the company their refineries, their oil wells, their shops in which wooden barrels were made from oak logs, and $25,000 in cash, which constituted the total of Imperial's assets. The original shareholders included some of Canada's first oil men. One of the 16, William Spencer, had worked with James Miller Williams in the initial development of Oil Springs, and had established his own refinery in 1862.

The real wheel in Imperial, however, was Jacob Lewis Englehart, who came from Cleveland in 1866 to make his fortune in Canadian oil. Just 19 when he started, he was probably the youngest operator in the Ontario oil patch. Englehart and Company was soon a substantial producer in the Oil Springs and Petrolia fields, and later built refineries at London and Petrolia. Englehart's refinery at Petrolia was reputed to be the largest and finest in Canada, and one of the best in North America. It was built on the site of a pair of previous plants, ill-fated as were so many of that era. Known as the Big Still, the initial plant featured a cheese-box shape still made of boiler plate instead of the customary cast iron, and held 2,500 barrels of oil, 10

Jacob Englehart

The Great Canadian Oil Patch

Above: Imperial Oil refinery at Sar
in 1969 — Canada's largest refinery
Opposite page: The Sarnia refinery
— then also Canada's largest refine

times the size of most stills of that era. It produced prodigious quantities of kerosene for a year and then blew up. It was rebuilt and when the fires were re-lit, it blew up again. Englehart bought the rubble that was left, and built a refinery that worked.

Imperial Oil moved quickly to rationalize the maze of refineries it had inherited. It closed many of the smaller ones, expanded the larger ones to achieve more efficient and economic operation, and improved its refining processes. Herman Frasch, perhaps the leading petroleum chemist of his day who later developed the Frasch process for producing sulphur from deep mines, was hired by Imperial Oil to find a means of making a cleaner kerosene from sulphurous crude. His method of treating kerosene with metal oxides for the first time produced a truly suitable product from Ontario crude, and greatly helped not only Imperial but all Ontario oil producers.

As the smaller plants were shut down, the ones built by Englehart at London and Petrolia became Imperial's principal refineries. When fire destroyed the London plant in 1883, the Petrolia plant became Imperial's only refinery. It was a $250,000 complex covering 50 acres, with an elaborate steam-operated pumping system which could

Petrolia plant

263

draw oil directly from nearby wells, or from the 100,000 barrels of underground storage. Six cylindrical stills with a crude capacity of 350 barrels each were heated by gas from the oil wells. The plant produced kerosene, waxes and lubricating oils. Ten-gallon tins of kerosene were shipped to markets in India, China, Japan, Australia and South America, while oak barrels carried Imperial's products west by rail and ox-cart to Hudson's Bay posts and east to the Maritimes. By 1883 Imperial had 23 branch offices from Halifax to Vancouver and its slogan was "Everywhere in Canada."

New capital from Standard

Imperial had to run fast to keep ahead of the octopus reach of Standard which was buying its way into Canada in much the same fashion as Rockefeller had set out to establish his monopoly position in the United States. By the late 1890's Standard had acquired control of three Canadian firms with refineries in London, Petrolia and Sarnia, and had captured a third of the Canadian market. To stay ahead of Standard, Imperial needed money for more bulk plants, distributing equipment, railway tank cars and refinery capacity. It was growing fast, but it had to grow even faster. Imperial searched in Canada and Great Britain for the expansion capital it required. From only one source was it able to find the money it needed – from Rockefeller.

Standard supplied the capital that Imperial required in 1898, and in return acquired majority ownership. The following year all of Standard's Canadian affiliates were consolidated into Imperial, which further strengthened Standard's ownership. Imperial's head office was moved from Petrolia to Sarnia, where Standard had purchased a refinery the year before. The Sarnia refinery was expanded and soon became Canada's largest, with a capacity of 900 barrels a day by 1900. Nearly 70 years later, with a capacity of 123,000 barrels a day, it was still the largest refinery in the country. Englehart remained with Imperial as a director and vice-president until his death in 1921.

The biggest by 1900

At the turn of the century, Imperial Oil was able to dominate the petroleum business in Canada with its coast-to-coast chain of bulk stations and its one remaining refinery at Sarnia. Imperial reckoned that its 900 barrels a day refinery capacity would be adequate for years to come. What it failed to foresee in 1900 was the impact of the automobile. In 1905 there were 565 automobiles in Canada, and three years later Imperial opened the country's first service station at its Vancouver warehouse, where a length of garden hose was con-

Crude oil
stills
at Imperial's
refinery
in Petrolia, 1883.

nected to a kitchen water tank filled with gasoline. By 1915, auto-mobile registration totalled 60,688, gasoline had graduated from the industry's cursed stepchild to its most important product, and Imperial was furiously building new refineries to meet motorists' demands. In one decade, 1909 – 1920, Imperial increased its number of refineries from one to five (with new plants at Vancouver, Regina, Montreal and Halifax), and its crude refining capacity from 900 to 23,000 barrels a day.

With a vastly enlarged market, rapidly growing sales, and dwindling Ontario production, Imperial established an exploration-production department in 1914 and set out to meet its supply problem on three fronts: by building a 153-mile pipeline to link its Sarnia refinery with oil fields in Ohio; establishing a subsidiary to develop oil production in South America, and launching an exploration campaign in western Canada which took 33 years to yield a major, commercial oil find.

Standard Oil of New Jersey, having been deprived of its west coast oil production by the 1911 dissolution order of the U.S. Supreme

265

South American ventures

Court, needed a Pacific crude supply source to compete for markets in the Orient. Imperial needed oil for its Canadian refineries. The result was the incorporation of International Petroleum Company in 1914 as a subsidiary of Imperial. International purchased a 347,000-acre estate (Hacienda La Brena y Parinas) in Peru from two English firms. In the following 33 years it drilled 2,200 oil wells and produced 280 million barrels of oil. In 1920, International Petroleum purchased a 2,000-acre concession in Columbia from famed U.S. wildcatters Mike Benedum and Joe Trees, who had discovered oil on the property two years earlier. International built a 350-mile jungle pipeline to the coast and by 1947 had produced more than 300 million barrels of oil from this concession.

The search for oil in western Canada was, alas, less successful. Imperial's first test, 225 miles northeast of Edmonton, was a dry hole. But by 1919 Imperial had fifteen geologists and five drilling crews looking for oil from the Arctic to the International Boundary. Its first discovery, at Norman Wells in the Northwest Territories in 1919 was Canada's first major oil field since the discovery of Oil Springs and Petrolia 60 years earlier, but it was too remote to be economically producible. Under a one dollar plus cost contract with the U.S. government, Imperial later developed Norman Wells for the second world war Canol project, producing oil for the pipeline and refinery at Whitehorse for one year before the Canol project was shut down. Imperial now operates Canada's smallest refinery at Norman Wells, producing aviation fuel and other products for the small northern market.

Royalite at Turner Valley

When Calgary Petroleum Products Company, which discovered a tiny, shallow oil pool at Turner Valley near Calgary in 1914, was on the verge of bankruptcy, Imperial purchased control and re-organized it as Royalite Oil Company. In 1924, the Royalite No. 4 well discovered the deeper gas formation at Turner Valley, and for the next 12 years the liquid condensate stripped from this gas was Canada's principal indigenous oil supply. When Calgary promoters R. A. Brown and George Bell in 1936 discovered the large pool of oil which lay at an even greater depth at Turner Valley, they were aided in financing their wildcat by $22,500 worth of drilling equipment obtained from Imperial, in return for a 7.5 percent gross royalty on any oil the well might produce. (They were also aided by a loan of $30,000 from Canada's number two oil firm), British American Oil.

266

These minor successes, however, far from covered the $33 million Imperial had spent on exploration in western Canada by the end of the second world war. By the end of 1946, its record was 133 dry holes in Western Canada, and not one significant, commercial oil discovery. Thus it was that Imperial was seriously considering the possibility of manufacturing a synthetic crude oil from Alberta natural gas, when it blew in its historic Leduc discovery in February, 1947.

Faced with a need for enormous sums of money to develop its new-found oil, step up its exploration program, and build pipelines and more refineries, Imperial in 1948 sold International Petroleum to parent Standard of New Jersey for $80 million. The following year it sold Royalite for $15 million, and subsequently sold its other interests in Turner Valley. In 22 years following the discovery of Leduc, Imperial invested several billion dollars in exploration and capital expenditures in Canada.

And that is how Imperial became the largest company in Canada.

British American

The British American Oil Company Limited was founded in 1906 by a man who seemed always afraid that some day he might lose control of his company to American investors.

One day he appointed an American as executive vice-president of his company. Later the American left British American to work for Gulf Oil Corporation in the United States, and became president and chairman of the board. The British American Oil Company Limited became a 69-percent-owned subsidiary of Gulf Oil Corporation of Pittsburgh. In 1969, its name was changed to Gulf Oil Canada Limited. British American Oil Company Limited, a name known to Canadians for more than half a century, was no more. It was instead, "the Canadian member of the world-wide Gulf family."

It took British American Oil just 20 years from its founding to rise from a small kerosene marketer to the second largest oil company in Canada, a position which it held until 1968 when Shell Canada pulled into the number two spot. Its range of operations, from uranium development in northern Saskatchewan to pipelines, petrochemicals and petroleum, is hardly less than that of Imperial Oil, although it is a fair-sized step behind with assets, in 1968, of $920 million, sales of more than $600 million, and net earnings of $48 million.

Ellsworth

Albert Leroy Ellsworth was 30 when he returned to Ontario in 1906 to establish British American Oil in Toronto, after working for 10 years as a statistician and cost accountant for Standard Oil at its

Buffalo refinery. It was considered an inopportune time to start an oil company, since every wise investor knew that the electric light bulb would soon trim the wicks of the kerosene lamps and put the oil companies out of business. But Ellsworth found seven other misguided investors, and between them they put up a total of $135,200. Silas Parson, prominent Canadian businessman and first president of the Canadian Manufacturers Association, became president of the new firm, and Ellsworth, although the founder and driving force of the organization, was secretary-treasurer for the next 15 years until he succeeded Parsons as president in 1921.

Only the best

It was at first a lean business, peddling kerosene and lubricating oils in Toronto, and in the first couple of years there were times when there was not enough cash on hand to fill the weekly pay envelopes. Then Ellsworth would climb into a company wagon and call on customers until he had collected enough money to get past pay day. From the start Ellsworth vowed that "no one shall sell better products nor give better service" than BA, but soon found that if the pledge were to be kept the firm had better start making its own products. So in 1908, BA completed its first refinery, a Toronto plant consisting of two secondhand cheese-box stills which produced primarily kerosene.

The new refinery was BA's pride and joy, but it did not solve the shortage of cash and the company soon found itself in debt to its American oil suppliers. Parsons and Ellsworth persuaded Charles L. Suhr of Oil City, Pennsylvania, and another associate to accept BA stock as collateral for the money it owed on the oil it had purchased from Suhr. W. K. Whiteford, a former BA president and later chairman of Gulf Oil Corporation, once recalled that "the loan continued to build up as conditions remained rather difficult for the new company, and the day came when Mr. Ellsworth realized that he had pledged enough stock to Mr. Suhr and Mr. McSweeney that they now owned control of the company. He was quite suspicious of American business and he was sure that he would soon be advised that they were taking over the company." They did not, but Suhr became a director in 1909 and at the time of his death 59 years later was still a director emeritus.

A demanding employer, Ellsworth had a bookkeeper's passion for detail. He reportedly even checked the junior clerks to make certain that they fixed the postage neatly to the company's mail because he hated slipshod work. But he lacked nothing in breadth of vision. Three years after the company was formed it obtained a federal

BA fleet
at Outremont,
Que., 1918.

charter and started selling its kerosene and lubricating oils in Quebec. Henry Ford had started mass-producing his automobiles just three years before BA was formed, but the impact was not yet great in Canada; there were less than 1,000 automobiles and a survey showed that five out of six Canadians preferred Old Dobbin for transportation. But by the end of the first world war the demand for gasoline had increased from 10 to 26 percent of the total petroleum market, and BA had enlarged and modernized its refinery to keep pace. In 1920 it purchased the Winnipeg Oil Company with its 115 outlets and extended its marketing operations across the three prairie provinces.

Its rapidly growing market requirements created a need for additional supply sources, which BA sought to provide by establishing, in 1924, the Toronto Pipe Line Company to build and operate crude oil

269

pipelines in the United States, and the following year establishing another subsidiary to explore for and develop U.S. oil production. This was BA's first step to a fully integrated operation, and met with immediate success. Initial investment in the two U.S. subsidiaries was $405,000. BA's U.S. oil production was built up to a rate of nearly 30,000 barrels per day by 1958. In 1966, BA sold its U.S. subsidiary to parent Gulf Oil Corporation for $196 million, providing funds for further expansion in Canada.

Montreal refinery

BA's second refinery was opened in Montreal in 1931. In 1934 it opened its Moose Jaw refinery in Saskatchewan; purchased a refinery in Coutts, Alberta and connected it by pipeline with oil fields in Montana; purchased another small refinery in Calgary from Bell Refining Company, and built the first absorption plant in the Turner Valley field to extract condensate from the vast volumes of natural gas which were then being flared. In 1936, BA helped finance the wildcat test which discovered the large oil reservoir at Turner Valley and three years later built a new refinery at Turner Valley to replace the small plant purchased from Bell.

Whiteford joins BA

It was in 1935 that BA hired, as vice-president of its U.S. subsidiary, a young man who had attended Stanford University and graduated from the roughneck school of drilling – William K. Whiteford. In 1942, Whiteford moved to Toronto as executive vice-president of the parent company, and years later recalled the event in a speech in Montreal.

"Mr. Ellsworth told me that it was with great reluctance that he was asking me to come to Canada," explained Whiteford; "first of all because he never wanted an American in charge of his Canadian company and second, he wasn't sure I would be accepted by the employees of the company or by the industrial world. Upon arrival I was told that, in order to ease the blow, there would be no announcement of my title, but that I would be assigned an office where I could get acquainted with the employees and that in time they would come to understand what my new position was. Furthermore, in order to keep the matter entirely confidential, I would not be paid a salary but could file an expense account to take care of any necessary expenses ... It was four months before my title and responsibilities were announced and my salary commenced."

Despite this inauspicious start, Whiteford was named president the following year when Ellsworth became chairman of the board, and the company growth continued. During the second world war, BA

BA Oil
refinery at
Toronto, 1918.

played a vital role in the building of the 1,600-mile Alaska highway by the U.S. Army Corps of Engineers, moving in 100 large storage tanks along the route and operating 350 tank trucks to haul in fuel supplies from the railhead through summer mud and winter blizzards. In 1943 it opened its largest refinery at Clarkson, Ontario to replace the Toronto plant which was shut down after the war. In 1945 the company extended its marketing operations to the west coast by purchasing the assets of Union Oil Company of Canada; in 1947 marketing was extended further east into Newfoundland; in 1950 a major expansion of the Montreal refinery was completed. Largest refinery program in the company's history was underway in 1969, when it was simultaneously building a 60,000 barrels per day refinery at Point Tupper, Nova Scotia, an 80,000 barrels per day refinery at Edmonton, and increasing the capacity of its Vancouver refinery by 20,000 barrels per day. Total capital investment involved was approximately $150 million.

Buys Union Oil assets

After the second world war and up to the mid-1950's, BA proudly advertised itself as the largest Canadian-owned oil company. But the basis for that claim was already being eroded. It was immediately after the war that BA began its association with Gulf, when the U.S. firm purchased a minority, 20 percent interest in the Canadian company. In 1951, Whiteford left BA to join Gulf, where he later became president and then chairman. Five years later Gulf acquired majority control of BA.

Gulf takeover

Gulf had started exploring for and developing oil and gas reserves in western Canada in the mid-1940's, and through its Canadian Gulf Oil Company had invested $135 million in western Canada. In 1956, BA issued 8.3 million shares, worth more than $300 million, to Gulf Oil Corporation to acquire the assets of Canadian Gulf. The acquisition increased BA's land holdings in western Canada from one million to eleven million acres, multiplied its Canadian oil production 10-fold, and made BA the largest holder of natural gas reserves in Canada. In 12 years following this acquisition, BA invested more than a billion dollars in capital and exploration expenditures in Canada.

Shell: a late bid

The venerable Royal Dutch/Shell Group, with the second largest oil operations in the free world, almost missed the boat in Canada. Actually, Shell had been one of the earlier passengers on board. But just before the boat started to move, Shell jumped off. To catch up later, it had to swim hard, pouring vast sums of money into Canada, and purchasing existing firms at high prices. Its purchases included the only fully-integrated, Canadian-owned oil company that was left. Shell, however, eventually made up for lost time, and in 1968 nailed down second place in the Canadian petroleum industry.

The Royal Dutch/Shell Group, whose member companies produce 14 percent of the non-Communist world oil production, resulted from a merger of Dutch and English interests which combined forces to meet the threat of Standard Oil. Shell Transport and Trading Company owed its start, in 1830, to a modest London trading concern which dealt in Oriental imports, including sea shells, much valued in Victorian decoration. With the establishment of the petroleum industry, the trading company graduated from sea shells to oil, carrying oil from Russia for lamps in the Far East. Eventually it built up a large fleet of ocean-going tankers, oil producing and refining operations in Borneo, and hundreds of ocean terminals and depots throughout the Orient. The Royal Dutch Company – or N. V. Koninklijke Nederlansche Petroleum Maatshappij, meaning The Royal Dutch Company for the Working of Petroleum Wells in the Netherlands Indies – came into existence as a result of discovery of oil in Sumatra in 1880.

By the turn of the century, Shell Transport and Royal Dutch were both integrated oil companies, with producing, refining, transporting and marketing operations, and were competing aggressively for markets throughout the Orient. It became evident, however, that both could be forced out of business by the growing competition from Standard Oil. To avert this they combined forces in 1907, creating the Royal Dutch/Shell Group, owned 60 percent by Royal Dutch of the Netherlands and 40 percent by Shell Transport of England. This ownership interest has remained unchanged. London became the financial headquarters of the Royal Dutch/Shell Group, and The Hague became headquarters for the technical side of the business.

Royal Dutch/Shell not only competed abroad with Standard, but moved the fight into Standard's back yard, establishing marketing and oil producing operations in the United States in 1912. Eventually the group's various interests in the United States were combined into Shell Oil Company, one of the largest oil firms in the United States, owned 65 percent by Royal Dutch/Shell.

The group entered Canada even before it entered the States, incorporating The Shell Company of Canada Limited in 1911 and building bunkering facilities in Montreal that year to handle shipments of gasoline brought in from Borneo by Shell tankers. Two years later another Shell firm built a small bulk plant at Vancouver to distribute products by horse-drawn tank wagon to a handful of service stations in the lower mainland area. The first Shell refineries in Canada, at Montreal and Vancouver, were placed on stream in 1932. Slowly the Shell marketing organization was built up in Canada, with Shell Oil Company of British Columbia operating in the west and Shell Oil Company of Canada operating in the east. Both were wholly-owned by the Royal Dutch/Shell Group.

Early arrival

Shell's search for oil reserves and production in Canada did not get started until 1939 when an exploration office was opened in Calgary. Even then it was not a venture directed by Royal Dutch/Shell, but by its 65-percent-owned U.S. subsidiary, Shell Oil Company. The search failed to find any oil, but it did result in the discovery of a large gas field in the Alberta foothills at Jumping Pound, near Calgary.

It was in 1946 that Shell almost missed the boat in Canada. It had been exploring for six years, with discouraging results, and in the aftermath of the second world war, the Royal Dutch/Shell Group was forced to retrench. Large producing properties in the Far East, which had been the foundation of the enterprise, were lost. Through-

Early departure

out Europe, much of the group's extensive refining and marketing facilities had been devastated by the war. It faced a major re-building program, and to finance this it had to cut costs. The decision, which seemed logical under the circumstances, was to drop all holdings of exploratory acreage in Canada and concentrate in Venezuela, where there seemed far better prospects for a more immediate return. The following year Imperial Oil discovered the Leduc field, and in 1948 it found the 800-million-barrel Redwater field. Much of the Redwater field lay under leases which Shell had dropped when it pulled out of Canada just two years before.

1950 program

Shell was back again exploring for oil in Canada in 1950, its program this time financed 50 percent by the U.S. firm, Shell Oil Company, and 50 percent directly by Royal Dutch/Shell. It paid a stiff penalty for its mistake. The most attractive looking exploratory holdings had already been picked up, and it was not until 1953 that Shell made its first, modest oil find in Canada. Even then its oil finding costs were higher than that of other majors who had been in on the ground floor in the Alberta play, either before or immediately after the Leduc discovery. But Shell this time persisted in its quest, and slowly built up appreciable reserves and production of both oil and gas.

Serious re-entry in 1957

Until 1957, Shell's operations in Canada appeared at best to be somewhat disjointed. Refining and marketing operations were carried out by two separate companies, both wholly-owned by Royal Dutch/Shell, while exploration and production was conducted by a third organization with ownership divided between Royal Dutch/Shell and its U.S. subsidiary. All of the interests were consolidated that year into Shell Canada, which for the first time became a fully integrated oil company, from oil well to service station.

Fully integrated it may have been, but it was a long way behind its major competitors, Imperial Oil and British American. It had regional marketing operations in the east and on the west coast, with a 55,000 barrels-per-day refinery in Montreal, an 18,000-barrels-per-day refinery in Vancouver, and a big gap across the rest of the country. Against its refining and marketing requirements of more than 70,000 barrels per day, its production comprised only 13,000 barrels of crude oil per day, plus about 50 million cubic feet of natural gas. Total assets were listed at a book value of little more than $200 million.

To catch up, Shell invested more than a billion dollars in expansion, exploration and acquisitions during the next dozen years.

Assets were increased from $200 million to $800 million; production from 13,000 to 68,000 barrels of oil per day; natural gas sales from 50 million to 370 million cubic feet per day; refining capacity (including projects under construction) from 73,000 to 213,000 barrels per day. In 1968 it passed Gulf Oil Canada in total sales ($622 million) and net earnings ($54 million), although net assets were still somewhat less than Gulf's.

Strangely enough, the large loss which Shell had sustained on its exploration operations in western Canada since 1950 helped in its later expansion. If Shell were able to acquire a profitable oil refining and marketing concern, it could then apply against future earnings of this acquisition, its backlog of tax credits resulting from the loss it sustained in its exploration program. This would allow Shell to pay a higher price for the acquisition of such properties.

First step in this direction was Shell Canada's purchase for $73 million of North Star Oil Limited, an independent producing-refining-marketing company based in Winnipeg. North Star had the third largest oil marketing operation in western Canada, and gave Shell its first marketing entry on the Prairie provinces.

Next step has been described as a "Shell shock" for Canadian Oil Companies Limited, one of the oldest oil companies in Canada which, in 1962, described itself as "the only major Canadian-owned company with completely integrated facilities from oil fields to refineries to service stations." Its boast sounded almost the same as British American's had, just before Gulf acquired controlling interest.

Canadian Oil was a product of the Ontario oil fields, organized in Petrolia in 1901 as the Canadian Oil Refining Company. Three years later it merged with several other small firms and became the Canadian Oil Company Limited. Another three years later it had declared itself bankrupt, and control was acquired by the National Refining Company of Cleveland, which in 1908 reorganized it once more as Canadian Oil Companies Limited. Under U.S. control for 30 years, it expanded its marketing operations across Canada until by 1938 National Refining Company itself was in financial trouble. The Montreal brokerage house of Nesbitt, Thompson and Company then purchased control.

"It was in December, 1938 that the most important event in Canadian Oil's history took place – an event which was to have a profound effect upon the company's personality and position within the petroleum industry," a company brochure later related. "At that

"Shell shock" for Canadian Oil

time, after three decades of control by United States interests, ownership of the company returned to Canada, thus reversing the trend which has prevailed with so many other segments of the industry."

By 1962, Canadian Oil had nearly $150 million in book-value assets, a 50,000 barrels-per-day refinery in Sarnia and a 5,000 barrels-per-day refinery in Alberta, 3,000 White Rose service stations from coast to coast, and 5,000 barrels-per-day oil production in Alberta.

Project Guardian

It was on a Saturday in July that year that representatives of Shell arrived at the Toronto home of Canadian Oil president H. W. Rea with an offer to purchase the company for $116 million. The offering was a thundering surprise to Canadian Oil, but Shell, in its typically thorough fashion, had been preparing the bid for months. A 30-man task force drawn from all company departments was assigned to the project, with a nine-member working committee and the others acting as advisers. To assure secrecy the project was given a code name, "Guardian," and the task force worked in a separate office building. Up to 100 Shell people were involved at different times in various aspects of the project. The job of the task force was to prepare an exhaustive evaluation of Canadian Oil, recommend the manner in which the bid should be made, and plan for the later integration of the operations of the two companies.

Resistance

Canadian Oil directors and Power Corporation of Canada, which held about 30 percent of Canadian oil stock, resisted Shell's offer. Once Shell had tipped its hand, the bidding for control of Canadian Oil became extensive. Shell upped its offer by $36 million to $152 million for the common stock, in addition to assuming long-term debt of $28 million. Shareholders accepted the bid. The "only major Canadian-owned oil company with completely integrated facilities" was no longer.

Greatly strengthened by the refineries and marketing facilities of Canadian Oil, Shell for the first time was in a strong competitive position across Canada, and was starting to tread on the heels of its two big competitors.

Stock listed

Shell Canada's capital structure was also again changed in 1962 when 13 percent of the company's equity was made available to the Canadian public. This was achieved when Shell Oil Company of New York distributed to its shareholders the stock which it held in Shell Canada. These shares were then listed for trading on the Toronto, Montreal and Vancouver stock exchanges. Conversion of outstanding preferred shares and exercise of share purchase warrants is expected to increase public ownership in Shell Canada to 20 percent by late 1972, leaving 80 percent with the Royal Dutch/Shell Group.

Shell Canada had yet another grand-slam play to make, a minimum $60 million gamble, the outcome of which might not be known until 1971 or 1972. It is a high-risk gamble, a wildcatter's plunge. Its gamble is the search for major oil fields along the continental shelves which lie beneath the Pacific and Atlantic coasts off Canada's shores, where it holds 95,000 square miles of oil and gas permits, an area larger than all of Great Britain, and six times as large as Denmark. Starting in 1963, Shell spent more than six years and $30 million exploring for oil on its holdings off the coast of British Columbia, drilling 14 dry holes before abandoning the search in mid-1969. Undeterred by its lack of success, Shell started a similar drilling program late in 1969 on its far larger holdings offshore from Nova Scotia, following several years of intensive geophysical and geological studies.

Shell's venture off the coast of Nova Scotia could prove to be another $30 million down the drain, or it could provide Shell's biggest prize in Canada. That is the type of risk required to stay in the league with the majors.

The Texas Company in Canada

Well back as number four in Canadian oil is Texaco Canada Limited. It can boast, like Imperial Oil and Shell Canada, that it can trace its origins in Canada to the pioneer Ontario fields of Oil Springs and Petrolia. Like Shell and Imperial as well as Gulf, it started out as a Canadian enterprise and eventually wound up under foreign control.

A small, integrated producing-refining-marketing partnership known as McColl and Anderson, established in 1873, was the start of what later became Texaco Canada. By the end of the first world war it had emerged as McColl Brothers, Limited, one of Ontario's leading petroleum marketers with a refinery and lubricating oil and grease manufacturing facilities in Toronto.

Late in 1927 it merged with Frontenac Oil Refineries, Ltd. of Montreal and became McColl-Frontenac Oil Company Limited. The Montreal financial house of Nesbitt, Thomson & Co. had purchased, earlier that year, all of the outstanding stock of McColl Brothers. Nesbitt, Thomson also owned Frontenac, put together from the pieces of the Nation's Oil Refineries which had gone bankrupt.

McColl-Frontenac, with a $7.5 million issue of public financing, started off with a promising future. Its Montreal refinery, which had been built by the Nation's Oil Refineries, was the second largest in Quebec. Crude oil supply was provided by production in Trinidad through its wholly-owned subsidiary, Antilles Petroleum Co. Its marketing position in Ontario was further strengthened in 1929 when it issued shares to acquire the Perfection Petroleum Company of Toronto. Shares of the company in 1929 sold as high as $45 and earnings the following year hit $1.4 million.

McColl Frontenac

Then the depression hit. Earnings were cut in half, and by 1937 the shares were selling as low as $8.50. The company faced increased competition with the construction of British American's Montreal refinery in 1930, and Shell's Montreal refinery in 1933. The old McColl Brothers refinery in Toronto, no longer able to compete with newer, more efficient refineries, was shut down. The Antilles Petroleum Co. was operating at a loss in Trinidad, and the company was faced with a squeeze on capital.

In the United States, The Texas Corporation (later, Texaco Inc., one of the largest international oil companies) saw a profitable opportunity for investment expansion in the struggling Canadian company. Despite the fact that it was hard pressed, under conditions of the depression, to raise the capital it required for growth, McColl-Frontenac still had a solid base and its shares in 1936 were selling for less than nine times earnings. The Texas Corporation began buying shares of McColl-Frontenac on the open market, and two years later disclosed that it had acquired a "substantial interest."

Takeover in 1938

During the annual meeting of McColl-Frontenac shareholders in Montreal in 1938, representatives of The Texas Corporation showed up to announce that the U.S. firm owned 35 percent of the company, and also held proxy statements from other shareholders. The Texas representatives voted down the slate of directors nominated by the company management, then nominated and elected a new board of directors.

The new board quickly set out to strengthen the financial position and expand the operations of McColl-Frontenac. More capital was raised with a $12.5 million bond issue, and further shares of McColl-Frontenac were issued to the U.S. firm to acquire the assets of The Texas Company of Canada Limited, which had made a modest start in petroleum marketing in Canada. Outbreak of the second world war in 1939, however, slowed down the expansion plans for several years.

Following the second world war, McColl-Frontenac launched an exploration program for oil and gas reserves in western Canada, even prior to Imperial Oil's discovery of the Leduc field in 1947. The parent Texas Company was also exploring in western Canada, and took over most of the operations of McColl-Frontenac, which, however, continued separate exploration and producing operations on a smaller scale.

McColl-Frontenac sold its Antilles Petroleum Co. to The Texas Corporation in 1957 for $11 million, and at the same time purchased a refinery in Toronto from Regent Refining in exchange for a block of shares worth some $15 million. Since Texaco had previously purchased Trinidad Leaseholds Ltd., the parent company of Regent Refining, it received most of the shares issued by McColl-Frontenac for the Toronto refinery, thereby further increasing its ownership of McColl-Frontenac. Two years later, McColl-Frontenac changed its name to Texaco Canada Limited.

In 1969, the giant Texaco Inc. of New York controlled two Canadian subsidiaries. It owned 68 percent of Texaco Canada, which sold some 150,000 barrels per day of refined products through 5,500 outlets coast to coast, operated refineries at Halifax, Montreal, Toronto and Edmonton, and produced some 15,000 barrels per day of crude oil in western Canada. It also held 100 percent interest in Texaco Exploration which was producing more than four times as much oil in western Canada as Texaco Canada.

Texaco Canada

The histories of Imperial, Gulf, Shell and Texaco in Canada all demonstrate one thing: attempts to maintain a significant, Canadian-owned, integrated oil operation, from wellhead to service station, have all floundered because of a lack of money. The international oil majors had money, and in the end, they took over.

There are a host of reasons why the Canadian enterprises lacked the resources to stay in the race. For one thing, the capital required to build the industry – more than $10 billion in exploration and capital investments to 1969 – was simply more than was available in Canada, and could only be raised with the help of outside money. National tax policies, with U.S. oil companies for decades receiving far more favorable tax treatment than Canadian companies, has been a factor. Perhaps the fact that Canadian-owned oil ventures were operated primarily on a national rather than a multi-national basis, has been a factor in the past, and will almost certainly be a factor if there are any future attempts to establish a Canadian position in the integrated petroleum industry.

But the biggest factor has undoubtedly been the history of the search for oil in Canada. The 90 years between the discovery of oil in

Why the internationals took over

The Great Canadian Oil Patch

Ontario and the discovery of oil at Leduc were largely barren years for oil in Canada. Elsewhere, oil discoveries and production were generating enormous profits and building the giant internationals. By the time Leduc came, these companies had the resources – the money, the know-how, the transportation, the manufacturing, and the marketing – to move in. For any major Canadian oil enterprise, Leduc came about a century too late.

Chapter Thirteen

The venerable institutions

Hudson's Bay Co., CPR

No two commercial organizations have so influenced the history and development of Canada as the venerable Hudson's Bay Company and Canadian Pacific Railway.

HBC – known to the early fur traders as "Here Before Christ" – is the oldest commercial company still in operation. It was 300 years old in 1970. Its extensive fur trading empire, which once extended from the Great Lakes to the Pacific Ocean, and from Alaska to California, provided the commerce responsible for the exploration and initial settlement of western Canada, and a good portion of what is now the western United States. The CPR tied the new-born nation together with a band of steel from coast to coast, and brought the second wave of settlement.

HBC and CPR each played a part in Canada's petroleum history, too. HBC teamed with a U.S. wildcatter, giving birth to a Canadian oil company which has now grown larger than HBC itself. The CPR, with a belated start, has developed the largest Canadian-owned oil and gas interests.

The wildcatter

Ernest Whitworth Marland was one of the most colorful wildcatters to come striding out of the early, brawling, booming history of the American petroleum industry – and into the quiet, dignified

board room of the Hudson's Bay Company in England where he concluded a deal for a large-scale joint petroleum exploration venture in western Canada.

Born in Pittsburgh, in 1874, the son of a Scottish mother and an English immigrant father who fought with the Confederate army in the U.S. civil war and later made a fortune manufacturing iron bands for bailing cotton, Marland inherited a life-long worship of aristocratic English manners and a compulsion for social reform, combined with a taste for wealth and a paternalistic attitude. As a boy he started school dressed in kilts and sporan. As a youthful promoter he arrived in the unsettled Indian country dressed in belted tweed jacket, knickerbockers and white spats. As a prosperous businessman he introduced polo and fox hunting to the plains of Oklahoma.

His father sent him to private schools patterned after English institutions and dreamed that some day Ernest might become a great jurist. But at the Michigan Law School, from which he graduated in 1893, Marland excelled only in poker.

Two years out of university, Marland had established his own law practice, and backed by his father's money and his sister's help, soon began acquiring coal leases with the hope of making a quick fortune. Instead of finding coal, however, he found some shallow oil and gas pools, and by the time he was 30, he was a millionaire.

It did not last. By 1907 his oil and gas production had been nearly depleted, he was deeply in debt, and an economic recession gripped the United States. That did not stop Marland from taking advantage of an unexpected opportunity. His nephew, an officer in the cavalry, had suggested to the owners of the 101 Ranch in Oklahoma that his "rich oil man" uncle in Pittsburgh might be persuaded to finance a search for oil on the ranch property. Marland did not own the fare to ride across Pittsburgh in a street car, but he was able to borrow enough money for a railway ticket to Ponca City, Oklahoma.

Beneath every hill he saw in Oklahoma, Marland envisioned huge structures containing vast quantities of oil. His unbounded optimism was his only real asset, but it was enough to raise financing from his eastern friends and organize the 101 Ranch Oil Company. His first half dozen holes in Oklahoma were either dry or found only small pockets of gas, and every hole put him deeper in debt. He pawned even his watch to pay for his room and board at one point, but eventually made his big strike with his ninth hole, on the sacred burial grounds of the Ponca Indians.

A race between his lavish spending and a string of discoveries marked Marland's career for the next two decades. The 101 Ranch

... and the Company of Adventurers

Marland Oil Co.

line
processing
ated
BOG.

Oil Company later became the Marland Refining Company with a small refinery at Ponca City, and in 1920, the Marland Oil Company, which was built into one of the largest oil producers in the U.S. mid-continent region.

Marland spent his way to success, sublimely confident the results would justify whatever expenditures he made. When the company treasurer dared to question how all the expenditures that Marland had authorized were to be met, Marland replied, "well, that's your job. Don't bother me with the details." And, for a time at least, the approach paid off.

One of the reasons it paid off was his faith in geology, and later in seismic, at a time when most wildcatters had as much faith in a divining rod. He felt certain the results would more than compensate for whatever it cost to acquire the best technical experts in the industry — and he was right.

Ponca City paternalism

At Ponca City he spent literally millions of dollars to build a 400-acre estate, with swimming pool, golf course, and acres of formal gardens. With his affluence he gave rein to his paternalistic regard for the welfare of his employees, offering social benefits unheard of in his day. Employees could purchase subsidized houses at low interest rates, invest in company shares on easy terms, obtain free medical and dental examinations, free accident and sickness insurance, and full salary not only during sickness but also during recovery from non-occupational accidents. When he built a new head office building in Ponca City, an entire floor was devoted to the exclusive use of employees, with shower baths, locker rooms, lecture and reading rooms. He established the Marland Industrial Institute for the dual purpose of providing employee technical training and "continuation of the educational opportunities . . . for all employees." The Institute's complex included a dining hall, assembly hall, clubrooms, classrooms, golf course and swimming pool. Senior employees were given generous stock options and profit sharing arrangements. Every working man, said Marland, ought to have not only "a living wage, but a saving wage."

Marland almost worshipped the European tradition of the great, baronial commercial empires, and was ever ready to align his interests with theirs. He negotiated personally with the president of Mexico for a blanket lease covering more than a million acres of oil rights in Mexico; negotiated a merger between Marland Oil and the U.S. interests of the Royal Dutch Shell, which fell through in the end, and in 1926 signed his exploration agreement covering the Canadian leases of the Hudson's Bay Company. Firms like Royal Dutch Shell, the

East Indian Company and Hudson's Bay, according to his biographer John J. Mathews, were "far more romantic to him than Standard and the American enterprises of the dollar princes . . . Even without his inherent Anglophile tendencies, he loved the Anglo-European atmosphere . . . the dignity, the quiet efficiency."

Marland was no doubt impressed by the charter which had been granted on May 2, 1670, by King Charles II to the Governor and Company of Adventurers of England Trading into Hudson's Bay. The charter granted to the Adventurers "the sole Trade and Commerce of all those Seas, Streightes, Bayes, Rivers, Lakes, Creekes and Soundes in whatsoever Latitude they shall bee, that lie within the entrance of the Streightes, commonly called Hudsons Streights together with all the Landes and Territoryes upon the Countryes, Coastes and Confynes of the Seas, Bayes, Lakes, Rivers, Creeks and Soundes aforesaid that are not already actually possessed by or granted to any of our Subjectes, or possessed by the Subjectes of any other Christian Prince or State:" and constituted them "the true and absolute Lordes and Proprietors of the same Territory, lymittes and places."

HBC's charter

It was an area as great as Europe, known as Ruperts Land, stretching from the Great Lakes to the Rocky Mountains, which the Hudson's Bay Company retained for 199 years as a result of this charter. In 1869, two years after the confederation of Canada, HBC sold Ruperts Land to the new nation for a total of $1.5 million. Under the terms of the sale, the company retained title to 7.5 million acres, or five percent of the total area. In general, the formula gave Hudson's Bay section eight and three-quarters of section 26 of each unoccupied township south of the North Saskatchewan River between Winnipeg and the Rocky Mountains. In each fifth township it got all of section 26. A township is divided into a grid composed of 36 mile-square sections. Because so much land had already been granted to railways, Hudson's Bay also got some acreage north of the North Saskatchewan river to make up its five percent allotment. The lands were sold to settlers and initially the mineral rights were sold with the surface rights, but after 1889 HBC followed the practice adopted by the government of Canada and the railways of retaining ownership of mineral rights. HBC eventually wound up with ownership of some 4.5 million acres of freehold mineral rights in the three prairie provinces.

A wealth in mineral rights

It was this 4.5 million acres of mineral rights that attracted Marland's interest, and on a visit to England he concluded a deal with

Charles Vincent Sale, governor of the Hudson's Bay Company, for a joint venture exploration program. The subsidiary company, Hudson's Bay Marland Oil Company, organized in 1926, was given an exclusive option to lease the HBC lands, and set out on an exploration program which also embraced other freehold lands and Crown-owned mineral rights. HBC initially held a one-sixth interest in the subsidiary, plus an option to extend this to 25 percent, which it eventually exercised in 1952.

HBOG shelves program

Initial exploration lasted two short years before the stock market crash of 1929. Marland lost control of his U.S. oil company that year, and, reflecting this, the name of the subsidiary company was changed to Hudson's Bay Oil and Gas Company. By 1934 HBOG had dropped all of its non-HBC leases, shelved its exploration program, and sent its books down to Ponca City to be kept. Discovery of crude oil at Turner Valley in 1936 brought some revival of exploration for HBOG in the Alberta foothills, but without encouraging results.

A few years before he had made his deal with the Hudson's Bay Company, Marland had given his firm's banking business to J. P. Morgan and Company, the great banking house which also acted as bankers for Standard Oil of New Jersey. Morgan and Company purchased $12 million worth of Marland stock with an option to purchase an additional $90 million. They soon controlled the company's board of directors.

Backed by Morgan money, growth of Marland Oil was accelerated, with gratifying discoveries throughout the mid-Continent regions and in the Los Angeles basin of California. The company's trademark, a red triangle with the word "Marland," soon hung at a growing chain of service stations throughout 11 states.

Continental Oil

Marland seemed blind to the control of his company exercised by the Morgan house until 1927 when, top-heavy with staff and a crushing burden of expenses, the company was running at a loss. The loss continued into 1928. Somehow, the old approach of results justifying expenditures seemed no longer to be working. Before the end of that year, Marland had been forced out of the company, new management was brought in to run a tighter ship, and several of Marland's associates had been fired. Marland Oil was merged into Continental Oil Company, a much smaller, mid-Continent oil and gas producer, also controlled by Morgan and Company. The red triangles were all re-painted and now read "Conoco."

Bitter over the loss of his company to the eastern bankers whom he now distrusted, Marland turned his energies to politics with the same idealistic approach, and reaped bitter fruit once more. He was elected to Congress and then, in 1934, elected state governor of Oklahoma, seeking a sweeping package of social reform measures which stunned the electors and taxpayers of his day. Two attempts to seek election to the U.S. Senate, while still serving as state Governor, resulted in defeat.

He returned, in 1938, to Ponca City to retire, and was forced to sell his great manor house, which had cost him millions, to the Carmelite Friars, for $66,000.

Broken and in ill-health, about his only satisfaction was that he was able to watch the sustained progress of Continental Oil Company, and know that he had started it all. "I was ambitious," he wrote, "to build a completely integrated oil company that would take its place in the petroleum industry and compete for markets with the Standard Oil companies." Others may have completed that dream, with Continental Oil Company, the successor to his Marland Oil Company, but it was he who had got it off to a robust start.

Marland did not live to see the alliance he had made with the Hudson's Bay Company bear fruit. He died in 1943, when Hudson's Bay Oil and Gas was still an inactive, almost defunct, organization.

Hudson's Bay Oil and Gas sprang back to life once more in 1948, following the discovery of the Leduc field, in the vanguard of the rush to Canadian exploration. In the following two decades it invested more than $300 million in land acquisition, exploration, oil field development, gas plants and pipelines.

HBOG springs to life

Revival of HBOG was mostly a matter of pouring in risk money. During the first eight years, its operations accumulated a loss of $5.8 million. The first profit was earned in 1956 – 30 years after the company had been formed. Thereafter, revenue and earnings climbed steadily. Hudson's Bay Company exercised its option to increase its ownership in the oil company from one-sixth to one-quarter in 1952. First public participation came with the sale of $19 million worth of HBOG shares in 1957, resulting in an initial 9.3 percent public ownership. Acquisition of two, smaller independent companies – Security Freehold Petroleums Ltd., and Consolidated Mic Mac Oils Ltd., in 1963 further increased the public ownership. In 1969, Hudson's Bay Oil and Gas was owned 65.7 percent by Continental Oil Company, 21.9 percent by the Hudson's Bay Company and had 12.4 percent public ownership. Conversion of preferred shares outstanding

Kaybob
South
No. 1 plant
operated
by HBOG.

in 1969 could, by 1972, further increase public ownership in HBOG to 15.6 percent, leaving 63.3 percent with Continental and 21.1 percent with HBC.

By 1968, Hudson's Bay Oil and Gas ranked as the third largest oil and gas producer in Canada, and its rate of growth during the preceding two decades had greatly outstripped that of either of its parent companies. Total revenues had risen to $67 million per year, generating $27 million per year in net earnings. The $274 million book value of its assets was for the first time greater than that of the parent Hudson's Bay Company ($272 million), while net earnings were nearly twice as great as HBC's $14.7 million.

Canadian Pacific Railway Company, the largest owner of freehold mineral rights in Canada, was endowed at its birth with enormous potential natural resources, including a vast petroleum potential in western Canada. Almost from its inception, the CPR was inevitably involved in the initial discovery and development of these petroleum resources. For more than half a century, however, it was a rather passive involvement, with the CPR content to let others explore and exploit its potential petroleum resources. Almost in spite of itself, the non-railway assets steadily grew in importance in the affairs and earnings of the CPR.

Canadian Pacific Railway

It was not until the middle 1950's that the CPR set out aggressively to develop these non-transportation resources. Since then, Canadian Pacific has come on strong – in hotels, real estate, mining, lumbering, and oil and natural gas. Non-transportation activities now account for more than half of Canadian Pacific's earnings. Its petroleum-related assets, carried at a book value of $195 million in 1968 but worth much more, now constitute the largest Canadian-owned oil and natural gas operations.

Organized in 1881 after several years of struggle by a group of gambling financiers and the government of Canada, Canadian Pacific Railway set out with a mandate to build the transcontinental railway which would bind Canada together as a nation, backed in its efforts by a cash subsidy of $25 million and a land grant of 25 million acres from the government. Less than five years later the line was completed and in operation, one of the all-time great construction achievements.

Like the government of Canada and the Hudson's Bay Company, the CPR started disposing of its 25 million acres of land grants without initially reserving ownership of the mineral rights, but soon

Land grants

289

started following Ottawa's example. It eventually wound up owing the mineral rights on more than 9.5 million acres of potential oil and gas lands in western Canada, plus another four million acres prospective for other minerals.

Gas find in 1883

The CPR was barely more than two years old before it had its first natural gas discovery, in 1883 at Langevin in southern Alberta, where it was drilling for a water supply for its locomotives. During the next decade it seemed to find almost more gas in southern Alberta than the water supplies it sought, with strikes at Medicine Hat, Brooks, Bassano, Dunmore and Bow Island. Right from the start it followed a policy of leasing its petroleum resources to others for development, and in 1911 it leased the Bow Island gas field to Eugene Coste who built what was then the longest gas transmission pipeline in the world, 170 miles from Bow Island to Calgary. In the protracted development of the Turner Valley field between 1914 and the second world war, a substantial number of the wells were drilled on CPR leases. Seeking to stimulate exploration for oil and gas on its lands, the CPR set up a Natural Resources Department in Calgary, and offered leases on easy terms. Exploratory leases could be had from the CPR for as little as five cents per acre. Producing leases carried a nominal annual rental of $1 per acre plus the standard one-eighth gross royalty. But the early search for oil on CPR lands, as everywhere else in western Canada, was unrewarding.

The Leduc discovery dramatically changed the outlook. The CPR, with its 9 1/2 million acres of prospective oil lands, was sitting on a potential bonanza. But it was slow to respond to the changed conditions, continuing offering leases on terms even more generous than those offered by the Alberta government on its lands, and imposed only minimal drilling commitments.

Enter Buck Crump

It was a moribund, problem-ridden organization that diminutive Norris Roy (Buck) Crump inherited when he became president of Canadian Pacific in 1955. CP was described, in an analysis by Fortune Magazine, as a tradition-encrusted monolith guided by an ultra-conservative board which saw its duty simply as "not to detract from earnings." Its vast and largely hidden non-transportation assets were operated primarily to build railway business and not essentially as enterprises to generate revenues in themselves. What earnings these assets did generate were mostly reported not as profits but as "additions to capital." Development of non-transportation earnings, the CPR is reported to have reasoned, might have had unwelcome effects on government regulation of rail rates.

The railway faced some tough problems. Its earnings were unsatisfactory, rates were rigidly controlled by government regulation, railway passenger business was declining, and government regulations precluded the dropping of uneconomic branch lines. With only half of its system converted to diesel power, the CPR faced a $1.5 billion modernization program over the next 15 years. Reported earnings had not advanced in the past 30 years, and at about $30 CPR shares were selling for less than 50 years earlier. All in all, the CPR project-ed an image of crying-towel gloom as it complained about the in-equity of competing with a tax-subsidized Canadian National Railway and the burdens of government control.

Buck Crump is the man generally credited with switching CPR onto a forward track. Born in 1904 in Revelstoke, B.C., Crump was the son of a CPR railroader, an Englishman from Gloucestershire who later became superintendent of the CPR's Kettle Valley line in British Columbia. Crump left high school at the age of 16 to work as a track laborer for the CPR, later completed his high school with night courses, and between 1926 and 1936 took time off to earn two railroad engineering degrees from Purdue University in Indiana. He then began a steady climb through the CPR ranks.

Onto a forward track

It was apparent to Crump that the CPR had little choice but to develop the latent earning power of its non-transportation assets, in order to help pay for the costly modernization program the railway faced, re-establish growth, and provide a more satisfactory return for investors.

Petroleum was only one of the non-transportation areas it sought to develop, but a vital one. First step was to terminate all non-producing CPR leases as they came up for renewal between 1957 and 1962. Next was the formation of Canadian Pacific Oil and Gas, a wholly-owned subsidiary formed to explore and develop the CPR land itself.

CP makes oil its business

Oil companies, accustomed to easy dealings with the CPR, were startled to see the railroad moving in. Many of them were openly critical, claiming that railroad men would never know how to run an oil company successfully. Who could ever have imagined the stodgy CPR gambling its investors' money in wildcat ventures? "Just let them drill a few dry holes and they'll soon forget all this nonsense," was the reaction of at least a few disgruntled oil men. They were due for a few surprises. In 1962, its first full year of operation, Canadian Pacific Oil and Gas pumped in $3.4 million to find and develop its own oil and gas, but steadily kept increasing the rate to a figure of

$20 million by 1968, putting in substantially more money than it was taking out. There were other surprises coming, too.

Initially, CPOG's task was to develop the 9.5 million acres of CPR mineral rights, located primarily in the central and southern parts of Alberta and Saskatchewan. Later, it started acquiring adjacent holdings of Crown acreage. Then in 1966 it made a major policy decision to acquire exploratory acreage wherever the opportunities might appear attractive. Less than three years later, by filings and by bidding at competitive sales, CPOG picked up more than seven million acres of exploratory holdings in western and northern Canada, offshore in Lake Erie, and in Britain's North Sea.

A plunge into the Arctic

The biggest plunge was in the Arctic Islands, when the Panarctic Oils syndicate in 1968 launched a minimum $30 million exploration program on 50 million acres of permit holdings, financed 45 percent by the federal government and 55 percent by some 20 private companies. By far the largest private interest in Panarctic is held by Canadian Pacific, with CPOG holding nine percent, and Cominco Ltd. (owned 53 percent by Canadian Pacific), holding another nine percent. Canadian Pacific views Panarctic's planned three to four-year exploration program in the Arctic Islands as only a starter. CPOG vice-president and general manager John Taylor has said that "Canadian Pacific is in the Arctic Islands to stay."

To facilitate development of its non-transportation assets, Crump spinned off most of these assets into a new company, Canadian Pacific Investments Limited, created in 1962. Five years later, CPI issued $100 million in preferred shares, the largest single public financing ever made in Canada. It was immediately over-subscribed. CPI was essentially wholly-owned by the CPR in 1970, but if all the outstanding preferred shares are converted into common shares, and the share purchase warrants exercised. CPR's ownership in its resource-based subsidiary could be reduced by 1974 to 77 percent.

Central-Del Rio

Late in 1969, Canadian Pacific Oil and Gas was merged into Central-Del Rio Oils on a share exchange basis. CPI had already invested $30 million for slightly more than a half interest in Central-Del Rio. This was increased, as a result of the merger, to 89 percent. The combined operations provided Central-Del Rio with annual sales of $36 million and varying interests in more than 80 million acres of oil and gas rights throughout Canada. CPI, by 1970, had also invested $53 million in Trans-Canada Pipe Lines to become the largest single

292

shareholder (17 percent) in the free world's longest natural gas pipe-line, and $6 million for 5 1/2 percent interest in Husky Oil.

With assets of $2.1 billion, Canadian Pacific was the second largest commercial organization in Canada in 1968. Its railways, planes, ships, trucks, communications networks and other related activities accounted for less than half of its earnings of $82 million. The balance came from Canadian Pacific Investments with its natural resources, hotels and real estate interests — a far different picture than in 1955 when its non-transportation assets were largely hidden. By 1969, oil, gas and pipelines were the biggest money makers for CPI.

Coinciding with the resurgent growth in Canadian Pacific was a marked change in ownership. In 1955, Canadian Pacific was owned only 15 percent by Canadians, with the balance owned mostly by English investors. By 1969, it was 63 percent Canadian-owned. By developing its latent natural resources, Buck Crump and his associates not only put the Canadian Pacific back on the tracks, but also returned it home to Canada.

Canadian control

Chapter Fourteen

The Athabasca Tar Sands

*God's
forgotten
country*

For more than half a century, the people of Fort McMurray had watched oil men come and go.

The oil men had come to dig from the banks of the Athabasca and Clearwater Rivers a plastic mixture of sand and bitumen known as the Athabasca tar sands. They had dug holes, drilled wells, experimented with underground fires, studied plans for an underground nuclear explosion and built plants to mine and process the tar sands. They came with visions of developing the largest known deposit of oil in the world, and they left, despairing, defeated and frustrated.

And Fort McMurray, a tiny fur trading settlement in the Athabasca country 250 miles northeast of Edmonton at the end of the Northern Alberta Railway line, shrank into a pocket of poverty in the midst of the affluence of oil-rich Alberta.

Fort McMurray has seen a lot of history since that day in 1788 when fur trader Peter Pond arrived to establish his "Fort of the Forks" (now Fort McMurray) near the junction of the Athabasca and Clearwater Rivers. This was the heart of the storied Athabasca country, hub of a fur-trading empire that stretched from the Great Lakes to the Pacific Ocean, from Alaska to California. From Montreal and Hudson Bay, the fur traders paddled their canoes to Athabasca – men like Peter Pond, David Thompson, Alexander Mac-

GCOS plant.

kenzie, George Simpson and Simon Fraser — men who first explored, mapped and tamed the northern half of the North American continent. More than a century and a half later, half the population of Fort McMurray was Metis and names like Mackenzie, Fraser and MacDonald are still common in the area.

Staging area

Fort McMurray became the staging area for transportation into the Arctic northwest, the start of a 1,700-mile transportation system down the Athabasca and Mackenzie Rivers as far as the Arctic coast. First canoes, then the steam-powered, wood-burning diesel tugs of the Hudson's Bay Company plied the broad, placid waterways downstream from Fort McMurray. In 1916 it became the terminus of the 250-mile Northern Alberta Railway from Edmonton, and heavy freight and supplies were loaded here on the barges towed by the throbbing diesel tugs of the federal government's Northern Transportation Company.

During second world war, some 2,500 members of the U.S. Army Engineering Corps and 50,000 tons of equipment were transferred from rail to barge at Fort McMurray for shipment 1,100 miles downstream for the Canol project. Later, Fort McMurray handled the freight moving in and out of Uranium City on Lake Athabasca where the government's Eldorado Mining and Refining was developing production from one of the world's richest uranium ore areas. These were hectic, exciting years for Fort McMurray.

Bypass

Then came the slump. A new highway and then a railway to Hay River on Great Slave Lake bypassed the transportation route to the far north through Fort McMurray. With a glut of world uranium supplies, activity at Uranium City ground to a halt. Tugs of the Northern Transportation Company were beached and many of them in 1970 were still rotting and rusting while summer employment by NTC at Fort McMurray dropped from 200 in 1958 to 35 a few years later. To top it off, Athabasca's historic fur trade industry had shrunk to a shadow and the dwindling number of trappers were hard pressed to earn enough for even groceries as prices for trapped furs fell drastically.

"This seemed like God's forgotten country," recalls Clair Peden, road construction contractor and former mayor of Fort McMurray. It looked like it, too. In 1960, it was a one-street town (a street of either mud, dust or snow, depending on the season) with a single clapboard hotel, a lonely service station, a few frontier stores and a collection of mostly unpainted shacks and log cabins, housing a population of 1,100. And still the oil men kept coming and going from Fort McMurray to drill their wells, study the tar sands, conduct their experiments and operate their pilot plants. The people of Fort McMurray no longer cared. They had long since lost all faith and hope in the plans of the oil men. They knew that literally beneath their feet lay the largest known deposit of oil in the world, and for all that they could tell it would be there forever.

"When the real thing finally came, hardly anyone would believe it," recalls Clair Peden.

The real thing finally came early in 1964 when first hundreds, and then finally as many as 2,000 men, together with hundreds of thousands of tons of equipment, supplies and material moved through Fort McMurray to the site of a vast construction project 20 miles northwest of the town. Slowly it dawned on the people of Fort McMurray that this time it was for real. By the time the $250 million complex of Great Canadian Oil Sands Limited was completed in 1967, Fort McMurray was a far different town. No longer a poverty-ridden backwash, Fort McMurray in 1968 was a thriving town of 5,000 people, as modern as tomorrow, "the oil capital of the world."

The real thing in 1964

The importance of the Athabasca tar sands, however, has really little to do with Fort McMurray. It has much to do with the future oil security of North America. And when the plant of Great Canadian Oil Sands Limited – controlled by Sun Oil Company of Philadelphia – was officially dedicated on September 25, 1967 it brought into effect a petroleum insurance policy. The spectre of a petroleum shortage has long haunted North American oil men, particularly in the United States. In 1920 the U.S. Geological Survey had predicted that only seven billion barrels of oil were still left to be found in the United States, and within the decade there would not be enough oil to meet requirements. Since that forecast, more than 50 billion barrels of oil have been discovered in the United States. But today the spectre of an oil shortage still haunts North America.

If a shortage of petroleum does develop, North America could turn for supplementary supplies to the Athabasca tar sands. Locked in these sands is enough bitumen (a very heavy grade oil) to yield 300 billion barrels of premium quality synthetic crude, equal to 75 percent of the world's proven reserves of conventional crude oil in 1969. If North America had no other petroleum supply, the Athabasca tar sands alone could meet 1969 demand rates for 60 years.

Stir a gallon of heavy molasses into a child's sand box, add a little clay, and the resultant mixture would give you some idea of what the Athabasca tar sands are like. Only in this case it is bitumen – blacker and heavier than molasses – which is mixed with the clean, white sand. Multiply this image until it is up to 300 feet thick, spread over an area of 30,000 square miles — 20 percent of Alberta — and covered with anywhere from a few inches to 2,000 feet of overburden. All of this is set in a gently rolling land covered by scrub trees, cut by deep-banked rivers, pockmarked by a myriad of lakes and embracing endless miles of muskeg. The problem faced in extracting the bitumen is something like the problem you would face in trying to recover clean molasses from the sand box.

A $250 million plant

To extract the bitumen on a commercial scale required an investment of $250 million by Great Canadian Oil Sands Limited. From lease number 86, the GCOS plant was built to produce synthetic crude oil at a rate of 45,000 barrels per day. Lease number 86 covers a mere 4,000 acres, about one-fiftieth of one percent of the total area of the Athabasca tar sands. Yet lease number 86 contains enough bitumen to maintain the 45,000 barrels per day production rate of Great Canadian for 30 years.

Anyone flying over northeastern Alberta who had never heard of this tar sands project would have rubbed his eyes in disbelief when he came across lease number 86. All that can be seen from a plane is an expanse of unsullied wilderness. Suddenly there is a clearing in the scrub forest of pine, spruce and poplar. Here, seemingly in the middle of nowhere, are a pair of gigantic excavators chewing into the earth; a thermal-electric power plant large enough to serve a town of 50,000 people with a concrete stack that towers 360 feet high to dwarf the trees; a complex of towers, vessels and piping much like a conventional oil refinery; and great storage tanks that can hold a million barrels of oil.

93,000 tons of sand per day

Production of the tar sands starts with the strip mining operation. Two crawler-mounted, bucket-wheel excavators are used to mine the sands. Ten scoops mounted on the outer rim of a wheel mine at a rate of 93,000 tons of sand a day, which is shipped on a conveyor belt to the extraction plant. Here the sand is mixed with hot water and chemicals and in a series of steps yields nearly 60,000 barrels a day of heavy black bitumen while 80,000 tons a day of tailings are dumped into vast disposal areas.

The recovered bitumen, too heavy to be moved by pipeline, is then treated in the six largest coker units in the world, which remove coke from the bitumen at a rate of 2,600 tons a day. The coke is burned in the thermal electric plant to provide power requirements for the complex. The steam also provides the hot water required in the primary extraction unit. By the time it leaves the coker units, the bitumen has been converted into distillate products which are further

298

Workings on GCOS property.

processed to recover sulphur at a rate of 314 tons per day, and yield the end product, 45,000 barrels a day of synthetic crude oil, the color of straw. From the Athabasca plant the synthetic oil is shipped by pipeline to refineries as far away as Toledo, Ohio.

If the whole scheme sounds something like a Rube Goldberg invention, it is still not half so weird as many other methods which have been unsuccessfully tried or proposed at Athabasca during the past half century. Underground fires, a nuclear explosion, microorganisms, steam injection and a washing machine have all figured in the abortive plans and ideas to exploit the wealth of the tar sands.

First mention of the tar sands was by Peter Pond who, in 1788, noted the black guck oozing from the banks of the Athabasca River and reported that the Indians used it to caulk their canoes. "Some bituminous fountains in which a pole 20 feet long may be inserted without the least resistance," were described the next year by Alex-

On the trail

299

ander MacKenzie. R. G. McConnell, working for the Dominion Geological Survey, reported in 1892 that "the tar sands evidence an up-welling of petroleum unequalled elsewhere in the world."

Promoters were quick to sniff the sweet scent of money mixed with the pungent odors of the tar sands and grandiose schemes to exploit the treasure were soon launched on paper. One prospectus issued in 1905 is said to depict Fort McMurray as "a miniature metropolis with a network of railway sidings, tall plumed stacks and steamers furrowing adjacent waters."

Sidney Ells

In 1913, a young engineer, Sidney Clarke Ells, set out for Athabasca to survey the prospects of commercial production for the federal mines branch, a task to which he devoted the next 32 years. It was pioneering under conditions as difficult as any fur trader ever faced – travelling by foot with a 70-pound pack the 250 miles over trackless muskeg and forest between Edmonton and Fort McMurray; camping out under northern stars at temperatures as low as 50 below; hauling on a tracking line 20 hours a day to help pull barges up the Athabasca River.

Ells set out from Athabasca Landing (north of Edmonton) with a 30-foot scow, a 22-foot freight canoe and a "crew of three white men and an alleged native pilot." Floating down stream it took the party only nine days to cover the 240 miles to Fort McMurray. In the following three months Ells' party located 247 tar sands outcrops extending over a distance of 185 miles along the banks of the Athabasca and tributary rivers, collected more than 200 samples from hand-augered holes to depths of five to seventeen feet. It took 23 days, with Ells and a 12-man crew of natives pulling 20 hours a day on a track line, on the return trip which brought out the first meaningful tar sand samples.

First samples

Ells' report of his field work in 1913 concluded that "certain areas should lend themselves to large scale commercial development," with the most promising use as a paving material. He also reported that "discovery of petroleum fields in western Canada will have a direct bearing on the development of Alberta bituminous sands."

Paving experiment

In the early winter months of 1915, Ells shipped out 60 tons of tar sands from McMurray to Edmonton by horse team "in temperatures ranging from 20 to 50 below zero and without tents for men or horses." The following year the Northern Alberta Railway was completed to within 17 miles of Fort McMurray (it was another 10 years before the final stretch was built). That summer Ells used the tar sands for experimental paving of Edmonton streets, pavement that was still in use half a century later. Tar sands material was also

Sidney Ells
and his party
haul a barge
containing tar
sand samples
up the
Athabasca
River, 1914.

subsequently used for paving in the Jasper National Park and in 1930
Ells had completed construction of a large mixing plant, housed on a
railway flat-car, for preparing paving material at a rate of 700 tons
per day. The plant was used for a period of two months, but with
Alberta gripped by the depression of the thirties, there was very little
road construction underway, and the plant was eventually sold for
scrap. In the end, the cost of transporting raw tar sands from Athabasca made its use economically unfeasible.

A host of government researchers, oil companies and individuals,
meanwhile, continued the attack on the tar sands, mostly with a

Getting the oil out

notable lack of success. One adventurous entrepreneur tried lighting a fire at the bottom of a shallow bore hole in the hope that the heat would induce the bitumen to flow from the sand. About all that happened, unfortunately, was that the fire kept sputtering out. Years later oil companies tried far more sophisticated underground fires, which they called "experimental in situ thermal recovery projects," but without much greater success. Another unsuccessful idea involved the use of micro-organisms which were to feed upon the tar sands and in the process extract the bitumen. That didn't work, either.

A method using centrifugal force was developed by Calgary inventor Gordon Coulson and first tested on his wife's spin-dry washing machine. So impressed with the process was Royalite Oil Company that, early in 1957, it announced it would proceed immediately with a $50 million project which would be producing synthetic crude from the tar sands by 1960 at a rate of 20,000 barrels per day. Royalite never did build the project and later sold most of its tar sands interests to other oil firms which quietly dropped the "washing machine method" in favor of other processes. Great Canadian Oil Sands, however, uses centrifuges in the final extraction process at its plant to remove the "fines" — small particles of clay described as being "finer than talcum powder."

The atomic blast proposal

The most spectacular idea of all first occurred to M. L. Natland of Richfield Oil Corporation in 1957 in Saudi Arabia, as he watched the setting sun which, he later wrote, "looked like a huge orange fire-ball sinking gradually into the earth." The sunset reminded Natland of a nuclear explosion, causing him to wonder why the intense heat generated by such a blast could not be harnessed to cook the bitumen out of the tar sands and allow it to be produced by conventional oil wells.

Richfield (now Atlantic Richfield Company) and its partners carefully worked out plans to set off an experimental nine-kiloton nuclear explosion at a depth of 1,250 feet and at a site 64 miles south of Fort McMurray. The plans were studied and approved during 1958 and 1959 by the U.S. Atomic Energy Commission and by special technical committees established by the Alberta and federal governments. But in the end, final approval was withheld by the federal government because of an international moratorium on nuclear explosions. In 1970 the oil companies were still awaiting a chance to set off their big bang.

Ultimate conquest of the tar sands was not the result of efforts in a single chain of continuous events. It was the result of a number of threads of events stretching back nearly half a century, each of which represented the hopes of men working on separate projects and all of which were eventually woven into the fabric of the Great Canadian Oil Sands project.

One of the most important threads was spun by the late Dr. Karl Adolf Clark who, as a young scientist at the newly formed Research Council of Alberta, started basement experiments in 1923 on his "hot water flotation" process, developing the basic technology now being used by Great Canadian to separate the sand and bitumen. In theory the process is simple; raw tar sands are mixed with hot water, causing the bitumen to rise to the surface as a froth which is skimmed off, while residue sand settles out at the bottom. In application, the process is highly sophisticated. Clark spent more than 40 years perfecting his hot water flotation process, experimenting with pilot projects, and assisting in its application in proposed commercial projects, all of which ended in failure. When Clark retired from the Research Council he was appointed by GCOS as a special consultant to help once more to apply his process in a commercial application. But he never did see it brought to fruition. He died in December, 1966, just seven months before the GCOS plant began production.

Karl Clark's process

About the time that Clark started his research work, a group of New York city policemen somehow acquired leases in the tar sands and formed Alcan Oil Company, selling out in 1923 to R. C. Fitzsimmons, who re-organized it as the International Bitumen Company.

Fitzsimmons experiment

Fitzsimmons developed his own hot water flotation process — in principle similar to Clark's process but differing substantially in application — and, using less than $50 worth of materials, managed to construct a make-shift hot water separation unit. Fitzsimmons' operation was enlarged several times (by 1941 the firm had invested more than $300,000) and was really the first successful commercial tar sands project. The bitumen that Fitzsimmons produced was not completley free of sand or clay particles and certainly was not suitable for refinery feedstock. But it was a fine product for waterproofing roofs and was sold for this purpose through a western Canadian chain of hardware stores. Following a series of changes in name and ownership, Fitzsimmons' company eventually became the present Great Canadian Oil Sands Limited.

Another attempt at tar sands production resulted from a visit to Denver in 1929 when Ells outlined possibilities of the Athabasca deposit to U.S. oil man Max W. Ball and his associates. The following year Ball formed Canadian Northern Oil Sands Products Limited, which later became Abasand Oils Limited, and during the next 15

Max Ball and Abasand

Karl Clark

years funnelled more than $2 million into tar sands development, some of it financed by the federal government during the second world war in an effort to secure more oil supplies.

After conducting laboratory research and pilot plant work, Ball had a plant in operation by 1940, capable of processing 400 tons per day of tar sands. By September of 1941 the plant had produced 17,000 barrels of bitumen which was refined into gasoline, diesel oil, fuel oil and coke. Then the plant was destroyed by fire.

Canada by this time was at war, and victory depended on ample supplies of oil. Head of the government's Wartime Oil Administration was Harold Rea, later chairman of the board of Great Canadian Oil Sands, but even then involved in Athabasca development. "During the dark days of world war two, Canada was hard-pressed to meet even essential petroleum needs," Rea later recalled. "Submarine warfare had already closed down a large east coast refinery. The Canadian Wartime Oil Administration was forced to initiate development of every known Canadian source of petroleum, including the Athabasca tar sands."

The government took over the Abasand property on a temporary basis, redesigned the facilities to incorporate some improved separation methods, and by 1944 once more had the plant in operation. But in the following year, the ill-fated Abasand plant was for a second time destroyed by fire. Abasand, however, has managed to retain a 25 percent interest in certain Athabasca leases – including the 4,000-acre lease from which GCOS is now producing. Now controlled by Power Corporation of Canada, Abasand in 1967 started receiving its first royalty revenues from the tar sands, after 37 years of frustration.

Despite initial success in selling bitumen as a waterproofing compound, Fitzsimmons' International Bitumen Company also had its share of troubles. In 1942 Fitzsimmons sold out to a group of Canadian and British investors headed by L. R. Champion and the firm's name was again changed, to Oil Sands Limited. In 1944, Oil Sands and the Alberta Government started work on a $500,000 pilot plant to further test the hot water separation methods developed by Clark and the Research Council. The plant was completed in 1949 and based on the results an economic study sponsored by the Alberta Government in 1950 concluded that commercial production of the Athabasca tar sands was economically feasible. But there was no great rush by oil companies to exploit the tar sands on the basis of the findings of a government study. The large fields of conventional oil then being discovered in Alberta offered far more economic and profitable sources of petroleum than those star-crossed tar sands. With a string of great discoveries like Leduc, Redwater, Bonnie Glen and Wizard Lake, who needed the tar sands?

Pilot plant

In Philadelphia, the Pew family, which controls the billion-dollar Sun Oil Company, had long been aware of the Athabasca tar sands. Ranked (in 1967) as the 12th largest U. S. oil company, Sun's operations embrace ship building, oil producing in the United States, Canada and Venezuela, petroleum marketing in eastern United States, Quebec, and Ontario, and refineries in Pennsylvania, Ohio, Texas and Ontario. But Sun has historically been a crude-deficit

Pew's Gamble

company, its refining and marketing operations demanding more oil than it has been able to find and produce.

Sun's interest in Athabasca extended back at least as far as 1944 when the late J. Edgar Pew, then vice-president in charge of production and later Sun's chairman, held discussions with Champion, whose Oil Sands Limited was seeking funds to build a tar sands plant. Sun decided that the time for the tar sands was not quite ripe, but in 1954 acquired a 75 percent interest from Abasand oils in 4,000-acre lease number 86 at Athabasca. Oil Sands Limited, meanwhile, had again changed its corporate coat and in 1953 emerged as Great Canadian Oil Sands. In 1958, GCOS contracted with Sun Oil for the rights to mine and process the sands from lease number 86 (subject to royalty payments to Sun and Abasand) while Sun also contracted to purchase 75 percent of production from a plant proposed by GCOS which would produce 31,500 barrels per day of synthetic crude.

Application for production

GCOS formally applied in 1960 for Alberta government authorization for its complex. It finally won approval in October, 1962, and the permit stipulated that construction was to start by 1964 with completion by September 30, 1966. But this was far from the end of troubles for GCOS.

During hearings before the Alberta Oil and Gas Conservation Board, competing applications for tar sands projects were made by Imperial Oil and three other affiliated oil companies, and by Shell Canada. Both the Imperial group and Shell sought authorizations for projects that would each produce 100,000 barrels per day of synthetic oil, maintaining that this was the minimum economic production and implying that the GCOS project was too small to be feasible.

The government was anxious to see commercial production from the tar sands, for this would ensure the availability of adequate petroleum supplies in the event that the reserves of the province's conventional oil ever proved to be inadequate. In its request for a permit, GCOS pointed to evidence "that additional sources of Canadian oil must be brought into production if Canada is to supply its domestic and U.S. export needs and still keep a prudent life of reserves," especially in the face of dwindling supply and increasing demand in the United States. The government appeared to agree, yet it was also determined that tar sands production, with the benefit of preferential government treatment, should not impair the conventional oil producing industry which generates a quarter of a billion dollars a year in Alberta government revenues. So the government authorized the smaller GCOS plant, and deferred until 1969 a decision on the other two applications.

Now GCOS had its permit, and all it needed was the money to build the plant, an amount estimated at $110 million in 1960 but revised to $122 million by 1962. Up to this point, financing for GCOS had come primarily from Canadian and English investors, and L. R. Champion, who had bought out International Bitumen in 1942, was still a major shareholder in GCOS. In order to help raise the money it would now need, GCOS had granted an option to the Canadian Pacific Railway to purchase a 51 percent interest in the company; the CPR in turn had assigned one-third of this option to Sun Oil and one-third to Canadian Oil Companies, which by that time, however, had been acquired by Shell Canada.

Before putting up the money, the CPR and Shell took another hard look at the project and dropped their options, which left Sun holding the ball. Sun wasn't certain that it wanted it either – certainly not at a production rate of 31,500 barrels a day which looked too small to be economic.

Financing

The final decision came down to John Howard Pew, chairman of the board of Sun Oil, son of the company's founder, industrialist, philanthropist, and patriarch of the Pew family. The proposal facing Pew was that GCOS go back to the Alberta government and ask for an increase in the authorized production volume to a rate of 45,000 barrels daily. To ensure financing, Sun would invest $67.5 million in GCOS, acquiring 81 percent interest, and assist in raising remaining funds required. The cost, for a plant of 45,000 barrels per day, was now estimated at $190 million.

It was a big gamble – larger, perhaps, than the company realized, because by the time the project was completed the cost was not $190 million but $250 million. It meant committing a substantial portion of Sun's financial resources in a venture where operating costs and results were unproven, where the technology was mostly untried, where profit would at best be modest.

But there were certain offsetting advantages. To meet its product sales, Sun in 1963 was a net buyer of some 75,000 barrels a day of crude oil and refined petroleum products. GCOS would help bring production closer into balance with product sales. Sun refineries would be assured of a continuing supply source at a constant price, regardless of future supply-demand trends or government restriction

Pew decides to go ahead

Oil sands
excavator.

on foreign oil imports (Canadian crude was exempt from U.S. oil import controls). With conventional U.S. crude supplies declining, development of a synthetic crude oil industry — based on tar sands, oil shales and coal — might well be the answer in meeting future U.S. petroleum requirements.

The first firm to establish such production would have a big competitive edge, and might thereby reap large benefits eventually, even if initial rewards were slim. U.S. government agencies and private companies had budgeted hundreds of millions of dollars for pilot plant and experimental work in developing such synthetic fuel sources. But tar sands development would likely come from a crude deficit company; a firm with crude production and refinery runs in balance could hardly afford to cut back its conventional oil production to accommodate more expensive synthetic crude at its refinery.

And if the GCOS plant did turn out to be the precursor of a large synthetic oil industry, Sun's crude deficit position could really turn out to be an advantage after all. Sun and the Pew family had been watching the Athabasca tar sands for more than 20 years. If they were ever going to act, the time was now. John Howard Pew decided to take the gamble.

The Alberta government approved the revised plans of Great Canadian in April, 1964. One of the conditions of the approval was that the plant was in production by September 30, 1967.

On September 25, 1967, some 500 government, industry and press representatives from throughout North America flew to Fort McMurray to attend the dedication of the complex, which was already producing synthetic crude. Within a few weeks the product would be starting its pipeline journey of nearly 3,000 miles to refineries in Ontario and Ohio. The dedication ceremonies were held in the

Completion

Cokers at
GCOS
plant.

309

Conveyor
system
carries sand
to plant
for processing.

J. Howard
Pew

"bubble", a huge canvas structure supported by compressed air and formerly used to cover winter construction at the plant site. The sound of heavy equipment and the shrill siren blast from the excavating machines reverberated through the bubble, signifying that here was a project so urgent that production couldn't be stopped even momentarily for the official dedication.

There was a long head table of company officials and visiting dignitaries, and an endless procession of speakers with an equally endless procession of cliches. Sidney Ells was there, a living witness to the 54 years of hopes and frustrations that had passed since that day he had first arrived at Athabasca by river scow to assess possibilities of developing the tar sands.

At the head table, an old man sat silent, impassive, through the lengthy speeches, huddled deeply into a blue overcoat with the collar turned up at the back, and with rimless spectacles riding down an ample nose. When everyone else had had his say, the old man got up to speak, and it was evident that John Howard Pew, at 85, was still the undisputed captain of Sun Oil.

"No nation can long be secure in this atomic age unless it be amply supplied with petroleum," said Pew. "It is the considered opinion of our group that if the North American continent is to produce the oil to meet its requirements in the years ahead, oil from the Athabasca area must of necessity play an important role."

Only time will tell what role the Athabasca tar sands will play in supplying the future petroleum requirements of North America. But this much is certain: the Athabasca tar sands are the best petroleum insurance that North America has.

311

Chapter Fifteen

The Arctic

The lands that fringe that Arctic Ocean at the top of the world may contain a storehouse of petroleum reserves, as well as metallic minerals, as large as any the world has known.

The potential oil-rich lands sweep in a circular path across Alaska, the northernmost reaches of Canada, Greenland and the Soviet Union, and may yield reserves to rival or even surpass those in the area which circles the Persian Gulf and which, in 1970, accounted for more than 60 percent of the world's proven oil reserves.

Could transform world patterns

Successful discovery, development and exploitation of the Arctic potential could transform world oil reserves and shift the focal point of supply from the eastern hemisphere back to North America. Canada, which in 1970 accounted for only two percent of the world's oil reserves, may well emerge as one of the major suppliers if the Arctic potential lives up to the hopes.

The fabulous potential, however, is matched well by formidable problems to be overcome before the Arctic is conquered – problems now being tackled with expenditures measured in the billions of dollars.

For Canada, and to a lesser extent, Alaska, hurdling the obstacles will require the opening of the legendary Northwest Passage, the fabled shorter shipping route between Europe and the Orient, a climax to a quest which has spanned nearly five centuries. That the

Imperial (
Atkinson F
oil discov

obstacles will be cleared and the prize captured, there can be little doubt, the question is mostly one of time – months, years or decades.

Prudhoe Bay points the way

It was the discovery of oil in 1968 on the North Slope of Alaska, at Prudhoe Bay, the largest oil field found in North America after more than a century of exploration, which fully awakened the world to the possibilities of Arctic oil prospects. As Leduc had triggered the exploration explosion throughout western Canada, so Prudhoe Bay two decades later set in full motion the Arctic play of North America, on a scale which could well dwarf that in western Canada.

The North Slope basin spans 600 miles on the northern fringe of Alaska, squeezed between the Beaufort Sea to the north and the rugged, snow-bound rocks of the Brooks mountain range to the south. It includes a treeless and table-flat Arctic coastal plain and, farther south, the undulating foothills of the Brooks mountains. The North Slope basin stretches inland from the ocean a distance of 20 to 200 miles, embracing an area of nearly 70,000 square miles.

Naval field

Geologists had long recognized the rocks of Alaska's North Slope as holding attractive possibilities for substantial accumulations of oil and gas. In 1923, the U.S. government designated an area of 37,000 square miles of the North Slope as U.S. Naval Petroleum Reserve No. 4, an area where all potential oil reserves have been preserved to meet possible future naval requirements. During the following three years, field parties from the U.S. Geological Survey conducted reconnaissance studies, and in 1944 the Navy started an eight-year, $50 million exploration program which resulted in the discovery of several modest-sized oil and gas fields, the largest of which was Umiat. Combined reserves discovered on the naval reserves were in the order of 300 million barrels of oil and a trillion cubic feet of natural gas which, had they been located in a more accessible area of the United States and off a naval reserve, would have been worth more than a billion dollars.

The oil and gas fields on the Naval reserve for years failed to attract more than sporadic interest by oil companies. Oil reserves here were considered much like those at Canada's Norman Wells field – too remote to be of economic value. A few daring explorers persisted in geologic studies, seismic surveys and some drilling, resulting in expensive abandonments. The American Association of Petroleum Geologists, in a review of exploration activities in 1967, noted that only one wildcat was drilling on the North Slope, a joint-venture test by Atlantic Richfield Company and Humble Oil (subsidiary of Standard Oil of New Jersey). The AAPG review concluded that "little or no geophysical or geologic work will be conducted on the Arctic slope during 1968 unless the currently drilling well is successful."

The "currently drilling well" discovered the Prudhoe Bay field.

Known as ARCO Prudhoe Bay No. 1, the wildcat was located on the flat tundra near the ocean, 190 miles southeast of Point Barrow. Drilling started in April, 1967, and late that year the well encountered a Triassic sandstone section some 400 feet thick, the bottom 70 feet oil bearing and the balance yielding natural gas. Below that a second, smaller pay section was found in the rocks of Mississippian age. The two companies knew they had a good discovery, but it was not until the middle of 1968 that the real dimensions of the strike were indicated. A followup well drilled seven miles away and down-dip on the giant structure which had been mapped by seismic, found the same Triassic sandstone at a lower elevation, below the gas cap in the reservoir, and containing an oil column 300 feet thick. Further followup wells by Atlantic Richfield and Humble, and by others such as British Petroleum, which held leases on the structure, confirmed that Prudhoe Bay was indeed the largest oil field ever discovered in North America, with possibly 10 billion barrels of recoverable oil reserves. A second strike on another structure at Ugnu, northwest of Prudhoe Bay, was made by British Petroleum and Atlantic Richfield in 1969.

ARCO discovery

With the Prudhoe Bay strike, oil companies poured men, equipment and money into the North Slope in a feverish race to find new treasures. Tugs and barges of the Canadian government-owned Northern Transportation Company moved drilling rigs, mud, cement, pipe and other equipment from Hay River down the Mackenzie River and across the Beaufort Sea to Prudhoe Bay, some 1,400 miles. From Seattle, other tugs and barges moved more equipment up the west coast, through the Bering Strait and past Point Barrow to the North Slope. During the winter months, when sea navigation was closed, a fleet of a dozen giant Lockheed Hercules cargo aircraft shuttled steadily back and forth between Anchorage and Fairbanks and the North Slope, carrying 20-ton loads. Everything was flown in — drilling rigs, portable camps, fuel, men, food. Even spruce logs, a foot in diameter and 30 feet long, were flown in from Fairbanks, to be used

Arctic oil rush

as pilings set through the permafrost to make a firm structure to hold the rigs. On the North Slope, there are no trees. In the winter of 1968-69, an estimated $15 million was spent by oil companies just on Hercules transportation to the North Slope.

Drillers from Texas, California, Oklahoma, Wyoming and throughout the U.S. oil patch, manned the rigs, working seven days a week, 12 hours a day – three weeks on and one week off – in isolated camps where the temperature can hit 50 degrees below zero with a 40 mile-per-hour wind, and the night is four months long. They were earning big money. A Cat skinner, tough enough to stick it out, could make as much as $30,000 a year.

To get the oil from the North Slope to refineries, Atlantic Richfield, Humble Oil and British Petroleum planned to start construction in 1970 on the biggest crude oil pipeline in North America. Eight hundred miles of 48-inch diameter steel pipe, it would stretch from Prudhoe Bay, across the Brooks Mountains through the Ana-

316

tuvik Pass to a deep-sea terminal at Valdez on the Pacific coast. From there, tankers would carry the oil to refineries along the U.S. west coast. Estimated cost of the pipeline was in excess of $1 billion. Studies were being prepared for other possible pipelines – a 3,000-mile oil line from the North Slope, east along the Arctic coast to the Mackenzie River, and across Canada to markets as far as Chicago and possibly even the U.S. eastern seaboard; natural gas pipelines from the North Slope to supply consumers in the U.S. midwest and in California. More than $40 million was invested in sea trials designed to determine if supertankers with icebreaker bows, strengthened hulls and extra power could bust through the Northwest Passage to move the oil to the eastern U.S. more economically than by overland pipeline.

Confirmation of the North Slope basin potential was provided on September 10, 1969, when the State of Alaska sold by auction the oil rights on 400,000 acres of the North Slope for total cash payments of $900 million. It was the largest amount of money ever paid at a single sale of oil and gas leases.

The Prudhoe Bay and Ugnu fields may have anywhere from 10 billion to 20 billion barrels of recoverable oil reserves — one quarter to one half of all the other proven conventional oil reserves in Canada and the United States in 1969. And the potential of the entire North Slope has been little more than scratched.

Potential of the Islands

Far greater than that of the North Slope, however, may be the oil potential of Canada's Arctic Islands. Geologically, the rocks of the Arctic Islands are considered at least as prospective for large oil reserves as those of the North Slope basin, and the area is five times as great — some 350,000 square miles as compared with 70,000 square miles.

The islands of the Canadian Arctic Archipelago form a polar desert where a thin skiff of snow sweeps across 525,000 square miles of empty land, an area almost as large as the sand-swept Arabian desert. Two thirds of this region contains potential oil bearing rocks which range in thickness up to nearly five miles. The remaining area, which flanks the sedimentary basin, is comprised of the igneous and metamorphic rocks of the Precambrian shield, promising a vast array of metallic minerals. The desert also stretches for a thousand miles along the narrow Arctic coastal plain on the mainland where it embraces an additional 20,000 square miles of potential oil bearing rocks and some 30,000 square miles of Precambrian shield.

First exploration in 1959

Exploration for oil on the Arctic Islands did not start until 1959, and 10 years later only three dry holes had been drilled and some $8 million spent. During the 1970's, at least $100 million is likely to be spent on the search for oil among the islands, and if large reserves result, the expenditures will be many times greater.

"The Arctic Islands aren't that awfully damn cold" says a driller who worked the winter of 1961-62 on what was then the most northerly wildcat drilled in the world, on Melville Island. "But the winters are sure as hell dark, and damn long."

In fact, moderated by prevailing winds from the Greenland Sea, the temperatures in this Arctic desert are not as cold as continental Arctic areas. Average July temperatures range between 35 and 65 F., while in January it averages -41, with a record low of -60. By contrast, absolute recorded low at Snag in the Yukon Territories is -84, while at Verkhoyansk in sub-Arctic Russia the thermometer has dipped as low as -94. Precipitation in the lowland and plateau areas, which embrace 92 percent of the islands, averages only 2.5 inches per year, compared with 18 inches at Calgary, located in a dry belt.

The winter snow is quickly lifted by the brilliant, 24-hour summer sunshine, which melts the top few inches of the permafrost layer that extends more than 1,500 feet below the surface. Landing on relatively flat areas with their island-hopping aircraft, equipped with soft, over-sized wheels, geologists can cover a lot of ground in the continuous days of the short summer. But late August can bring the first of the blizzards, and the end of the summer field season.

Indications of oil have been noted in the Arctic Islands for nearly a century and a half. Arctic explorer William Edward Parry noted in 1831 that some island rocks, when broken, gave off a petroliferous odor. Wallace Pratt, former chief geologist with Standard Oil of New Jersey, in 1947 postulated that the Arctic Islands might some day become one of the world's major oil producing areas. Pratt observed that the most important world oil reserves had been found in three inter-continental areas which had been occupied during much of geologic time by Mediterranean seas; the area bordering the U.S. Gulf coast, the Caribbean, and the Middle East area bordering the Persian Gulf. The land-ringed Arctic sea, between the continents of North America, Europe and Asia, is a fourth such area, said Pratt.

Geological survey

The Geological Survey of Canada, in 1947, started extensive geological reconnaissance surveys of the islands, supported by aeromagnetic and aerophoto surveys. A paper on the "Geology and petroleum possibilities in the Canadian Arctic Islands," by Y. O. Fortier and R. Thorsteinsson of the GSC and A. H. McNail of Dartmouth College, published by the American Association of Petroleum Geologists in 1954, attracted considerable attention. The authors concluded that "the analysis of the sedimentary and tectonic elements of the Arctic Islands . . . indicates that several large areas appear to have many similarities to other regions that produce, or have in reserve, large quantities of petroleum."

Oil companies showed no more than a cursory interest in the oil prospects of the Arctic Islands. There were many, far more favorably located areas in the world in which to search for oil.

Submarine voyage

It was the U.S. nuclear submarine, Nautilus, which triggered the first interest of the oil industry in the Arctic Islands. In 1958 Nautilus made the first voyage beneath the ice of the polar cap, while later another nuclear submarine, Skate, demonstrated that it was possible to surface a submarine through the ice right at the North Pole. The oil industry saw in this a possible means of solving the problem of shipping oil from the Arctic Islands in nuclear-powered submarine tankers. This prospect, however remote at the time, coupled with further encouraging GCS reports on the geology of the islands, was enough to set off one of the greatest land rushes in Canada's oil history. In late 1958 and early 1959, oil and mining companies filed with the federal government for oil rights covering more than 120,000 square miles.

Land rush

It was more than a year before the permits were formally issued. They had to first await the promulgation of the Canada Oil and Gas Lands Regulations which provided for the issuance of federal oil and gas permits in the far north and offshore areas under regulations designed to promote the development of oil reserves at the lowest possible cost, and encourage the participation of Canadian capital. Meanwhile, geological survey crews flocked to the islands for the hectic two-month field season each summer, extending the broad reconnaissance work that had been launched by the Geological Survey.

All the right signs

What the geologists found was highly encouraging. The Arctic Islands had every known ear-mark of a major petroleum basin. The geological column present in the islands embraces the known oil bearing rocks of every age. Ample indications of petroleum were found, in the form of oil seeps, bitumen and even tar sands. The known source rocks capable of generating oil were found to be present, as were reservoir rocks capable of containing vast petroleum supplies. Every known type of geological condition capable of trapping oil accumulations is believed to be present. Possible oil bearing sections are more than a thousand feet thick, and there are large surface-indicated structures, some more than 100 miles long and capable of holding several billion barrels of recoverable oil reserves.

Geologists soon found another unique geologic condition which could facilitate the discovery of major mineral reserves, including both petroleum and metallc minerals. Throughout the inland areas of Canada, the potential oil bearing rocks are invariably covered with a relatively thick layer of glacial drift aluvium, which masks the presence of structures which could contain oil. On the Arctic Islands, the sedimentary rocks are far better exposed, greatly facilitating the study of the possible oil bearing rocks and disclosing the presence of large structures.

Flanking the sedimentary basin in the islands are the Precambrian and igneous rocks of the Precambrian shield, the source of one of the great mineral-bearing areas of North America and potentially one of

Panarctic
Oils camp
on Melville
Island.

the greatest on earth. But metallic minerals may be found not only in the shield flanking the Arctic Islands sedimentary basin, but within the basin area itself.

Other minerals

"There are few other large areas on earth where such a happy geographic relationship exists between metallic mineral resources and readily available and relatively inexpensive sources of hydrocarbon energy with which to develop the minerals," consulting geologist J. C. Sproule has stated.

Substantial mineral reserves had already been discovered in the Arctic Islands by 1970. At the northern tip of Baffin Island, Baffinland Iron Mines Ltd. had outlined two iron ore deposits containing an estimated 127 million tons of ore grading 68 percent iron. On Cornwallis and Little Cornwallis Island, Cominco, under a farmout agreement from Bankeno Mines, was exploring several lead and zinc deposits found during field geology studies for petroleum exploration.

Winter Harbor

In the summer of 1961, the M. V. Thora Dan, loaded with the drilling rig of contractor Peter Bawden Drilling Limited and thousands of tons of equipment and supplies, shipped out of Montreal, headed for Winter Harbor on Melville Island. The eyes of the oil industry turned north to watch the drilling progress at the most northerly wildcat ever drilled, 1,050 miles south of the North Pole. Winter Harbor No. 1 well was drilled by Dome Petroleum as operator for a consortium of independent oil companies.

"It will be primarily a stratigraphic test for subsurface information," Dome's exploration manager E. J. Baltrusaitis explained. "We hope it will find oil, but of course, the odds are always against any wildcat making a discovery. Even if the well finds no oil, it could still add tremendous incentive to Arctic Islands exploration by confirming our surface interpretation of subsurface conditions. This is our primary objective in drilling."

Drilling possible year round

Winter Harbor No. 1 spudded on September 10, 1961 and drilled through the long Arctic night until March 24, when it was abandoned at a depth of 12,543 feet. It did not discover oil, although there was a slight show of natural gas at a depth of 1,000 feet. But neither was it a failure. It proved the feasibility of year-round drilling in one of the most inhospitable areas of the world — at a cost of several million dollars — and further confirmed the presence of geologic conditions favorable for the accumulation of petroleum reserves. Two other wells were drilled in the Islands during the following two years, both abandoned. One near Resolute on Cornwallis Island was taken to a depth of 4,840 feet by December 15, 1963, and the other, on Bathurst Island, was abandoned on February 19, 1964, at a depth of 10,000 feet.

Interest lags

With the abandonment of the first three tests, the Arctic Islands play appeared headed for the deep freeze. The independents, with limited financial resources, were unwilling to risk the multi-million dollars required for a meaningful exploration program. The major international companies had, with few exceptions, shunned the Arctic Islands play. Burgeoning offshore exploration programs in the North Sea and in Canadian waters off the coasts of Newfoundland and Nova Scotia, diverted interest and possible exploration funds away from the Arctic Islands. Only the French government-controlled Elf Exploration continued with an aggressive program in the area, with extensive geological and geophysical surveys aimed at eventual exploratory drilling. With the possible exception of Elf, it looked as though the Arctic Islands might well be abandoned for another decade or two, perhaps even longer.

The man who kept the Arctic Islands oil play alive was John Campbell Sproule, the consulting geologist who first envisioned a $20-$30 million joint-venture exploration program for the area, and refused to let the vision die. For three years it was touch and go for Sproule's planned Panarctic Oils Ltd., and several times it looked as though it had gone. But refusing to give up, Sproule ultimately managed to win enough support from a group of companies headed by Canadian Pacific Railway interests, and from the government of Canada, to initiate the first comprehensive oil exploration program in the Arctic Islands.

J. C.
Sproule

Son of a Peace River, Alberta, dentist, Sproule has had a confessed, life-long love affair with the north country. His career in geology stemmed from a gold find along the banks of the Peace River.

It was 1925, and Sproule, then 20, was a dental technician working for his father, whose practice was spread throughout the small communities of the northern Peace River country. Traveling with his father, Sproule had acquired an interest in the geology of a spectacular country where rumors of gold and other metallic riches abounded.

The dental practice took the Sproules that August to Hudson Hope, now the site of the Peace River dam, one of the continent's largest hydro-electric power projects. It was on a Sunday that Sproule hiked seven miles up the Peace River from Hudson Hope to fish. The river was the lowest it had been in 25 years, and the flat, rock-bottomed river bed was exposed for a considerable distance from the river banks.

The river bottom was pockmarked with the occasional sinkhole, where softer concretionary areas had been washed out to form pot-shaped bowls. What was probably Sproule's first geologic theory was put to immediate use. He reasoned that if gold nuggets had ever bounced along the river bottom they might well have become trapped in these sinkholes. "I reached into one, and pulled out a handful of gravel and several gold nuggets," Sproule recalled years later.

Dreams
of a
fortune

Excited by the discovery and filled with dreams of a fortune, Sproule resolved to keep his strike quiet until he had a chance to do some prospecting and perhaps file some claims. The next day, equipped with a frying pan to pan for gold, Sproule hiked back from Hudson Hope to the scene of his gold strike. But the river, fed by

Panarctic in the Arctic Islands, 1969. Copter transfers supplies from ship to shore. Below, Ellesmere Island camp. Opposite, Drake Point test site, Melville Island.

mountain flash-floods, had risen overnight, and the sinkholes were covered with 14 feet of water.

"The river has never been that low since," Sproule later recalled, "and I guess the gold must still be there."

His future now determined, Sproule headed the following year for the University of Alberta at Edmonton and a course in geology. He spent the next 13 years studying geology, lecturing at the University of Toronto, earning a Ph.D. degree, and working on government-sponsored geological surveys across Canada, the final four years with the Geological Survey of Canada. In 1939 Sproule joined Imperial Oil as Saskatchewan exploration manager, and later moved to International Petroleum (then an Imperial Oil subsidiary) as chief advisory geologist, supervising exploration activity in South America. In 1951 he established his Calgary consulting firm, J. C. Sproule and Associates, and within a few years had the largest petroleum consulting organization in Canada.

Birth pains of Panarctic

When the rush to pick up Arctic Islands oil rights hit in 1959, Sproule was already established as one of the leading experts on the petroleum geology of the far north, particularly in the Lower Mackenzie River area where his firm had conducted geologic studies for a number of independents over a period of more than five years. It was inevitable that he would lead the new play too, and in the summer of 1960, Sproule set off on the first of his firm's geological field parties on the Islands. Sproule and others from his firm were to return to the Islands each summer during the following decade.

In his studies of the Arctic Islands oil prospects, Sproule adopted a novel approach. During the next seven years he spent $1.25 million more in studies of this area than he received in fees from the 25 clients for whom he was doing the work. Sproule pooled the geological data gathered from the studies of his client's permit areas so that each would have a more comprehensive picture, and paid the cost for studies of areas between the permit holdings of his clients. In

$5 million in data

return for the benefits they received from this extra work, the clients agreed to let Sproule use as he saw fit the complete package of geological data he had gathered. By 1967, Sproule had a file on the geology of the Arctic Islands representing an investment of more than $5 million in field studies and interpretation.

Sproule was investing heavily in the future of the Arctic Islands, and by 1964 the threat that exploration activity here might be shelved for a decade or more became only too apparent. In the face of this it seemed likely that Sproule's clients, mostly small firms, would let their permits lapse and drop out of the Arctic Islands play. This would happen unless, Sproule reasoned, a plan could be devised whereby dozens of permit holders could pool their acreage and resources to conduct a comprehensive exploration program large enough to provide an opportunity for success.

The plan began to take shape late in 1964 during a conversation with Eric Connelly, president of Pembina Pipe Lines Limited, one of the early Arctic Islands permit holders. "With $30 million, a controlling position in the Arctic Islands could be acquired and a real exploration program launched which would prevent these permits from being dropped and the area from being locked in a deep freeze," Sproule commented.

Control would cost $30 million

(Later Sproule was to write in a report to the backers of his planned project that "it became evident that a workable project could be developed, providing a dominant portion of the lands within the Arctic Islands sedimentary basin could be controlled by a single company. The advantage of a single company control would be that the entire basin area could be operated as though it were a concession, thus enabling the operator to study the complete basin prospects and then select those areas as drilling sites that are most likely to produce oil.")

The two agreed that if Sproule could put together the necessary land, Connelly would investigate means of financing the project. Sproule was able to obtain options on more than 35 million acres of permits, and further agreed to seek $15 million from private investors and government assistance. It was a quest that took nearly three years, and repeatedly it seemed that failure would be the certain result.

Money hard to find

Connelly, in August 1965, approached Dean Nesbitt of the Montreal investment firm of Nesbitt, Thomson and Company, who was intrigued with the possibilities of participating in the play, but pointed out the record of failure in raising substantial private money from Canadian sources for oil exploration under prevailing tax legislation (which contrasted sharply with U.S. tax legislation in this regard). An approach was made to the federal government which, eager to see active exploration in the Arctic Islands, was sympathetic. The tax rules were not changed, but instead Ottawa devised the "northern mineral exploration program" whereby the government would loan to Canadians unable to write-off exploration expenditures for tax purposes, up to 40 percent of the cost of approved exploration programs in the far north, with repayment only if commercial production were attained.

By early 1966 the project appeared well advanced. Panarctic Oils Ltd. had been formed and held options to earn interests in some 40 million acres of permits in return for a $30 million exploration program which was to start January 1, 1967. A plan for financing had been devised as follows: Panarctic was to raise $15 million from oil and mining companies, which were not eligible for the government's northern loans. A public company – Great Circle Petroleum Ltd. – was to raise the remaining $15 million, of which it would obtain $9 million through a public underwriting by Nesbitt, Thomson and Company, and $6 million under the government's new loan program.

Handful of eels

Things did not, however, work out that way. By May 15, 1967, when Sproule held a meeting to report progress to the permit holders, Panarctic had still only $11 million of the required $15 million from oil and mining companies, and the deadline was six weeks away. Sproule had, in fact, obtained commitments that totalled more than $15 million, but as several had dropped out at various times he never had the required amount at any one point in time. "It was like trying to hold a handful of eels," Sproule later commented. "I couldn't hang on to all of them."

Ottawa gets involved

Sproule sought – and obtained – approval from the farmers to scale down the exploration program from $30 million over five years to $20 million over three years, with a corresponding reduction in the interest to be earned, but with an option to later extend the program to the original $30 million. Panarctic was to then seek $12 million from industry and $8 million from Ottawa under the northern loan program.

"Despite the several problems that have arisen in the past, we are convinced that the necessary funds to proceed can be raised prior to June 30, and that we will, therefore, be able to proceed with the program planned," Sproule reported.

Once again it did not work out quite as planned. Panarctic did not raise the money by June 30, and when the deal was finalized on December 12 that year, it was not with a loan from the federal government, but with a $9 million government equity investment.

Thus it was that Hon. Arthur Laing, Minister of Indian Affairs and Northern Development, was able to announce in the House of Com-

mons on December 12, 1967, that Canada was to join the ranks of
nations (which includes Great Britain, France, Italy, Japan, Mexico
and a host of others) with active government participation in the
search for oil.

Panarctic's initial $20 million financing included $9 million from
the government, which gave it 45 percent ownership in the new
company, and $11 million from 20 private groups which held the
remaining 55 percent. Leading the list of private participants were
two affiliates of Canadian Pacific Investments (in turn a subsidiary of
the CPR): Cominco, 53 percent owned by CPI, and Canadian Pacific
Oil and Gas, wholly-owned by CPI.* Cominco and CPOG subscribed
for nine percent interest each in Panarctic, while other major participants included the Dome Petroleum and Dome Mines group, International Nickel Company, and Noranda Mines.

How the pie was sliced

Panarctic's initial financing was the product of the vision, persistence and $1.25 million risk of J. C. Sproule, by all odds the boldest
gambler in the Arctic Islands. "Sproule was in deep financial waters,"
recalls a business associate. "He had risked nearly everything on Panarctic, was deeply in debt to his bank, and his bank was starting to
press him."

Ironically, a few months after financing had been secured for Panarctic, the Prudhoe Bay discovery was brought in on the North Slope
of Alaska, confirming the enormous Arctic oil prospects which geologists had long forecast. The rush to explore for Arctic oil soon became a stampede. Within months, holdings of oil and gas permits in
the Arctic Islands doubled to nearly 200 million acres, embracing not
only all of the potential areas of the islands but also the ice-clogged
ocean areas between the islands. Companies which a few months
earlier had completely spurned the Arctic play were now desperately
seeking to join the play. Had the Prudhoe Bay discovery been made
earlier, financing for Panarctic's joint-venture program would have
been instantly over-subscribed.

With Panarctic's initial financing completed, Sproule was able to
recover a portion of his investment from fees and from the sale of his
extensive Arctic geology files. In addition, he received a net carried
eight percent interest in the Panarctic project, while Connelly received two percent. These carried interests will generate no revenue

*Late in 1969, Canadian Pacific Oil and Gas was merged into Central-Del Rio Oils, which
became 89 percent owned by Canadian Pacific Investments. See Chapter 13.*

Quantity is the key

until Panarctic has completely recovered the costs of whatever investment it makes in the Arctic Islands which, at best, will require
decades.

Key to exploiting the petroleum resources of the Arctic Islands
will lie in the discovery and development of prolific reserves at a low
cost per barrel in order to offset higher operating and transportation
costs. Finding vast quantities of prolific oil reserves would not auto-
matically solve all the problems confronting development of the Arctic oil potential. But it would provide the resource base which would
enable the problems to be solved.

Quest for the Northwest passage

Exploitation of the potential oil and mineral resources of the
Arctic Islands will, in the final analysis, require the opening of the
Northwest Passage, the shipping route for which English seamen first
explored in vain, nearly 500 years ago. There is no other way to get
the oil out economically, and the Northwest Passage will have to be
opened for commercial shipping, whether by supertankers designed
as the world's largest icebreakers, or by submarine tankers, if the
Arctic oil potential is to be realized.

John Cabot, in 1497, five years after Columbus landed in America,
was the first to seek the Northwest Passage as a trade route to India.
He discovered Nova Scotia and Cape Breton, but came nowhere near
the Passage. Martin Frobisher in 1576, nearly a century later, marked
the start of more concerted efforts, exploring the approaches to the
Northwest Passage along the coast of Baffin Island. Others followed,
each reaching a little closer to the goal; many of them perishing in
the attempt. England ruled the seas when John Franklin led his party
in 1845, confidently expecting to sail across the top of North America, only to disappear with all men in the unknown Arctic. Forty
expeditions, English and American, set out in the next decade to find
Franklin's party, many of them perishing in the same manner. But
they did discover the Northwest Passage, parties led by men like
Perry, M'Clure, Ross, Collinson and others, and if they did not actually sail all the way through, they at least managed to cover the
route, dragging their sleds across the ice, filling in the map at the top
of the world.

Amundsen in his 47-ton Gjoa made the first sailing in the Northwest Passage in 1903 to 1906, and the 80-ton Royal Canadian
Mounted Police patrol ship St. Roche was the first to complete the
voyage in a single year, sailing from west to east in 1940.

The impact of the Northwest Passage on the potential resources of the Arctic Islands is blazed on every globe. From Resolute, Cornwallis Island, a focal point near the centre of the Arctic Islands, a 4,000-mile radius embraces most of the industrialized nations of the world; all of North America and Europe, most of the Caribbean, Russia and Japan. Population within this circle in 1970 amounted to more than three quarters of a billion people, who consumed petroleum products at a rate of more than 30 million barrels a day.

Shipping routes, of course, do not lie along straight lines; they have to curve around such things as continents. But if you could ship through the fringes of the polar ice cap, the seaboard areas of all these countries would lie within 5,000 miles of Resolute. England and Western Europe would be 3,700 miles; Montreal, 3,100 miles; San Francisco, 4,600 miles; Tokyo, 4,700 miles. And if you could ship directly through, or under the polar ice cap, the distance to England and Western Equope would be only 3,000 miles. These are short distances in oil world traffic. From the Persian Gulf, where more than half of the world's supply of proven oil reserves are located, tankers move crude oil 8,000 miles to England through the Suez Canal, and 12,000 miles for the supertankers which skirt around Africa. From the Persian Gulf to Japan, tankers move nearly three million barrels of oil a distance of 7,800 miles every day.

"Opening of the Northwest Passage," Sproule has stated, "could go farther towards advancing Canada as a world power than any single event in our history. The new perspective provided by this convenient transport artery will be certain to bring Canada into closer association with all our circumpolar neighbors."

Central for shipping

Take 150,000 tons of steel and ballast and try to smash it through sheets of ice 10 feet thick, rows of pressure ridges where the ice is twice as thick, hummocks, small bergs, floes and islands of ice which may be 60 to 100 feet thick — and see what happens.

This was the task that Humble Oil and Refining Company, the U.S. operating subsidiary of Standard Oil of New Jersey, had assigned to the supertanker S.S. Manhattan, the first commercial class vessel to attempt a voyage through the Northwest Passage.

The first seven months of 1969 were spent preparing the Manhattan for its voyage. The ship was cut into four sections, and each section towed to a different shipyard on the U.S. eastern seaboard for strengthening and other modifications. A new 125-foot bow was built at a fifth shipyard. Designed to improve the ice breaking capability by 40 to 60 percent, the bow was built to hit the ice at an

Manhattan in the passage

331

*Extra
steel*

angle of 18 degrees, rather than the conventional 30 degrees on icebreaker ships, and was 18 feet wider than the rest of the ship's hull. Ice fenders, nine feet wide and made of 1 1/4 inch steel, were installed behind the bow on either side of the hull. Extra beams were strung across the hull to provide greater strength. When the sections were put back together at the yard of Sun Shipbuilding in Chester, Pennsylvania, the Manhattan measured 1,005 feet long – three times the length of a football field – with 155 feet of beam. Fully loaded, the ship's hull extended into the water 54 feet, the heighth of a five-storey building. Steam turbines provided 43,000 shaft horse-power for the twin propellers. The Manhattan emerged as the world's largest, most powerful icebreaker.

*Objects
of the
exercise*

Immense though it was, the Manhattan was never intended to operate through the Northwest Passage on a year-round, commercial basis. To cope with the worst of the polar ice would require ships far larger and more powerful, with special design characteristics. The Manhattan was but a half-scale, under-powered, test model.

Humble had in mind the year-round use of tankers capable of hauling 250,000 tons of oil, more than double the 115,000-ton load capacity of the Manhattan, on the 4,500-mile route from Prudhoe Bay through the Northwest Passage to the U.S. eastern seaboard. The first of these might be in operation as early as 1972, and by 1980 there could be a fleet of as many as 30 such tankers, costing $1.5 billion, each making the round trip from Prudhoe to New York in about 35 days and moving oil at an average rate of two million barrels per day. Cost of moving the oil from Alaska by tanker to the U.S. eastern seaboard could save as much as 40 to 50 cents per barrel as compared with the alternative of moving it to the same market by pipeline. If successful, the icebreaker tankers could save as much as $400 million a year in the cost of moving oil from Prudhoe Bay to New York.

"The Northwest Passage could become the catalyst which opens up the resources of far northern Alaska and Canada to the world," Humble president Dr. Stanley Jones declared as preparations neared completion for the Manhattan's voyage. "A year-round sea route in this area could do for the Arctic areas of Alaska and Canada what the railroads did for the western United States – and might do it quick-er."

The essential purpose of the Manhattan's voyage was to collect the data which would determine the requirements of the larger, com-

Manhat
in
Northw
Passa

The Great Canadian Oil Patch

Icebreaker
Sir John A.
Macdonald.

mercial ships which might follow – size, horsepower, design and
other features – and more accurately assess the costs and economic
feasibility. Could the larger tankers plow through ice ridges 100 feet
thick? Could highly sophisticated ice reconnaissance locate and
identify the thicker, tougher ice accumulations so that ships could go
around them, rather than fighting through? What assistance might be
required from powerful icebreaker ships located at strategic positions
along the route? How much would it cost?

To collect the data, the Manhattan was equipped as a floating
research vessel. Hundreds of tiny pressure gauges on the ship's hull
measured the pressure as the ship pushed into various types of ice at
varying speeds and varying horsepower. Closed-circuit television was
installed to monitor continuously the impact and effect on ice of
150,000 tons of force. A custom designed, integrated electronic navigation system employing digital computers, a satellite receiver using
radio signals from U.S. Navy polar-orbiting satellites, special sonar
devices, and other equipment were set up to measure forward speed,
bearing, side-slip and acceleration of the ship against such factors as
ice thickness, bow strain and horsepower. Surface parties were equipped to core, sample and analyze ice conditions along the route. The
U.S. Coast Guard and the Canadian Department of Transport assisted
in aerial ice reconnaissance using side scanning radar, infrared photo-
graphy and laser beams. The mountains of data collected on the two
voyages planned for the Manhattan – in August and September of

Manhattan
rou

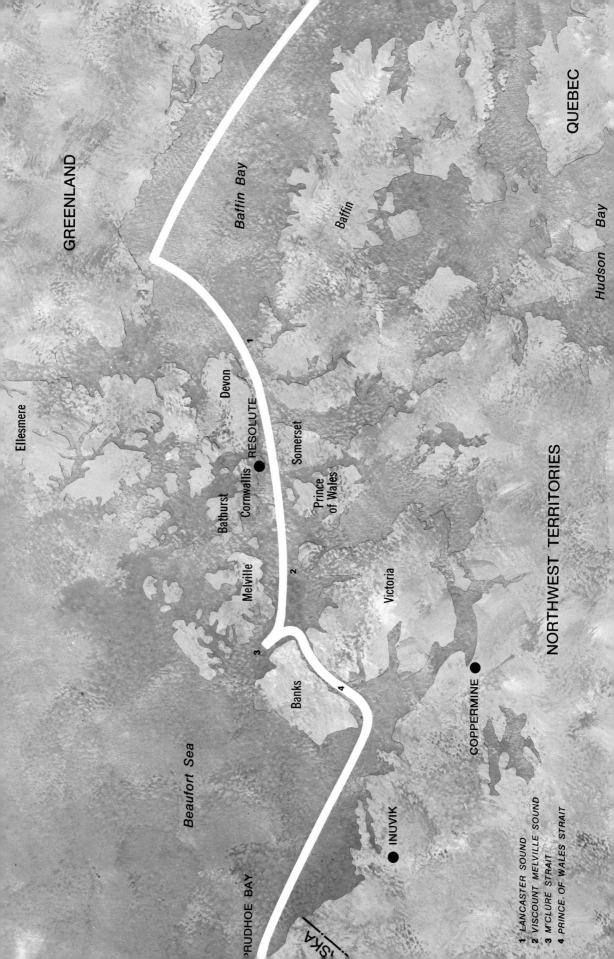

GREENLAND

QUEBEC

Baffin Bay

Baffin

Hudson Bay

Ellesmere

Devon

Bathurst

Cornwallis

RESOLUTE

Somerset

Prince of Wales

Melville

Victoria

Banks

Beaufort Sea

INUVIK

COPPERMINE

NORTHWEST TERRITORIES

PRUDHOE BAY

1

2

3

4

1 LANCASTER SOUND
2 VISCOUNT MELVILLE SOUND
3 M'CLURE STRAIT
4 PRINCE OF WALES STRAIT

1969 and the Spring of 1970 — were shipped to Humble's head office at Houston, Texas, to be processed and interpreted by computer. It would be, said Jones, "one of the most promising — yet most difficult — experiments that American industry has ever undertaken" — an experiment costing more than $40 million.

September 12, 1969; Manhattan has been out to sea from Philadelphia for three weeks, and has less than 1,000 miles left on its voyage to the Alaskan North Slope. Accompanied by the Canadian Coastguard icebreaker John A. Macdonald, the Manhattan had cleared most of the Northwest Passage which stretches 900 miles between the islands of the Canadian Arctic Archipelago. Not until it was well into the passage, did Manhattan find tough ice conditions to test. Several times, in areas of thick ice and intense pressure, Manhattan had become stuck, unable to move astern or forward, the ice clamping against her hull like a vice. Each time the Macdonald, 9,000 tons of steel propelled by 15,000 horsepower from its diesel-electric engines, had come crashing and bashing through the ice alongside Manhattan. By breaking the ice which has gripped the giant tanker, the Macdonald has freed the Manhattan, allowing her to charge back and forward until she has once more gained sufficient momentum to crack through the ice cover. This time, however, the getting out was not so easy.

Johnny Mac to the rescue

The position was a few miles into M'Clure Strait, a body of water between Banks and Melville Islands at the western edge of the Northwest Passage. Butting up against the edge of the permanent polar ice pack, M'Clure Strait is not the intended route for commercial shipping through the Northwest Passage; an easier route lies through the Prince of Wales Strait along the southeast coast, rather than the northwest coast, of Banks Island. The more northerly route was taken in order to find tougher ice conditions to test the capabilities of Manhattan. No ship had ever sailed all the way through M'Clure Strait.

Captain Robert Le M'Clure and his crew of 60 from H.M.S. Investigator, a 400-ton wooden sailing ship, had found this Strait nearly 120 years before. They were the first ever to traverse the entire Northwest Passage, but they did not make it all the way with their ship. Pulling sleds, they had walked more than 200 miles over the ice.

Sailing from England in 1850, M'Clure and the men of the Investigator had spent four winters in the Arctic, seeking to find and cross the legendary Northwest Passage. They had approached the passage from the west, sailing around Cape Horn, up the Pacific Coast of the Americas, through Bering Strait, past Point Barrow, and into the region of the Arctic Islands. They had been blocked by ice in attempting to sail through the Prince of Wales Strait, and had turned around to circumnavigate almost the entire coast of Banks Island. Along the northern coast of Banks Island, the Investigator had drifted for weeks in a narrow lead, hardly wider than the ship, pressed on one side by the awesome polar ice pack and on the other by the towering, vertical cliffs of Banks Islands, which rose to heights of as much as 1,000 feet. Caught in this trap, it had seemed almost inevitable that the Investigator would be crushed to a pulp, until finally it found the sanctuary of a harbor, Mercy Bay. Here it was locked in by the ice for 18 months. Eventually the crew abandoned the Investigator at Mercy Bay. Three men had already died. The survivors, suffering from malnutrition, scurvy, frostbite and some from temporary insanity induced by their long Arctic ordeal, walked from Mercy Bay across the ice to another expedition of ships waiting at Melville Island, and became the first to complete the crossing of the Northwest Passage.

Problem in M'Clure Strait

For 34 hours, the Manhattan and the Macdonald were beset in a polar ice flow in M'Clure Strait, on the path of the route over which M'Clure and his men had trekked in 1853. Thin snow covered the ice which stretched unbroken in all directions. It looked like a prairie landscape, anywhere between Winnipeg and Edmonton, in the middle of winter — a vast, snow-covered prairie in which two ships had somehow got stuck. The temperature was 23°F., the wind was blowing at 30 miles per hour, and the combination produced a wind chill factor -13° F. In the Arctic winter, there would be continuous darkness, the temperature would be between -40°and -60°F., and the wind would blow at rates approaching 100 miles per hour.

For a day and a half, the two ships made little headway through the polar pack, which had moved down to clog the eastern entrance of M'Clure Strait. Four hours of steady ramming through the ice produced less than a mile of progress.

The Macdonald charged the ice like an angry bull. As the bow hit the unbroken edge of the pack, it would rise from the water, come crashing down and through the ice, and the whole ship would rumble and shake and shudder as it came to an abrupt halt. Then the "Johnny Mac" would roar full power astern, reverse props with another shudder, and charge full speed again at the ice.

The massive Manhattan, which requires a good many miles to gain full speed, could never lift its hull more than 50 feet to put the whole bow on top of the ice. Against the ice, the bow rose slightly, gently. Nor did it rumble, shake or shudder. There were muffled bangs, like the sound of empty barrels hit with rubber hammers, as the ice clanged against the bow, and the ship cut through, gliding sedately as if nothing in the world could ever stop its momentum. But when the ice got thicker and stronger and the pressure greater, its progress grew slower and slower until gradually the ship had stopped. Motionless for a few minutes, it would then inch astern, imperceptibly at first, preparing for another run at the ice. But sometimes it was not able to move astern, and that is when the Johnny Mac would come crashing up alongside, breaking the ice and relieving the pressure which held the Manhattan fast.

Mercy Bay

The polar flow which held up the Manhattan off Mercy Bay was a pan of ice, several miles across, thicker and stronger than most of the other ice which clogged M'Clure Strait. Where it was flat, it was 10 feet thick, and in the pressure ridges, it was twice as thick. It was crystal-blue ice, clear, sparkling, drained of its salt, seemingly stronger than concrete. In front of the bow, the impact of 150,000 tons caused the ice to buckle and fold in accordion pleats. Farther back, against the shoulders of the bow, massive hunks of ice, as large as houses, were broken off, pushed down into the water, then came swooshing up, like some gigantic whales at play.

Yo-yo system

Captain Roger Steward, who had never broken through ice with a ship before, was learning the intricate techniques, with the advice of experienced Canadians. Ramming back and forth in what he dubbed the "yo-yo system," he declared that "you just gotta keep a-swinging."

Thanks to the assistance of the Macdonald, the Manhattan "kept a-swinging" until it eventually broke through the polar ice floe, made a large U-turn, and, skirting the floe this time, headed out of M'Clure Strait to take the easier way through the rest of the Northwest Passage, down Prince of Wales Strait.

Passage possibilities

If the Manhattan's epic voyage leads to regular commercial shipping through the Northwest Passage – possibly as early as 1972 – it will be the catalyst which will open up the Canadian Arctic for development on a scale undreamed of.

Icebreaking tankers are one possible means of opening the Northwest Passage. Submarine tankers afford another possible means.

"The icebreaking tanker is at best a stop-gap that will be defeated by the submarine tanker," an official of General Dynamics Inc. of Groton, Mass., told a seminar of Arctic shipping and logistics experts in Montreal, shortly before the Manhattan's sailing. General Dy-

Manhattan's
bow, constructed
to slide up
on ice and crush
it by ship's
weight.

namics had spent nearly a decade on design and feasibility studies of both nuclear-powered and diesel-electric powered submarine tankers. "Submarine tankers will be used in Arctic waters within a few years," General Dynamics forecast, adding that "oil shipping terminals and offshore drilling rigs also will go underwater in the Arctic."

Design studies of submarine cargo ships have been made in the United States, Great Britain, Germany and Japan. Mitchell Engineering Limited and Saunders-Roe Ltd. of England in 1962 had completed design studies for a 50,000-ton, nuclear-powered submarine, the Moby Dick, capable of carrying a 28,000-ton payload at speeds up to 50 knots, and which the company claimed could "operate under the ice to trade with specific terminals in the Canadian north during their closed season."

Submarine cargo ships

Cost of building a nuclear-powered cargo submarine has been estimated at five to seven times the cost per ton of carrying capacity as compared with a surface supertanker. Projected payload capacities for the submarines studied during the early 1960's ranged from 20,000 to 50,000 tons, compared with supertankers capable of carrying more than 300,000 tons. The submarine tanker, however, with the same horsepower to tonnage ratio, could travel at more than double the speed of a supertanker on the surface. Thus a submarine with a 25,000-ton payload could deliver as much oil as a 50,000-ton surface tanker. And when you consider also the shorter distances through the Northwest Passage, the possibilities of submarine cargo vessels may be seen in a new light. A submarine carrying 25,000 tons at a speed of 35 knots or better, could deliver as much oil over the 3,000-mile route from the Arctic Islands to Western Europe as a supertanker carrying 200,000 tons a distance of 12,000 miles from the Persian Gulf to Western Europe at a speed of 17 knots.

It will require several years of studies, design engineering, research, experiments and ship construction before the Northwest Passage is opened to commercial shipping on a regular basis. That it will be ultimately accomplished is the assumption on which is based the expenditure of hundreds of millions of dollars in the search for the mineral resources of the Arctic Islands.

SELECTED BIBLIOGRAPHY

In addition to that listed here, substantial source material for this book was drawn from Oil in Canada (1949-1963), and its successor publication, Oilweek (established in 1955), with individual articles too numerous to list. The author drew upon interviews, newspapers, company reports and other corporate sources, material from the archives of the Glenbow Foundation in Calgary, from the Oil Museum of Canada at Oil Springs, Ontario, and from other sources.

Alcock, F. J., A Century in the History of the Geological Survey of Canada (Ottawa: Department of Mines and Technical Surveys, 1947).

American Petroleum Institute, Facts About Oil (New York, N. Y.).
Petroleum Facts and Figures (New York: 1959, 1969).

Beach, F. K., Alberta's Petroleum Paternity (Gardenvale, Quebec: National Business Publications, 1956).
and Irwin, J. L., History of Alberta Oil (Edmonton, Alberta: Department of Lands and Mines, Government of Alberta, 1940).

Beaton, Kendall, "Dr. Gesner's Kerosene: The Start of American Oil Refining," in Business Review (New York: March, 1955).

341

Beck, J. M., Pendulum of Power: Canada's Federal Elections (Scarborough, Ontario: Prentice-Hall, 1968).

Behrendt, Ernest, "The Arctic, land of Frozen Assets," in Petroleum Today (New York: American Petroleum Institute, Fall, 1966).

Chapman, E. J., Mineral and Geology of Canada (Toronto, Ontario: W. C. Chewett & Co., 1864).

Canadian Association of Oilwell Drilling Contractors, An Introduction to Drilling (Calgary, Alberta).

Canadian Petroleum Association, Oil in Alberta (Calgary, Alberta).

Report of the Geological Reserves Committee on Ultimate Potential Hydrocarbon Reserves in Canada (Calgary, Alberta: April, 1969).

1968 Statistical Year Book (Calgary, Alberta: 1969).

Christian Guardian, "The Oil Wells of Enniskillen," anon. (London, England: February 19, 1862).

Cronin, Fergus, "North America's Father of Oil," in Imperial Oil Review (Toronto, Ontario: Imperial Oil Limited, June, 1958).

"The Day Leduc Came In," in Imperial Oil Review (February, 1967).

Dack, W. L., "McMahon Ready to Build a Gas Line," in Financial Post (Toronto, Ontario: April 4, 1956).

Elford, Jean Turnbull, A History of Lambton County (Sarnia, Ontario: Lambton Historical Society, 1967).

Ells, Sidney C., Recollections of the Development of the Athabasca Oil Sands (Ottawa: Department of Mines and Technical Surveys, Information Circular 1C-139, 1962).

Fanning, Leonard M., Men, Money and Oil (Cleveland, Ohio: The World Publishing Company, 1966).

Finnie, Richard, Canol (San Francisco: published by the prime contractors for the Canol Project, Price-Bechtel-Callahan, 1945).

Gale, Thomas A., The Wonder of the 19th Century: Rock Oil, in Pennsylvania and Elsewhere (Erie, Pa.: Sloan and Griffeth, 1860).

Geological Survey of Canada, Reports of Progress: 1849-1850; 1851-1852; 1860; 1861 (Ottawa).

Gesner, Abraham, A Practical Treatise on Coal, Petroleum and Other Distilled Oils — second, revised edition (New York: Bailliere Bros., 1865).

Gesner, G. W., Dr. Abraham Gesner, A Biographical Sketch (St.

John, New Brunswick: Bulletin of the Natural History Society of New Brunswick, 1896).

Goodall, D. P., Gas Export, 1950-1960 (Calgary, Alberta: Alberta Oil and Gas Conservation Board, 1961).

Gray, Earle, "Beating the Oil of the Tar," in The Star Weekly (Toronto, Ontario: March 19, 1966).

"Turner Valley Oil Stampede," in The Canadian Weekly (Toronto, Ontario: October 24, 1964).

The Impact of Oil (Toronto, Ontario: Ryerson Press/Maclean-Hunter, 1969).

Griffin, Selwyn P., "Petrolia, Cradle of Oil Drillers," in Imperial Oil Review (Toronto, Ontario: September, 1930).

Hammond, M. O., "The Rush to Enniskillen," in Imperial Oil Review (Toronto, Ontario: September, 1929).

Hardy, W. G., (ed.), Alberta, A Natural History (Edmonton, Alberta: M. G. Hurtig, 1967).

Harkness, R. B., "Ontario's Part in the Petroleum Industry," in Canadian Oil and Gas Industries (Gardenvale, Quebec: February and March issues, 1951).

Henry, J. T., The Early and Later History of Petroleum (Philadelphia, Pa.: Jas. B. Rodgers & Co., 1873).

Horizons, "Fire Flood is Key to Unlocking the Athabasca Tar Sands," anon. (Tulsa, Oklahoma: Pan American Petroleum Corporation, December, 1968).

Hume, G. S., Oil and Gas in Eastern Canada (Ottawa: Geological Survey of Canada, economic geology series No. 9, 1932).

Hume, G. S., "History of Pipeline Construction," in Canada Year Book, 1954 (Ottawa: 1955).

Hunt, Sterry S., "Notes on the History of Petroleum, or Rock Oil," in Canadian Naturalist, Volume 6 (Montreal, Quebec: 1861).

Imperial Oil Review, Imperial Oil Limited, Toronto, Ontario:

"The Conquest of Atlantic No. 3," anon., January, 1949.

"Oil Argonauts of the farthest North," anon., December, 1919.

"Tidings from Arctic Outposts," anon., March, 1920.

"Our Well at Fort Norman," anon., February, 1921.

"Flying Across the Edge of the Great Unknown," anon., June, 1921.

"Releasing the Titan in the Black Diamond Field," anon., November, 1924.

Jackman, C. W., Oil and Gas Exploration and Development in Alberta, 1883-1960 (Edmonton, Alberta: Department of Mines and Minerals, Government of Alberta, 1960).

Klauss, Robert L., "Athabasca, Land of Expectation," in Our Sun (Philadelphia, Pa.: Sun Oil Company, Summer and Fall issues, 1964).

"Great Canadian Oil Sands: The Way in Works," in Our Sun, Fall, 1967.

Knowles, Ruth Sheldon, The Greatest Gamblers (New York: McGraw-Hill, 1959).

"Arctic Oil – it could set off a new era," in The Wall Street Journal (New York: January 6, 1969).

Lauriston, Victor, Lambton's Hundred Years (Sarnia, Ontario: Haines Frontier Printing Company, 1949).

Link, T. A., "A Trip to the Fort Norman Oil Fields," in Imperial Oil Review, February, 1921).

"Fort Norman or Bust," in Imperial Oil Review, September, 1921.

Locke, Jeannine, "Publisher Max Bell," in The Star Weekly (Toronto, Ontario: February 12, 1966).

Mathews, John J., Life and Death of an Oilman; the career of E. W. Marland (Norman, Oklahoma: University of Oklahoma, 1951).

McLaurin, John J., Sketches in Crude Oil (Harrisburgh, Pa.: Published by the author, 1896).

"Oil Springs," in Oil City Derrick (Oil City, Pa.: July 22, 1914).

Mining Journal, "Arctic Challenge," anon., (London, England: July 25, 1969).

Myers, C. V., Oil to Alaska (Edmonton, Alberta: published by the author, 1944).

Nevins, Allen, John D. Rockefeller: The Heroic Age of American Enterprise (New York: Charles Scribner's Sons, 1940).

Nickle, C. O., Valley of Wonders (Calgary, Alberta: published by the author, 1941).

Oil and Gas Journal, "Hunt pushed for Arctic tanker route," anon. (Tulsa, Oklahoma: February 17, 1969).

Petroleum Panorama, Special issue to commemorate 100th anniversary of first successful well drilled for oil production in United States. (Tulsa, Oklahoma: January 28, 1959).

Petroleum Press Service, "Through the Northwest Passage," anon. (London: July, 1969).

Porter, McKenzie, "Frank McMahon's Five Lucky Strikes," in Maclean's (Toronto, Ontario: January 5, 1957).

Purdy, G. A. Petroleum, Prehistoric to Petrochemicals (Toronto, Ontario: Copp Clark Publishing Company, 1957).

Robb, Charles, "On the Petroleum Springs of Western Canada," in Canadian Journal, Volume 6 (Toronto, Ontario: 1861).

Research Council of Alberta, Athabasca Oil Sands (Edmonton, Alberta: Reprint of papers presented at second conference on the Athabasca Oil Sands, 1963).

Roberts, Leslie, Clarence Decatur Howe (Toronto, Ontario: Clarke, Irwin & Co., 1957).

Ross, Victor, Petroleum in Canada (Toronto, Ontario: 1917).

Sanders, Wilfred, "Quest for Petroleum," in Maclean's, (Toronto, Ontario: July 15, 1937).

Sarnia Observer, an account of the discovery of oil at Enniskillen, anon. (Sarnia, Ontario: August 26, 1858).

Sclanders, Ian, "He gave the world a brighter light (biographical article on Abraham Gesner), in Imperial Oil Review (Toronto, Ontario: Imperial Oil Limited, February, 1955).

Shaw, Charles L., "Alberta's Oil Riddle," in Maclean's (Toronto, Ontario: February 1, 1939).

Shell Oil Company of Canada Ltd., Canadian Oil, a Century of Progress (Toronto, Ontario: 1950).

Sproule, J. C., "Arctic Islands exploration," in Canadian Oil and Gas Industries (Gardenvale, Quebec: February, 1961).

"Exploration for Oil and Gas in the Arctic Islands of Canada," address to International Oil Scouts Association (Banff, Alberta: June, 1965).

"Canada's North, address to annual meeting of Association of Professional Engineers of Alberta (Calgary, Alberta: March, 1967).

Tait, Samuel W. Jr., Wildcatters, (Princeton, New Jersey: Princeton University Press, 1946).

Taylor, Robert, "The Great Pipeline Debate: After 10 years the scars still show," in The Daily Star (Toronto, Ontario: June 8, 1966).

Thorburn, Hugh G., "Parliament and Policy Making: The Case of the Trans-Canada Gas Pipeline," in The Canadian Journal of Economics and Political Science (Toronto, Ontario: University of Toronto Press, November, 1957).

345

Toronto Globe, (Toronto, Ontario):

Series of articles on Oil Springs, Aug. 27, Sept. 2 and Sept. 6, 1861.

Report of discovery by H. N. Nixon of flowing oil well at Oil Springs, January 28, 1862.

Report on inquest into death of H. N. Nixon, February 14, 1863.

Series of articles on oil fields at Petrolia, Aug. 30, Sept. 2, 3 and 5, 1881.

United States Department of the Interior, An Appraisal of the Petroleum Industry of the United States (Washington, D. C.: 1965).

Western Oil Examiner, Special issue on history of oil development at Turner Valley (Calgary, Alberta: June 15, 1956).

Whipp, Charles, and Phelps, Edward, Petrolia, 1866-1966 (Petrolia, Ontario: Petrolia Centennial Committee, 1966).

Williamson, Harold F. and Daum, Arnold R., The American Petroleum Industry, 1858-1899, The Age of Illumination (Evanston, Illinois: Northwestern University Press, 1959).

Williamson, Harold F.; Andreano, Ralph L.; Daum, Arnold R., and Klose, Gilbert C., The American Petroleum Industry, 1899-1959, The Age of Energy (Evanston, Illinois: Northwestern University Press, 1963).

Wilson, Neill C., and Taylor, Frank F., The Building of Trans Mountain (Vancouver, British Columbia: Trans Mountain Oil Pipe Line Company, 1954).

Winchell, Alexander, Sketches of Creation (New York: Harper & Bros., 1870).

Yackulic, George, "Max Bell," in Western Business and Industry (Vancouver, British Columbia, 1963).

ACKNOWLEDGEMENTS

On various plane trips across the country, from St. John, New Brunswick to Vancouver, B.C.; at an exploration base camp in the Arctic Islands; aboard the Canadian coastguard icebreaker John A. Macdonald as she accompanied the tanker SS Manhattan on an historic cross of the Northwest Passage. Spare moments in places such as these and other unlikely locations, when the assignments and tasks of the day had been completed, were used to complete the writing of this book. It was during a six-year period, in the time left over from my tasks as editor of Oilweek, that this book was researched and written.

Only the assistance, support and encouragement of dozens of people has made it possible.

I am indebted to all those who generously made time available to talk to me, provided me with information, or made certain files or other sources of corporate information available to me. I cannot name them all; the list is too long.

The support of those who particularly went out of their way to assist me, must, however, be acknowledged: the late Percy Timms, who loaned me valuable material concering events at the time of the initial discovery of oil at Turner Valley; Mrs. Beatrice MacLaughlin, curator of the Oil Museum of Canada, Oil Springs, Ontario, who

Acknowledgements

spared no effort to find original source material for me; the staff of the Glenbow Foundation archives, Calgary, for similar generous help; the staff of the Calgary Public Library, who scoured the continent to find obscure books and articles, some of them more than a century out of print; the staff of the Petrolia, Ontario, public library.

Some of the material for certain sections of this book I had gathered originally as source material for articles appearing in Oilweek. Also of assistance were Oilweek files, and back copies of its predecessor publication, Oil in Canada. For such assistance, I am indebted to Maclean-Hunter Limited, publisher of Oilweek.

To Vernon Myers, with whom I first started writing about the petroleum industry 20 years ago, and from whom I learned so much, I am also greatly indebted.

My heart-felt thanks to my family for their enduring patience; to my wife, for her continual support and encouragement, and assistance in the work; and to Dorothy Barraclough, who typed my copy to make of it a neat manuscript.

To a very few, the Canadian petroleum industry has brought some modest measure of fame and fortune. Some of these persons are discussed in this book. But it is upon the resources, the talents and efforts of many thousands of others that the petroleum industry is really dependent. The investors, who risk their money, some who profit, some who lose. The wildcatters of an earlier generation of whom none know today; those who didn't hit the big discovery to reap their bonanza, but lost their savings and years of efforts instead. The thousands more who work in the industry in every conceivable job and profession: executives, typists, clerks, geophysicists, chemists, accountants, engineers of all types, geologists of all classifications, landmen, roughnecks, tool pushers, cat skinners, welders, aircraft pilots, doctors, nurses, sailors, mechanics, draftsmen, and many more. To all these, this book is dedicated.

Earle Gray
Calgary, 1970

348

INDEX

Index

Index

Index